CONTENTS

PLACES TO VISIT

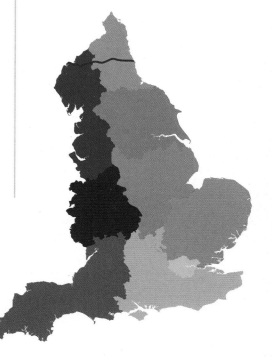

ENGLISH
HERITAGE

WELCOME

Welcome to your new handbook. It's packed with everything you need to plan brilliant days out in 2019. This year we'll be exploring England's rich myths, legends and folklore that were passed on through England's history, discovering where fiction met fact and old stories that were lost along the way.

It is difficult to understand the full significance of the subject of our front cover – **Tintagel Castle** – without relating to the Arthurian legend and the importance this myth had for the kings of Cornwall. Today it's a beautifully rugged place on the wild edges of the Cornish coast. Over the past two years we have been planning for the building of a new bridge at the castle which will recreate the historic link between the mainland and the island. It will be a spectacular new addition to a visit, so keep an eye on our website for more information.

The grounds of **Walmer Castle** in Kent have been the focus of another major project, and two areas of the gardens have been restored and reopened to visitors. There are improved catering facilities, new trails and we've taken care to make room for wildlife by conserving and improving natural habitats, including a wildflower meadow.

Another site with ties to a well-known tale is **Whitby Abbey** in North Yorkshire – the inspiration for a scene in Bram Stoker's *Dracula*. Over the past few months we've been installing innovative new interpretation across the site, and we've created a new visitor centre with a café, shop and a reinvigorated museum.

This year will see our experts undertake essential work at **Saxtead Green Post Mill** in Suffolk, where a specialist millwright is restoring the sails and stairs of this local landmark. We're also removing invasive vegetation from the walls of **Pevensey Castle** in East Sussex.

For walkers amongst you we've been working with the British Pilgrimage Trust to identify some of the country's ancient pilgrimage routes. These take in a selection of our lesser-known sites, and they're a wonderful way to gain a new perspective on an often overlooked part of England's past. The routes are highlighted in each regional introduction section of this handbook, and you can find full details online.

Look out for our *Members' Magazine*, the *What's On Guide* and our *Kids Rule!* Magazine for more ways to make the most of your membership. You'll find plenty of inspiration for your adventures into England's past, and ideas on how to make 2019 your most legendary year yet.

We couldn't carry out this important conservation work without Members like you – thank you so much for your support.

Kate Mavor
Chief Executive

Opening Times

All information is correct at the time of going to press, but please always check the website or give us a call before you visit in case there are any changes or temporary closures.

In some circumstances, such as urgent repairs or filming, we may need to change some opening times, and properties showing this symbol ⊡ may be closed at certain times for private events.

At a few properties you can't enter less than one hour before closing time. Some of our smaller staffed sites may close between 1pm and 2pm. Our customer services team will be able to give you more information where relevant.

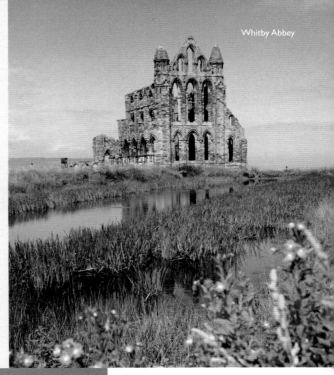
Whitby Abbey

Walmer Castle

Where properties have key keepers, please give them a ring before setting off. For those open at 'any reasonable time' please visit during daylight for safety reasons.

Please remember to always take your valid membership card(s) with you when visiting. To check opening times before setting off, please visit: english-heritage.org.uk/daysout/ properties

All dates shown run from
1 April 2019 to **31 March 2020**

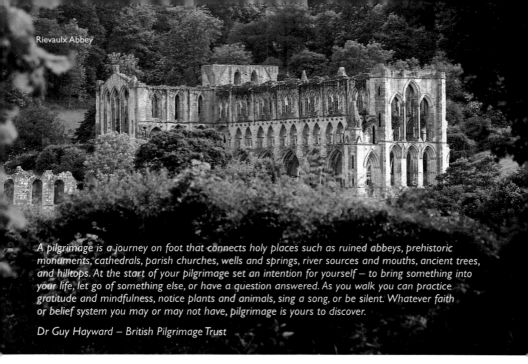

Rievaulx Abbey

A pilgrimage is a journey on foot that connects holy places such as ruined abbeys, prehistoric monuments, cathedrals, parish churches, wells and springs, river sources and mouths, ancient trees, and hilltops. At the start of your pilgrimage set an intention for yourself – to bring something into your life, let go of something else, or have a question answered. As you walk you can practice gratitude and mindfulness, notice plants and animals, sing a song, or be silent. Whatever faith or belief system you may or may not have, pilgrimage is yours to discover.

Dr Guy Hayward – British Pilgrimage Trust

INSPIRE ME

—— PILGRIMAGE ——

Pilgrimages in England aren't just a thing of the past, and you don't have to follow any – or any particular – religion to make a pilgrimage. A revival is being spearheaded by the British Pilgrimage Trust, and we've worked with them to offer you suggestions for short pilgrimages in each of our regions. You'll find details in the regional introductions, and discover more English Heritage-related pilgrimage routes at **english-heritage.org.uk/pilgrimage**

Pilgrimage to sacred places plays an important part in many world religions. In England, the heyday of pilgrimage was the Middle Ages, when our roads and seaways were thronged with pilgrims journeying to holy shrines. You can trace their devotion in many of the sites we care for.

The greatest English shrine, immortalised in Chaucer's *Canterbury Tales*, was the tomb of St Thomas Becket in Canterbury Cathedral. Pilgrims to it also visited **St Augustine's Abbey**, and were welcomed along their way at **Dover Castle** and **Maison Dieu**.

Bury St Edmunds Abbey enshrined the martyred Saxon king Edmund, England's original patron saint. But the greatest East Anglian pilgrim magnet was the Virgin Mary's Holy House at Walsingham in Norfolk; pilgrims travelled there via **Castle Acre Priory** and **Thetford Priory**, which itself treasured a miraculous statue of the Virgin.

Wenlock Priory

Lindisfarne Priory

Many English monasteries founded their prosperity on donations from pilgrims, including **Wenlock Priory**, shrine of the local Saint Milburga, and especially **Hailes Abbey**, home of the 'Holy Blood'.

Further north, pilgrims visited the tomb of St Aelred at **Rievaulx Abbey**, and made the hazardous crossing to St Cuthbert's **Lindisfarne Priory**, which retains its powerful atmosphere today. **Finchale Priory** honoured one of the most indomitable English pilgrims, the sea rover-turned-hermit St Godric He journeyed to Santiago de Compostela in Spain, twice to Jerusalem and three times to Rome, once allegedly carrying his elderly mother.

The Camino Inglés, an official route to Santiago de Compostela, starts at the port city of A Coruña in Spain, where medieval pilgrims arrived from England. To complete the full 100km pilgrimage and collect a 'Compostela' certificate, pilgrims must prove that they have walked the 75km Spanish section, as well as 25km in the UK. The Finchale Camino Inglés route on p.275 is a recognised English section where you can collect official stamps.

Individuals from all levels of medieval society, from princes to paupers, would go on pilgrimage to the shrines of Christ and the saints. There can be little doubt that the primary motive was religious, pilgrims hoping that their journeys to visit holy relics – which could be long, arduous and sometimes involve real danger – would lead to the forgiveness of sins or a miraculous cure. Several monasteries in the care of English Heritage were important pilgrimage destinations. Especially close to my heart is Hailes Abbey in Gloucestershire. Mentioned in Chaucer's Canterbury Tales, it was home to what was believed to be a portion of the very blood shed by Christ on the Cross.

Dr Michael Carter
Senior Properties Historian

Brodsworth Hall and Gardens

INSPIRE ME

HISTORIC GARDENS — ALL YEAR ROUND

We lovingly care for, restore and develop some of England's historic gardens. They're a delight to visit at any time, but here are just a few highlights for each season.

SPRING

Snowdrops are the welcome heralds of spring. You'll find more than 500,000 of them, along with 200,000 yellow aconites, at **Brodsworth Hall and Gardens**, and the carpets of snowdrops at **Belsay Hall, Castle and Gardens** remember the 18th-century tradition that the ladies of the hall gathered to plant them every year. Daffodils aren't far behind; you'll discover 28 Victorian varieties at **Osborne**, and swathes of narcissus (appropriately including the 'Sir Winston Churchill' variety) at **Walmer Castle and Gardens**, where we're opening new areas of the gardens

this spring. If fruit-tree blossom inspires you, you'll see plenty in **Audley End House and Gardens'** famous organic kitchen garden and **Carisbrooke Castle's** Princess Beatrice Garden.

SUMMER

In summer, you'll be spoilt for choice. **Kenilworth Castle's Elizabethan Garden** was designed to look at its best in July, the month of the Queen's famous 1575 visit. **Eltham Palace and Gardens'** 1930s garden is also in fullest bloom, and you can admire the rich hot summer colours of Victorian plantings at Osborne. Look out for the

Osborne wedding myrtle, used in bouquets by royal brides from Queen Victoria's own daughters to Princess Eugenie in 2018. At Brodsworth, you can savour the fragrance of the Rose Dell's wild roses, and if you love naturally growing wild flowers, you'll find honeysuckle in **Witley Court and Gardens'** great wilderness; May bluebells in **Stott Park Bobbin Mill's** newly opened woodlands; and sometimes wild orchids on **Scarborough Castle's** headland.

AUTUMN

The vibrant yellow-orange-brown-red colours of changing leaves are autumn's great joy. There are over 6,000 trees in **Kenwood's** parkland, including the richly-hued Sweet Gum, and a vast variety in **Wrest Park's** immense 90-acre gardens, enlivened by charming garden follies. Seek out Belsay's Katsura tree, with its burnt-sugar scent, and Audley End's Howard Oak, one of only two in the world. Autumn's also a great time for misty garden vistas, like the view across Witley Court's lake.

WINTER

A crisp winter day can be an enchanting time to explore our gardens, revealing the shape and structure of trees, hedges and frosted topiary. Snow highlights the convoluted curves and bulges of Audley End's Cloud Hedge, and Brodsworth Hall offers seasonally-flowering Christmas Roses and over 100 varieties of hollies. In January and early February, visit the **Home of Charles Darwin, Down House,** where startlingly-coloured and powerfully-scented tropical orchids put on a show in the greenhouses. And before you know it, it's time for snowdrops again.

Eltham Palace and Gardens

Osborne

Mount Grace Priory, House and Gardens

Don't miss!

... our most recently opened garden, the revived Arts and Crafts style gardens at **Mount Grace Priory, House and Gardens.** It offers individual guide pamphlets for each season, helping you to get the most out of the gardens all year round.

Tintagel Castle

INSPIRE ME

TELLING TALES: THE MYTHS, LEGENDS AND FOLKLORE OF ENGLAND

This year we're uncovering some of the myths and legends that swirl around our historic places. From buried treasure to mysterious music, and from hobgoblins to ancient kings, these sites have many strange stories to tell.

TURNED TO STONE

Long before we began to understand prehistoric stone circles, people came up with different theories about what they were and how they got there. Some thought they were humans turned to stone as punishment for their sins – so **The Hurlers** were men transformed to boulders for playing the game of hurling on a Sunday, and the **Nine Ladies** and **Nine Stones** were girls 'petrified' for circle-dancing on that holy day. The stones of **Stanton Drew** were thought to be the remains of an entire wedding party, also punished for dancing on a Sunday.

KINGS AND WITCHES

It's been said that the **Rollright Stones** were once a king and his invading army who were turned to stone by a witch. The central stone at **Mitchell's Fold** was itself a witch – one who had been punished for maliciously milking dry a magic cow. Stone circles needed to be treated with respect, and merely trying to count their stones was thought unlucky. Moving them could be fatal. The body of a medieval barber, apparently killed by a falling prehistoric stone, was found at **Avebury** in 1938.

GODS AND GOBLINS

Other tales linked ancient sites to pagan gods. **Grime's Graves** and **Grimspound** are both named after 'Grim', an alias of Woden, a Saxon god. **Wayland's Smithy** was the haunt of a Saxon smith-god who would shoe any horses left nearby. The 'hobgoblin' of **Hob Hurst's House** would help around the farms of those he liked in return for a bowl of cream — but he could be a menace to anyone who offended him.

IMMORTAL ARTHUR

Tales of King Arthur can be found across England, famously at **Tintagel**. **King Arthur's Round Table** was said to be his jousting arena, and **Arthur's Stone** was either his grave or the place where he killed a giant. Many believed that Arthur never died — that he lies asleep with his knights, ready to return should England need them. Some say he sleeps near **Sewingshields** on Hadrian's Wall, others beneath **Richmond Castle**.

SECRET PASSAGES

Like many castles and monasteries — including **Whitby Abbey** and **Beeston Castle** — **Richmond Castle** is rumoured to conceal a secret passage. Legend has it that a drummer once volunteered to explore it, beating his drum to signal his progress. He got lost and disappeared — but legend declares you can still hear his drum. You might also hear a fiddler stuck for eternity in a secret tunnel beneath **Binham Priory**.

BURIED TREASURE

According to legend there's hidden treasure to be found beneath **Beeston Castle**, **Stokesay Castle** and **Caister Roman Fort**, among other places. And sometimes real treasure does come to light. In 1964 a hoard of revealing Roman artefacts — more precious to archaeologists than gold — was dug up near **Corbridge Roman Town**, where it's now on display.

Mitchell's Fold Stone Circle

Richmond Castle

Whitby Abbey

You can find more tales about the myths, legends and folklore of our sites on each regional introduction page, as well as on our website.

Some of our historic sites are quite remote, so use the handbook to plan your visit and investigate these myths and legends for yourself. Listen for peculiar noises, keep an eye out for buried treasure, and whatever you do, don't go dancing on a Sunday…

Step into t

PREHISTORY
BEFORE AD 43

c. 950,000 YEARS AGO
Earliest human activity in England

c. 12,000 YEARS AGO
Continuous human settlement begins

c. 4000-2500 BC
Neolithic Period (First Farmers)

c. 3000 BC
Stonehenge begun

c. 2500-750 BC
Bronze Age

FROM c. 750 BC
Iron Age

The earliest known humans came to England nearly a million years ago. But continuous settlement began only after the end of the last Ice Age, some 12,000 years ago.

THE FIRST FARMERS
Nomadic 'hunter-gatherer' people left few visible traces, but with the arrival of farming in the Neolithic (New Stone Age) period, people began constructing monuments. Among the earliest are ritual enclosures like *Windmill Hill* and communal tombs like *West Kennet Long Barrow*.

MONUMENTS AND METAL-WORKING
Circular earthwork 'henges' appear from about 3000 BC, when *Stonehenge* was begun. The later Neolithic and early Bronze Ages saw massive stone circles like *Castlerigg Stone Circle* and *Avebury Stone Circle* raised, sometimes becoming elements of 'ritual landscapes' like that including mysterious *Silbury Hill*. *Grime's Graves* flint mines were in use by 2600 BC: but before *Stonehenge* was completed in about 2000 BC, the working of bronze was known in England.

ROUND BARROWS, VILLAGES AND HILL FORTS
Individual burials in Bronze Age 'round barrows' (like *Flowerdown Barrows*) meanwhile replaced communal tombs. From about 1500 BC landscapes were divided up by great field systems, with dwellings grouped into villages such as *Grimspound* and *Chysauster Ancient Village*. New iron-working technology from around 750 BC coincided with the spread of hill forts like *Maiden Castle*. Then town-like tribal power centres such as *Lexden Earthworks* developed – a process interrupted by the Roman Conquest.

WE CARE FOR 57 SITES WITHIN THIS PERIOD, INCLUDING:

- Avebury Stone Circle
- Castlerigg Stone Circle
- Chysauster Ancient Village
- Grime's Graves
- Lexden Earthworks
- Maiden Castle

- Mayburgh Henge
- Silbury Hill
- Stonehenge
- West Kennet Long Barrow
- Windmill Hill

ROMANS
AD 43-C. 410

AD 43
Roman Conquest
begins

AD 84
Furthest extent
of Roman rule
in Britain

AD 122
Hadrian's Wall
begun

**c. AD
260-360**
Saxon Shore
defences built

**c. AD
410-425**
Imperial rule
by Rome fades

Roman Britain lasted for over three and a half centuries, leaving an indelible mark on the nation's landscape. English Heritage's Roman sites reflect the era from its violent beginning to its obscure close.

CONQUEST
Though Julius Caesar raided Britain in 55 and 54 BC, full-scale conquest began when Roman forces landed near *Richborough Roman Fort* in AD 43. Despite resistance by Boudica (Boadicea) and others, Roman armies had reached northern Scotland by AD 84, before eventually retiring to the permanent frontier of *Hadrian's Wall*. Incomparably the most impressive Roman monument in Britain, the Wall's defensive system includes major forts like *Birdoswald*, *Chesters* and *Housesteads*.

CIVILISATION
Away from the frontiers, Roman Britain was for long periods peaceful and prosperous. 'Country houses' like *Lullingstone Roman Villa* flourished, bath-houses and amphitheatres were built, and many towns were founded – including large *Silchester* and *Wroxeter* and smaller *Aldborough* and *Corbridge* – often at existing British tribal centres. Most were later walled against increasing external threats.

THE SAXON SHORE
Towards the end of the 3rd century, attacks by seaborne Germanic raiders prompted the creation of 'Saxon Shore' coastal fortifications like *Burgh Castle*. Further trouble saw the system strengthened in the next century, and *Pevensey Castle* added. Garrisons were by now mainly British-born, and little distinguished 'Romans' from 'Britons' when imperial rule petered out. There was no clearly definable end to Roman Britain.

WE CARE FOR 57 SITES WITHIN THIS PERIOD, INCLUDING:

* Birdoswald Roman Fort
* Burgh Castle
* Chesters Roman Fort
* Corbridge Roman Town
* Hadrian's Wall
* Housesteads Roman Fort

* Lullingstone Roman Villa
* Pevensey Castle
* Richborough Roman Fort and Amphitheatre
* Wroxeter Roman City

EARLY MIDDLE AGES
C. 400-1066

This momentous era between the end of Roman Britain and the Norman Conquest, when Britons, Anglo-Saxons and then Vikings struggled for dominance, saw the gradual emergence of a unified English nation.

THE ENGLISH CONQUEST

Post-Roman Britain was assailed by sea-borne Germanic peoples – Angles, Saxons, Jutes and Frisians. Though delayed by Romano-British resistance (perhaps inspired by a fabled 'Arthur') these 'Anglo-Saxon' invaders conquered most of lowland England by the mid-600s, establishing several independent kingdoms. Tantalising hints about this shadowy period come from sites like *Birdoswald Roman Fort*, *Tintagel Castle* and *Wroxeter Roman City*.

CHRISTIAN CULTURE BLOSSOMS

Increasingly called 'English', the pagan conquerors were converted to Christianity by missionaries from Rome and Ireland. Christian culture blossomed: *Lindisfarne Priory* produced its illuminated Gospels, while Bede's writings at *St Paul's Monastery, Jarrow* fostered the concept of an English nation. The architecture and craftsmanship of *St Peter's Church, Barton-Upon-Humber* and *Sandbach Crosses* likewise reflect the English Church's vitality.

THE VIKING THREAT

Towards the end of the 8th century, soon after *Offa's Dyke* defined its western boundary, England's development was imperilled as Viking raids became invasions. King Alfred of Wessex turned the tide, and his descendants reconquered Viking-held lands: his grandson Aethelstan became the first ruler of a unified English state. But Danish pressure was revived by King Cnut, and it was a weakened England which faced the Normans in 1066.

WE CARE FOR 18 SITES WITHIN THIS PERIOD, INCLUDING:

* 1066 Battle of Hastings, Abbey and Battlefield
* Lindisfarne Priory
* Lydford Castle and Saxon Town
* Offa's Dyke
* St Augustine's Abbey
* St Paul's Monastery, Jarrow
* St Peter's Church, Barton-upon-Humber
* Sandbach Crosses
* Tintagel Castle
* Whitby Abbey

MEDIEVAL
1066-1485

Nearly half of all English Heritage sites date from the 'medieval' centuries between the battles of Hastings in 1066 and Bosworth in 1485. Their variety mirrors the era's developing character.

THE LAND FILLED WITH CASTLES

Earthwork and timber 'motte-and-bailey' castles were the instruments and symbols of the Norman Conquest. Many, like *Clifford's Tower* and *Totnes Castle*, were later refortified in stone. The great stone keeps of the Norman and Angevin kings and their barons formed the core of major early fortresses like *Dover Castle*, *Conisbrough Castle* and *Richmond Castle*. The focus then shifted to many-towered enclosure walls with powerful gatehouses, as at *Framlingham Castle* and *Goodrich Castle*. Equipped with halls, chapels and many domestic buildings, some strongholds like *Beeston Castle* or *Kenilworth Castle* were immense in scale. More compact fortresses – including *Farleigh Hungerford Castle* and *Nunney Castle* – developed towards the end of the era, with some (like *Berry Pomeroy* and *Kirby Muxloe* castles) equipped for artillery defence.

TOWN AND COUNTRY

Only a tiny minority of medieval people lived in castles. English Heritage's collection also includes lightly fortified or undefended manor houses like *Stokesay Castle* or *Old Soar Manor*; and urban houses like Paignton's *Kirkham House*. Country life is represented by *Wharram Percy Deserted Medieval Village* and farm buildings like imposing *Harmondsworth Great Barn*.

WE CARE FOR 203 SITES WITHIN THIS PERIOD, INCLUDING:

- Beeston Castle
- Carisbrooke Castle
- Carlisle Castle
- Castle Acre Priory
- Clifford's Tower
- Conisbrough Castle

- Dover Castle
- Eleanor Cross, Geddington
- Framlingham Castle
- Goodrich Castle
- Harmondsworth Great Barn
- Kenilworth Castle

MEDIEVAL
1066-1485

1337-1453
Hundred Years War
with France

1349
Black Death

1381
Peasants' Revolt

1455-1485
Wars of the Roses

1476-1477
First books printed
in England

OASES OF PEACE

Whether in castle, town or country, medieval life was dominated by the Church: in the 14th century about one in fifteen Englishmen were clergy of some kind. English Heritage cares for parish churches like *St Mary's Kempley* with its impressive wall-paintings, and bishops' mansions including *Lincoln Medieval Bishops' Palace:* and the evocative remains of many monasteries, from big, prosperous *Castle Acre Priory* to tiny *Mattersey Priory*.

Each reflects the characteristics of the monastic order which inhabited it: 'mainstream' Benedictines at *Binham Priory* and *Whitby Abbey*; solitude-seeking Cistercians at *Furness Abbey* and *Rievaulx Abbey*; decoration-loving Cluniacs at *Wenlock Priory*; Augustinian canons at tranquil *Lanercost Priory*; hermit-like Carthusians at *Mount Grace Priory, House and Gardens* or the urban friars of Gloucester's *Blackfriars* and *Greyfriars*.

MEMORIES OF CONFLICT

Many of English Heritage's medieval sites, by contrast, recall the foreign or internal wars of medieval England. Some – like *Carlisle Castle* – guarded land borders against Scots or Welsh, or like *Carisbrooke Castle* and *Dartmouth Castle,* defended coasts against sea-borne invasion and raiding. Others, including *Rochester Castle*, endured conflicts between monarchs and barons, or like *Dunstanburgh Castle* or *Warkworth Castle,* witnessed the dynastic Wars of the Roses, ended by the Battle of Bosworth which began the Tudor age.

WE CARE FOR 203 SITES WITHIN THIS PERIOD, INCLUDING:

- Aydon Castle
- Cleeve Abbey
- Lanercost Priory
- Middleham Castle
- Mount Grace Priory, House and Gardens

- Old Sarum
- Rievaulx Abbey
- St Mary's Church, Kempley
- Scarborough Castle
- Stokesay Castle

TUDORS
1485-1603

The pivot of medieval and modern history, the Tudor era saw strong royal government established; England transformed from a Catholic to a Protestant nation; and the flowering of a distinctively English culture.

THE TRIUMPH OF MONARCHY
Ending the Wars of the Roses, Henry VII curtailed aristocratic power and castle-building, and his successors strengthened the grip of monarchy. Henceforth fortresses would be raised only by the crown, most notably Henry VIII's coastal artillery forts – the first co-ordinated system of national defence – including *Deal Castle, Pendennis Castle* and *Portland Castle*.

RELIGIOUS UPHEAVALS
Henry's new-style forts defended England against European Catholic reaction to the religious changes he initiated: English Heritage's outstanding collection of monastic ruins bear witness to his Dissolution of the Monasteries. After swinging from Edward VI's radical Protestantism to Mary's revived Catholicism, the nation settled down to religious compromise under Queen Elizabeth I.

THE FLOWERING OF ENGLISH CULTURE
Elizabeth's long and glorious reign witnessed the expansion of English sea power (reinforced by her defeat of the Spanish Armada) and the flowering of English culture epitomised by Shakespeare. It also saw the burgeoning of the great English country house. Some were converted monasteries or adapted medieval fortresses like *Kenilworth Castle and Elizabethan Garden*, but most were built from new, like *Kirby Hall*. All these developments expressed a new-found English self-confidence.

WE CARE FOR 50 SITES WITHIN THIS PERIOD, INCLUDING:

- Deal Castle
- Hailes Abbey
- Hardwick Old Hall
- Kenilworth Castle and Elizabethan Garden
- Kirby Hall
- Norham Castle
- Pendennis Castle
- Rushton Triangular Lodge
- Titchfield Abbey
- Tynemouth Priory and Castle

STUARTS
1603-1714

Following a long peace, the intense political and religious conflicts of the Stuart era transformed England's government. Developments in architecture and living standards are reflected in this era's English Heritage sites.

GRACIOUS LIVING
The earlier ('Jacobean') part of the period saw many lavish mansions like *Audley End House* and *Bolsover Castle* built, and fine interiors created in more modest dwellings like *Great Yarmouth Row Houses*.

THE ENGLISH REVOLUTION
The Civil Wars between Charles I and Parliament (1642-51) brought much devastation; epic sieges of *Pendennis Castle* and many other places; and (after his imprisonment at *Carisbrooke Castle*) the king's execution and the creation (1649-53) of the Commonwealth, the only republic in English history. Young Charles II narrowly escaped capture near *Boscobel House*.

RESTORATION AND NEW STYLES
Epitomised by Pepys's diary, the reign of the restored Charles II brought continuing scientific advances, but also plague and fire in London and humiliating Dutch attack, provoking the building of defences like *Tilbury Fort*. The 'English Baroque' style of Christopher Wren and *Abingdon County Hall* came increasingly into fashion towards the end of the period.

ENGLAND AND BRITAIN
The era's long-simmering religious disputes were addressed in 1689, after the Catholic James II was deposed by the Protestant William and Mary. Under Queen Anne, the Acts of Union with Scotland made England part of 'Great Britain'.

WE CARE FOR 40 SITES WITHIN THIS PERIOD, INCLUDING:

- Abingdon County Hall
- Audley End House and Gardens
- Berry Pomeroy Castle
- Bolsover Castle
- Boscobel House and The Royal Oak
- Carisbrooke Castle
- Great Yarmouth Row Houses
- Langley Chapel
- Pendennis Castle
- Tilbury Fort

GEORGIANS
1714-1837

An age of contrasts, counterpointing elegant aristocratic mansions with grimy, overcrowded mills, the Georgian era saw Britain become the world's first industrial nation, at the hub of a rapidly growing empire.

ELEGANT MANSIONS

English Heritage's outstanding collection of Georgian and Regency mansions reflect the period's progression of fashionable styles, from the Palladian of *Chiswick House* via Robert Adam's *Kenwood* to the 'Regency' Greek Revival of *Belsay Hall* and *The Grange at Northington*. Extravagant or tasteful interiors (as at *Marble Hill House*) were matched by formal or 'landscaped' gardens – an English gift to the world – often adorned (as at *Audley End House* and *Wrest Park*) with charming garden architecture.

INDUSTRIAL REVOLUTION

The wealth which financed these mansions was increasingly founded on England's pioneering Industrial Revolution, itself founded on entrepreneurial enterprise and new developments like canals, the 'factory system' and steam power. The *Iron Bridge* was the world's first of its kind, and the world's first steam trains ran in England in 1825.

WAR AND EMPIRE

International trade boomed alongside an expanding empire, particularly in India and the Americas. Yet as *Dover Castle* and *Dymchurch Martello Tower* demonstrate, Britain's growing military and especially naval power did not go unchallenged, notably during the long wars with Revolutionary and Napoleonic France. The Duke of Wellington, the greatest military hero of these wars, is remembered at *Apsley House*, *Walmer Castle* and *Wellington Arch*.

WE CARE FOR 41 SITES WITHIN THIS PERIOD, INCLUDING:

- Apsley House
- Belsay Hall, Castle and Gardens
- Chiswick House
- Derwentcote Steel Furnace
- Iron Bridge
- Kenwood
- Marble Hill House
- The Grange at Northington
- Wellington Arch
- Wrest Park

VICTORIANS
1837-1901

The long reign of Queen Victoria saw Britain at the zenith of its international power and status, and the greatest manufacturing nation in the world.

MASTERS AND SERVANTS

Queen Victoria's strong personality is reflected at *Osborne*. Her wealthier subjects also continued to build great mansions like *Brodsworth Hall* and *Witley Court,* operated by armies of servants – as *Audley End's* kitchens, nursery wing and stables demonstrate.

A HIVE OF INDUSTRY

J.W. Evans Silver Factory and *Stott Park Bobbin Mill* recall Victorian England as a hive of manufacturing industry. Rural life was also transformed by machinery, as seen in English Heritage's collection of windmills.

DOUBT AND CERTAINTY

The publication of Charles Darwin's ideas on evolution (matured and written at *Down House*) shook Victorian religious certainty, but did not stem the period's flood of chapel and church building – the latter almost always in the ubiquitous 'Gothic Revival' style. *St Mary's Church, Studley Royal* is a flamboyant example.

AN IMPERIAL POWER

Despite the 1860s French invasion scare which produced new fortifications like *Fort Brockhurst* and the updating of older defences like *Dartmouth Castle*, Britannia's fleets continued to rule the waves and her armies to fight far-flung colonial wars. The Indian Mutiny of 1857 and the Boer War of 1899-1902 dented 'Imperial' confidence, but at the Queen's death the British Empire was still rapidly expanding.

WE CARE FOR 28 SITES WITHIN THIS PERIOD, INCLUDING:

* Audley End House
* Brodsworth Hall
  and Gardens
* Home of Charles Darwin,
  Down House
* Fort Brockhurst

* J.W. Evans Silver Factory
* Osborne
* Sibsey Trader Windmill
* St Mary's Church, Studley Royal
* Stott Park Bobbin Mill
* Witley Court

MODERN
1901-PRESENT

During a century of rapidly-developing technologies, the two World Wars which dominate the modern age of British history acted as catalysts for previously unimaginable social changes.

TWO WORLD WARS – AND A THIRD?
The First World War, with its terrible carnage, and the Second World War – whose far greater impact on civilian life is underlined at *Great Yarmouth Row Houses* – are both reflected in English Heritage properties. Old fortresses like *Tynemouth Priory and Castle* were updated for new types of warfare, and the *Secret Wartime Tunnels* beneath *Dover Castle* played a crucial role in saving the nation in 1940. The dead of both wars are remembered by the London war memorials cared for by English Heritage, including the poignant *Royal Artillery Memorial* at Hyde Park Corner. But *York Cold War Bunker* is a chilling reminder that the threat of even greater mass destruction remained ever-present.

SOCIAL TRANSFORMATION
Both World Wars transformed the social structure of England: *Brodsworth Hall* tracks the decline of the country house and its servant-dependent lifestyle – though remodelled *Eltham Palace* displays the stylish living still enjoyed by the millionaire few.

AN ONGOING REVOLUTION
The post-Second World War creation of the Welfare State made life easier for the many. The advent of radio and TV and more recently of affordable computer technology fostered a still greater (and still continuing) revolution in lifestyles.

WE CARE FOR 22 SITES WITHIN THIS PERIOD, INCLUDING:

- Brodsworth Hall and Gardens
- Calshot Castle
- Dover Castle (Secret Wartime Tunnels)
- Eltham Palace
- Great Yarmouth Row Houses
- Portland Castle
- Royal Garrison Church
- Tynemouth Priory and Castle
- York Cold War Bunker

MEMBERSHIP AND EVENTS

Your membership is helping to care for over 400 historic sites across the country. Every day, you're playing a vital role in keeping the story of England alive for future generations. Thank you for your support.

"Membership of English Heritage gives me the sense that I am helping to preserve locations that are the very essence of our beautiful island."

READ ALL ABOUT IT
Our superb Members' Magazine is packed with inspiration and ideas for making the most of your membership, including a full list of our events. You can also be the first to hear about special events, offers and the latest news by signing up to our e-newsletter www.english-heritage.org.uk/newsletter

KIDS GO FREE
We allow free unlimited entry to our sites for up to six children per member. Children must be under 18 and within your family group.

EVENTS
We offer a whole host of fantastic days out, from live action spectaculars to ghost tours, arts and crafts fairs, talks, tours,

exhibitions and children's quests and trails.
www.english-heritage.org.uk/events

MEMBERS' EVENTS

As a Member, you can delve far deeper into our sites. Our experts will invite you behind the scenes, let you handle artefacts, lead you in workshops and take you on walking tours. We have over 150 Members-only events across the country every year. Look out for these in your Members' Magazine or on your Members' Area
www.english-heritage.org.uk/members

MEMBERS' REWARDS

Get access to exclusive competitions, deals and special offers on great brands through our Members' Rewards programme **www.english-heritage.org.uk/rewards**

MORE DAYS OUT

Your membership card opens doors to many other associated attractions and properties – either at no extra charge or for a discounted rate. See p.293 and details on your Members' Area online.

SHARE YOUR EXPERIENCE

Help us tell others how great English Heritage membership is. Follow us on Facebook, Twitter and Instagram and share your stories about fantastic days out at our sites, and your recommendations and general tips for making the most of your membership.

Get inspiration and tips from our Members Panellists in our Members' Voices section at **www.english-heritage.org.uk/members**

 Subscribe to our YouTube channel and watch history being brought to life from your own home. From a Victorian cookery series with world-renowned Mrs Crocombe, to our kids interviews with characters throughout history, and 360° and aerial views of our properties, you'll find a myriad of videos to keep you entertained and inspired.

*The Members' Magazine is mailed directly to UK Members, and to Life Members overseas.

Don't forget...

Your benefits as a Member entitle you to:

- Unlimited entry to all our sites.
- Free entry for up to six accompanied children (under 18) within your family group per member.
- Your free handbook (RRP £10.95).
- Our exclusive Members' Magazine – packed with ideas, inspiration and news.
- Free or reduced-price admission to over 100 associated attractions.
- Access to exclusive Members' events.
- Access to the exclusive personalised Members' Area on our website.
- Free or discounted entry to our events programme.
- Members' Rewards – exclusive special offers on great brands.

LONDON

GLITT

ERING

Hertfordshire

Essex

Enfield

Barnet

Harrow

Haringey

Waltham
Forest

Redbridge

Havering

Hillingdon

Brent

Islington

Camden

Hackney

Barking
and
Dagenham

Westminster

City of
London

Tower
Hamlets

Newham

Ealing

Kensington

Hammersmith

2.

11
14 12 9 10
13

6

5

Hounslow

Wandsworth

Southwark

Greenwich

Bexley

8

Richmond-
upon-
Thames

Lambeth

Lewisham

4

3

7

Kingston-
upon-
Thames

Merton

Bromley

Sutton

Croydon

1

Kent

Surrey

THE HERMIT'S REVENGE

The **Jewel Tower** was built in the 1360s to safeguard Edward III's
royal treasures. But it was raised on land confiscated from the monks
of Westminster Abbey – an offence they never forgot or forgave.
Their chronicler later gleefully recorded (or invented?) the terrible
punishments inflicted on the land-grabbers. A leadworker who had
stolen a hermit's lead coffin during the building work was almost
immediately struck dead in his own workshop. And when Master
William Usshborne, the king's palace-keeper, made a fish pond
on the site, he choked as he tried to eat a fish from the pond.
He suddenly fell down dead without confessing his sins, therefore
bound directly for Hell.

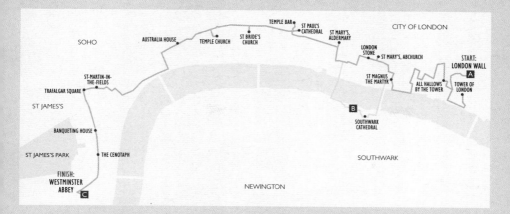

THE ROYAL ROUTE

5 miles | 1 day
Tower of London to Westminster Abbey

Delve into the heart of England's history through the streets of the modern city. Discover relics of traditional belief in the Trojan ancestry of British kings, when London could claim to be the New Troy, and Westminster Abbey was the holy of holies. Pick out holy wells and ancient stones, places of sanctuary and peace, the tombs of saints and the haunts of sinners, from the scrum of the modern city.

Linking the two traditional power centres of London, the City of Westminster and the City of London, you follow the ancient processional way from the Tower of London, once believed to replicate the lost palace of the Kings of Troy, through the popular and commercial City, to the political and priestly city of Westminster, in the shadow of the great Abbey church.

View more details and a downloadable version of this route at
www.english-heritage.org.uk/pilgrimage

Discover English Heritage sites along the pilgrimage route

A London Wall *(p.38)*

B Winchester Palace (see diversion) *(p.38)*

C Chapter House & Pyx Chamber *(p.38)*

In partnership with

APSLEY HOUSE

Revel in the dazzling interiors, glittering treasures and fabulous art collections of the Duke of Wellington's Apsley House. Enjoy our enhanced multimedia guide, and find out about the duke's crucial years in India.

HYDE PARK W1J 7NT

Home of the first Duke of Wellington and his descendants, and popularly known as 'Number 1 London', Apsley House stands right in the heart of the capital at Hyde Park Corner. It is London's only surviving aristocratic townhouse open to visitors today. Originally designed by Robert Adam for Baron Apsley – from whom it takes its name – it was lavishly and fashionably remodelled for Wellington by Benjamin Wyatt between 1819 and 1829.

Wellington is most famous for defeating Napoleon at the Battle of Waterloo in 1815, the culmination of a brilliant military career. But he was also a major politician, becoming Prime Minister in 1828. Reflecting the Duke's rising status, Apsley House's magnificent interiors provided the perfect backdrop for entertaining, particularly at the annual Waterloo Banquets, which commemorated the great victory.

Other highlights include the grandiose Dining Room, with its breathtaking crystal chandelier and gilt Portuguese tableware service, one of many treasures presented to Wellington by grateful nations.

The mansion's interior also displays Wellington's outstanding art collection. Paintings by many famous artists – including Velázquez, Rubens, Goya, Titian and Breughel

NEW FOR 2019

Wellington's years in India are often forgotten, but it was there that he first came to prominence as a military leader. Hear the stories, see the objects and enjoy the display of the Deccan silver service, a gift from his fellow officers at the end of his Indian campaign. Many of the objects will be on display at Apsley House for the first time.

— hang throughout the first floor rooms, and a colossal nude statue of Napoleon by Canova dominates the stairwell at the centre of the house.

Apsley House offers a layered multimedia guide and a children's multimedia guide. In the basement you'll find a new exhibition highlighting Wellington's campaigns in India.

When the seventh Duke of Wellington gave the house to the nation in 1947, the family retained the private rooms, which they still use today. This makes Apsley House the only property cared for by English Heritage in which the owner's family still lives.

Complete your visit by crossing the road to Wellington Arch, one of London's most iconic landmarks, which also honours the famous 'Iron Duke'.

Please note: Photography in the house is not permitted.

OPENING TIMES

1 Apr-1 Nov, Wed-Sun	11am-5pm
2 Nov-22 Dec, Mon-Tue	10am-4pm
2 Jan-31 Mar, Sat-Sun	10am-4pm
23 Dec-1 Jan	Closed

Last entry 30 mins before closing

VISIT US

Address: Apsley House, 149 Piccadilly, Hyde Park Corner, London

Direction: Adjacent to Hyde Park Corner tube station, next to the entrance to Hyde Park

Train: Victoria ½ mile

Bus: From surrounding areas

Tube: Hyde Park Corner

Tel: 020 7499 5676

NON-MEMBERS

Apsley House
Adult £11.60 | Concession £10.50
Child £7.00 | Family £30.20

Pre-booked guided tour
Adult £14.20 | Concession £13.20
Child £10.50 | EH Member £5.50

Joint ticket with Wellington Arch
Adult £15.00 | Concession £13.50
Child £9.10 | Family £39.10

Joint ticket with Wellington Arch Pre-booked guided tour
Adult £20.60 | Concession £19.50
Child £16.10 | EH Member £9.10

ACQ.1947 OVP

Disabled access very limited.
Please phone property for information.

MAP PAGE 338 (3E)
OS MAP 176, 161/173: TQ284799

CHISWICK HOUSE & GARDENS

CHISWICK W4 2RP

Chiswick House is one of the earliest examples of neo-Palladian design in England; its gardens are the birthplace of the English Landscape Movement.

Inspired by the architecture and gardens of ancient Rome, Richard Boyle, Earl of Burlington, designed and built Chiswick House from 1725-29. Its sumptuous interiors and major furnishings were designed by William Kent and display a rich collection of Old Master paintings.

Chiswick's 65 acres of gardens combine grand vistas, architectural delights, water features and wilderness areas. Extensive restoration has returned them to their mid 18th-century glory. They're a unique oasis in London, where you can now also enjoy picnic and play spaces.

Highlights include the magnificent Conservatory, home to the oldest collection of camellias in Britain. At the annual month-long Camellia Show starting in late February, you can explore this collection and stroll in the 19th-century Italian Garden. The walled garden is now a thriving community kitchen garden. You'll find details of pre-booked camellia and garden tours, kitchen garden open days and a year-round event programme at www.chgt.org.uk, where you can also download a guide before your visit.

Complete your day out by visiting the acclaimed modern café.

Managed by Chiswick House & Gardens Trust in partnership with English Heritage.
www.chgt.org.uk

⊤ Available for corporate and private hire – contact Chiswick House and Gardens Trust 020 3141 3351

▣ Licensed for civil wedding ceremonies

OPENING TIMES

House

1 Apr-31 Oct, Mon, Wed	11am-3pm
Sat-Sun	11am-4pm
1 Nov-31 Mar	Closed
Last entry 30 mins before closing	
Garden, daily all year round	7am-dusk
Conservatory, daily	10am-3pm

Occasionally the House or Conservatory is closed for private events – please check www.chgt.org.uk prior to visiting

House is available for private group and tour bookings on Tue, Thu and Fri Apr-Oct and all week Nov-Mar

VISIT US

Direction: Burlington Lane, Chiswick, London W4 2RP

Train: Chiswick ¼ mile walk (10 mins)

Bus: TfL 190, E3

Tube: Turnham Green 1 mile then bus E3

Tel: 020 8995 0508

NON-MEMBERS

House:
Adult **£8.25** | Concession **£5.50**
Child **Free entry for children under 18**

Entry to the gardens is free; donations welcome

Members may be charged for special events

Disabled access to ground floor only.

Dogs on leads (restricted areas only).

Parking (charges apply – disabled bays available) – off Westbound A4. Satnav: W4 2RP.

No photography allowed inside the house.

MAP PAGE 338 (3E)
OS MAP 176, 161: TQ210775

ELTHAM PALACE
AND GARDENS

There's no better place in Britain to immerse yourself in 20th-century design than Eltham Palace. See what 1930s millionaires could achieve when they built and furnished a mansion regardless of expense — it's a triumph of style, taste and ahead-of-the-time home comforts.

GREENWICH SE9 5QE

Stephen and Virginia Courtauld created a uniquely memorable masterpiece when they built their mansion adjoining the Great Hall of medieval Eltham Palace. Completed in 1936, the retro 'Wrennaisance' red brick exterior of the new house was built in sympathy with the old hall. But the interior is an outstanding showcase of 1930s high fashion; an eclectic mix of art deco, ultra-smart ocean-liner style and cutting-edge Swedish modernist design.

An extensive restoration programme has opened more doors at Eltham. An introductory film uncovers the history of the palace, how the Courtaulds used the foremost contemporary architects and interior designers to create it, and how they lived here. Multimedia handsets draw you into an elite circle of 1930s society, and let you feel what it was like to be a guest here. They include cine-film clips, oral history recordings and original photography of the family. Visual guides to each room help you admire the mansion's striking art deco design details and explore recently revealed features.

What impresses most is the house itself. The dining room is an art deco tour de force, with bird's-eye maple veneered walls, a shimmering aluminium-leaf ceiling and black-and-silver doors portraying animals and birds. Still more exotic is Virginia Courtauld's bathroom, complete with onyx bath and sink and gold-plated bath taps.

You can also take a look into her walk-in wardrobe, next to her bedroom. It displays glamorous period dresses based on those she wore, and you can try on replica 1930s clothes and accessories. Explore her nephews' bedrooms and bathroom, complete with a shower, then unusual in a private house. It's one of a pioneering range of ultra-modern conveniences you'll discover in this innovative 'high-tech' home, including underfloor heating, a centralised vacuum cleaner and a built-in audio system.

Admire the 1930s Map Room, displaying maps and paintings until recently hidden by wallpaper. This room records the Courtaulds' exotic holidays, often involving pioneering travel by air. Also on view are the basement rooms – a luxury wartime air-raid shelter and a billiard room, with a mural including the family's pet lemur, Mah-Jongg.

For a complete contrast with the 1930s rooms, step into the Great Hall – the only substantially

remaining part of the medieval palace. It has a magnificent hammer beam roof, built for Edward IV in the 1470s. Henry VIII spent much of his childhood at Eltham.

Be sure to leave time to wander the palace's 19 acres of beautiful gardens. They've been re-presented in the style commissioned by the Courtaulds, with the Rock Garden and cascade and Rose Garden replanted.

Eltham Palace also has a stylish visitor centre, with a shop and glasshouse café. For children there's a fantastic play area. Like the Courtaulds travelling around the globe in their luxury yachts and planes, little ones will have the world at their feet.

🎬 *The Crown; Trust; Stan & Ollie; Brideshead Revisited;* Florence and The Machine's *'Shake it Out'* music video; Jessie Ware's *'Alone'* music video.

🍽 Available for corporate and private hire

🔔 Licensed for civil wedding ceremonies

OPENING TIMES

1 Apr-30 Sep, Sun-Fri	10am-6pm
1-19 Oct, Sun-Fri	10am-5pm
20-25 Oct, daily	10am-5pm
26 Oct-3 Nov, Sun-Fri	10am-5pm
4 Nov-23 Dec, Sun	10am-4pm
2 Jan-16 Feb, Sun	10am-4pm
17-23 Feb, daily	10am-4pm
24 Feb-31 Mar, Sun-Fri	10am-4pm
Christmas Opening	
24-25 Dec	Closed
26 Dec-1 Jan, daily	10am-4pm
Last entry 30 mins before closing	

Please check the website for the most up-to-date Friday opening times, as the Palace may occasionally be closed for private functions throughout the year

VISIT US

Address: Court Yard, Eltham, Greenwich, London

Direction: Off Court Rd SE9, Jct 3 on the M25, then A20 to Eltham. Please use satnav postcode SE9 5NP to help direct you straight to the car park

Train: Mottingham ½ mile walk (best for visitor centre entrance). Eltham Station is also ½ mile walk

Bus: TfL bus services 124, 126, 160 or 161 and then a short walk

Tel: 020 8294 2548

NON-MEMBERS

Adult **£17.00** | Concession **£15.30**
Child **£10.20** | Family **£44.20**

Members may be charged for special events

[ACQ.1995] 🎧 ♿ ♿ ☕ f ✳ ⬛ ⵜ 🔔 🚹 🚻
✕ P 🏠 🍴 🛍 💷 🐦 ⚠ [OVP]

Pushchairs and large rucksacks need to be left at reception.

Parking charges apply to non-members.
Parking free for Members.

Some restrictions on photography in the house.

MAP PAGE 339 (4F)
OS MAP 177, 162: TQ424740

KENWOOD

Kenwood is among the finest of all the great houses in our care. Its breathtaking interiors and fabulous world-class art collection are free for everyone to enjoy. The mansion and its tranquil parkland are favourites with visitors seeking relief from the bustle of central London, and there's plenty here for families to discover together.

HAMPSTEAD NW3 7JR

Crowning Hampstead Heath, Kenwood House was bought by William Murray in 1754; he became Lord Chief Justice and, from 1776, the 1st Earl of Mansfield. The house was remodelled by Robert Adam between 1764 and 1779 to create the imposing mansion that greets visitors today.

Kenwood displays the Iveagh Bequest, an internationally renowned art collection. It was assembled by brewing magnate Edward Guinness, Earl of Iveagh, and bequeathed to the nation, along with the Kenwood estate, in 1927. It includes paintings by Rembrandt, Vermeer, Van Dyke, Turner, Reynolds, Gainsborough and Constable.

Enjoy the welcoming atmosphere of the house as you take in this extraordinary collection. There are comfortable sofas where you can relax and browse room booklets, and you can ask our volunteer explainers about the house and its paintings.

A lift to the first floor provides full access to all our collections. The original bequest of 69 paintings has been joined by the Suffolk Collection of Tudor and Stuart portraits, including full-length paintings of extravagantly dressed Jacobean courtiers.

Most striking of all Kenwood's glories, however, is its suite of magnificent Robert Adam rooms: Entrance Hall, Great Staircase, Ante-Room, and his masterpiece, the Great Library. These lavish rooms have been redecorated as they originally appeared over two centuries ago.

Through integrated interpretation, you can discover for yourself the story of Kenwood and its people, from Lord Mansfield and his mixed-race great-niece, Dido Belle, to brewing millionaire Edward Guinness. Feel free to wander through the house, opening desks and boxes to reveal the stories within. 'Growing Space', an activity base in the Orangery, features areas where families can stay and play together. Our explorer backpacks are perfect for families with under fives, and older children can look out for Mac and his doggy paw prints, leading you to hands-on activities.

WANDER THROUGH THE HOUSE, OPENING DESKS AND BOXES TO REVEAL THE STORIES WITHIN

House Highlights tours, free to members, are available from our team at weekends, Mondays, Wednesdays and Fridays; they last about an hour. Our volunteers also offer 15-minute Spotlight Tours, free to all, on Tuesdays and Thursdays.

Kenwood's 112 acres of leafy parkland, landscaped by Humphry Repton, is renowned for its fine views over London, its sculptures and its meandering woodland paths. Don't miss the conserved ornamental 18th-century Dairy. It's open on the first and third Sundays of every month, April-October. (Please call site for details.)

You can also download our free app before visiting: www.english-heritage.org.uk/kenwood

📖 *Notting Hill; Mansfield Park; Scenes of a Sexual Nature; Venus; Belle.*

OPENING TIMES

House

1 Apr-3 Nov, daily	10am-5pm
4 Nov-31 Mar, daily	10am-4pm
24-26, 31 Dec & 1 Jan	Closed

Brewhouse Café

1 Apr-30 Sep, daily	9am-6pm
1 Oct-30 Nov, daily	9am-5pm
1 Dec-31 Jan, daily	9am-4pm
1 Feb-31 Mar, daily	9am-5pm
24-25 & 31 Dec	Closed

Garden House Shop

1 Apr-30 Oct, daily	10am-5pm
31 Oct-31 Mar, daily	10am-4pm
24-25 & 31 Dec	Closed

Estate open from 8am to dusk (see park entrance for closing time)

Entry to the House and grounds is free; donations welcome. Pre-booked group tours available

Last entry 30 mins before closing

VISIT US

Address: Kenwood, Hampstead

Direction: Hampstead Lane, NW3

Train: Gospel Oak or Hampstead Heath (both London Overground)

Bus: TfL 210 (also bus H3 passes within a short walk)

Tube: Golders Green or Archway then bus 210

Tel: 020 8348 1286

ACQ.1927

Disabled access (lift to all floors for visitors with a disability or mobility problems; toilets).

Dogs on leads (restricted areas only).

Café open daily.

Parking charges apply. Disabled bays available.
Mobility service available on request.
Parking free for Members during visit.

MAP PAGE 338 (3E)
OS MAP 176, 173: TQ271874

🔲 Available for corporate and private hire

🔲 Licensed for civil wedding ceremonies

CHAPTER HOUSE AND PYX CHAMBER

WESTMINSTER ABBEY – SW1P 3PA

Built in 1250, the Chapter House was used for monks' daily meetings, and sometimes by medieval Parliaments. A beautiful vaulted building, it displays a medieval tiled floor and spectacular wall paintings.

Under the care and management of the Dean and Chapter of Westminster.
www.westminster-abbey.org

OPENING TIMES

1 Apr-31 Mar, Mon-Fri	10am-4.30pm
Sat	10am-4pm
19 Apr, 24-25 Dec & 1 Jan	Closed

May be closed at short notice on state and religious occasions

VISIT US

Direction: Within Westminster Abbey. Members who do not wish to visit the rest of the Abbey: enter Dean's Yard from Broad Sanctuary and turn left across the square to find the cloisters. All other visitors should use the normal visitor entry point for the Abbey

Train: Victoria and Charing Cross

Bus: From surrounding areas

Tube: Westminster and St James's Park

Tel: 020 7222 5152

NON-MEMBERS

Buy ticket from Westminster Abbey or online

ACQ.1872	Chapter House
ACQ.1901	Pyx Chamber

MAP PAGE 338 (3E)
OS MAP 176/177, 161/173: TQ299795

COOMBE CONDUIT

KINGSTON UPON THAMES – KT2 7HE

Two brick-walled chambers, connected by an underground passage. Part of a system collecting spring water and channelling it to Hampton Court Palace.

Managed by the Kingston upon Thames Society.

OPENING TIMES

Apr-Sep,
2nd Sun of each month   2pm-4pm

Group and education visits outside these hours by arrangement

VISIT US

Direction: Coombe Lane West close to corner with Lord Chancellor Walk

Train: Norbiton ¾ mile or Raynes Park 1 mile then bus 57

Bus: TfL 57

Tube: Wimbledon then bus 57

Tel: 020 8549 4586

ACQ.1978 🕱 ⚠

Disabled access (exterior only).

MAP PAGE 338 (4E)
OS MAP 176, 161: TQ204698

HARMONDSWORTH GREAT BARN

HILLINGDON – UB7 0AQ

Medieval timber-framed barn, built 1426-27. One of the largest barns ever built in England, and among the least altered medieval buildings in Britain.

Managed by the Friends of the Great Barn at Harmondsworth.

OPENING TIMES

Apr, 2nd & 4th Sun of the month	11am-4pm
May-Sep, 2nd & 4th Sun of each month	10am-5pm
Oct, 2nd & 4th Sun of the month	11am-4pm
1 Nov-31 Mar	Closed

VISIT US

Direction: Located in High Street, Harmondsworth Village

Train: West Drayton 2 miles

Bus: TfL U3 and 350

Tube: Heathrow Terminals 1, 2, 3 – 2 miles

Tel: 0370 333 1181

ACQ.2012 🕱

MAP PAGE 338 (3E)
OS MAP 176, 160: TQ056778

LONDON WALL

TOWER HILL – EC3N 4DJ

The best-preserved remnant of the Roman wall which formed part of the eastern defences of Roman Londinium. Built c. AD 200.

OPENING TIMES

Any reasonable daylight hours

VISIT US

Direction: Located outside Tower Hill Underground station, EC3

Train: Fenchurch Street ¼ mile or London Bridge 1 mile

Bus: From surrounding areas

Tube: Tower Hill

DLR: Tower Gateway

ACQ.1953

MAP PAGE 339 (3F)
OS MAP 176/177, 173: TQ336807

WINCHESTER PALACE

SOUTHWARK – SE1 9DG

Part of the 12th-century great hall of Winchester Palace, London mansion of the Bishops of Winchester, including a striking rose window.

Managed by Bankside Open Spaces Trust.

OPENING TIMES

Any reasonable daylight hours

VISIT US

Direction: On Clink Street close to corner with Stoney Street (between *Golden Hinde* replica ship and the Clink Prison Museum)

Train/Tube: London Bridge ¼ mile

Bus: From surrounding areas

ACQ.1967

MAP PAGE 339 (3F)
OS MAP 176/177, 173: TQ325803

JEWEL TOWER

Tucked away between the Houses of Parliament and Westminster Abbey, the Jewel Tower is an easily overlooked but precious fragment of English history.

It was built in c. 1365 as the 'Jewel House' to safeguard Edward III's silver plate and royal treasures. It's the sole surviving remnant of the 'Privy Palace', the private royal apartments within the great medieval Palace of Westminster. It's also the only part of the palace complex which survived the disastrous fire of 1834 and is regularly open to the public.

Displaying a finely carved medieval vault, its 14th-century architecture remains largely unaltered, with an anti-clockwise spiral staircase. You can still see the excavated remains of its original moat. The tower later became a royal Tudor lumber room, whose contents included dolls discarded by Henry VIII's daughters. Subsequently it housed the House of Lords records and then the National Weights and Measures Office, determining the value of weights and measures for Britain and its empire.

The Jewel Tower offers you magnificent views of the Houses of Parliament, and you can explore its history and changing roles over the centuries across three floors of recently expanded displays. Outstanding among its collection are the Westminster Capitals, eight rare and beautifully carved early Norman sculptures made in the 1090s, which once adorned William Rufus's Westminster Hall. You can also admire the Palace of Westminster Sword, part of a richly decorated Anglo-Saxon weapon dating from the 800s. Once the prized possession of a Saxon nobleman, it was re-discovered near here over a millennium after it was made.

⊤ Available for corporate and private hire

OPENING TIMES

1 Apr-30 Sep, daily	10am-6pm
1 Oct-3 Nov, daily	10am-5pm
4 Nov-31 Mar, Sat-Sun	10am-4pm

Last entry 30 mins before closing

VISIT US

Direction: Located on Abingdon Street, opposite the southern end of the Houses of Parliament (Victoria Tower)

Train: Victoria and Charing Cross ¾ mile, Waterloo 1 mile

Bus: TfL 3, 11, 12, 24, 53, 87, 88, 148, 159, 211 & 453

Tube: St James's Park and Westminster ¼ mile

Tel: 020 7222 2219

NON-MEMBERS

Adult **£6.30** | Concession **£5.70**
Child **£3.80** | Family **£16.40**

ACQ.1938 ◼ ◼ ◼ ◼ ◼ OVP

New café with indoor and outdoor seating.

Disabled access (limited).

MAP PAGE 338 (3E)
OS MAP 176/177, 161/173: TQ301793

MARBLE HILL HOUSE

TWICKENHAM TW1 2NL

A lovely Palladian mansion still set in riverside parkland, Marble Hill House is the last complete survivor of the elegant 18th-century villas which bordered the Thames between Richmond and Hampton Court.

It was begun in 1724 for Henrietta Howard, Countess of Suffolk, a remarkable woman of letters and friend of some of England's greatest writers. The house and gardens were planned by a coterie of fashionable connoisseurs, including the poet Alexander Pope.

Marble Hill was intended as an Arcadian retreat from crowded 18th-century London, and there can be few places in England which better recall the atmosphere of Georgian fashionable life.

WE'RE PLANNING EXCITING CHANGES TO MARBLE HILL AND ITS SURROUNDINGS

We're planning exciting changes to Marble Hill and its surroundings. We want to open Marble Hill House for free and more often, open up more areas in the park, create new habitats to improve the park's biodiversity and restore the 18th-century garden. See www.english-heritage.org.uk/marble-hill-revived for details and updates.

Please note: The house will remain open for the full 2019 season from Apr-Oct. Project works will commence on site from November 2019. The house will be closed for the 2020 season and then reopen Apr 2021 when the project is due to launch.

🎬 *Nanny McPhee 2: The Big Bang; Vanity Fair.*

OPENING TIMES

House (Guided Tour Only)

1 Apr-27 Oct, Sat-Sun	10.30am, 12pm, 2.15pm & 3.30pm
28 Oct-31 Mar	Closed
Park	
1 Apr-31 Mar, daily	7am-dusk
Café	
1 Apr-27 Oct, daily	10am-5pm
28 Oct-31 Mar	Check website for details

VISIT US

Direction:	Richmond Road, Twickenham, London
Train:	St Margaret's or Twickenham
Bus:	TfL 33, 490, H22, R68, R70
Tube:	Richmond 1 mile
Tel:	020 8892 5115

NON-MEMBERS

Adult **£8.60** | Concession **£7.70**
Child **£5.20** | Family **£22.40**

Café (Coach House Café, open all year).

Disabled access (exterior & ground floor only; toilets).

Parking charges apply to non-members.
Parking free for Members.

No photography allowed inside the house.

MAP PAGE 338 (4E)
OS MAP 176, 161: TQ173736

RANGER'S HOUSE
THE WERNHER COLLECTION

GREENWICH PARK SE10 8QX

The Wernher Collection is one of the greatest private art collections ever assembled in Europe. Now you can explore this glittering spectacle at your own pace, guided through its immensely diverse wonders by new interpretation.

Gathered by the fabulously wealthy diamond magnate Sir Julius Wernher (1850-1912), the collection is housed in an elegant Georgian villa, once the official residence of the 'Ranger of Greenwich Park'. It includes nearly 700 varied works of art, including early religious paintings and Dutch Old Masters, minute carved Gothic ivories, fine Renaissance bronzes and silver treasures, and the life-sized erotic marble statue, *The Love of Angels*. The 120 pieces of medieval and Renaissance jewellery – the largest collection in England – feature pendants set with opals, pearls, rubies, sapphires and diamonds. There are tapestries with fanciful scenes of Chinese life, a mechanical travelling cabinet whose drawers pop out by turning a handle, and little-known paintings by famous artists.

Sir Julius developed his keen eye for high-quality craftsmanship while assessing diamonds in South Africa. He could afford to buy the very best, and his particular passion was for what he called the 'splendidly ugly' – tiny, unusual artworks expertly crafted in rich materials. So you'll discover an enamelled gold skull pendant; a minute boxwood coffin with intricate contents; and a beautiful 2nd-century BC Greek gold earring of the goddess Victory. Everyone will have their favourite. What will yours be?

Explore a preview of highlights from the collection on our website.

⊤ Available for corporate and private hire
◆ Licensed for civil wedding ceremonies

OPENING TIMES

1 Apr-31 Oct, Sun-Thu	11am-5pm
1 Nov-31 Mar	Closed

VISIT US

Address: Chesterfield Walk, Blackheath, London

Direction: Ranger's House is on Chesterfield Walk and overlooks the junction of General Wolfe Road and Shooters Hill Road

DLR: Deptford Bridge then bus 53, or 20 min walk from Cutty Sark

Train: Blackheath ¾ mile

Bus: TfL 53 & 386. Also TfL 54, 202 & 380 will stop close by

River: Greenwich Pier

Tel: For enquiries, please call Eltham Palace on 020 8294 2548

NON-MEMBERS

Adult **£9.50** | Concession **£8.60**
Child **£5.70** | Family **£24.70**

ACQ.1986 ♿ 🏛 ⊤ ◆ 🚶 🚻 📷 OVP

Toilets (including disabled).

No photography allowed inside the house.

MAP PAGE 339 (4F)
OS MAP 177, 161/162: TQ388769

WELLINGTON ARCH

Visit this famous landmark to gain wonderful views over Royal London from the balconies, and see our new Royal Artillery exhibition.

HYDE PARK W1J 7JZ

Set in the heart of the capital at Hyde Park Corner, opposite Apsley House, Wellington Arch is one of London's most iconic monuments. It's crowned by the largest bronze sculpture in Europe, depicting the Angel of Peace descending on the 'Quadriga' – or four-horsed chariot – of War.

The balconies just below the sculpture offer you glorious panoramas over the Royal Parks and central London. It's a unique spot from which to view the Household Cavalry passing beneath to and from the Changing of the Guard at Horse Guards Parade.

On the first floor within the Arch, you'll discover a display revealing its fascinating and sometimes surprising story. Originally intended as a grand outer entrance to Buckingham Palace, it later took on the role of a victory arch proclaiming Wellington's triumph over Napoleon, and once housed London's smallest police station. By 1883, however, the Arch was causing traffic bottlenecks. So it was moved, stone by stone, some 100 metres (328 feet) to its current position. The great bronze Quadriga sculpture, by Adrian Jones, was added in 1912.

On the second floor, you'll find our recently-installed display about the Royal Regiment of Artillery, 1914-1918. Mounted in partnership with the Royal Artillery, it commemorates the wartime sacrifice of over 49,000 artillerymen, and considers how they were remembered by the nearby Royal Artillery memorial, controversial because it was the first war memorial in Britain to depict a fallen soldier. The exhibition also focusses on the human aspect, highlighting the story of Gunner Stone, VC and including rarely-seen artefacts from the Ypres battlefields.

The third- and fourth-floor exhibition, 'Waterloo 1815: The Battle for Peace' explains the context, the events and the aftermath of the battle. You can even see a pair of Wellington's boots and the sword he carried on that famous day, 18 June 1815.

Discover much more about the 'Iron Duke' by combining your trip to Wellington Arch with a visit to Wellington's London residence, Apsley House, just opposite.

🔲 Available for corporate and private hire

OPENING TIMES

1 Apr-30 Sep, daily	10am-6pm
1-31 Oct, daily	10am-5pm
1 Nov-31 Mar, daily	10am-4pm
24-26, 31 Dec & 1 Jan	Closed
Last entry 30 mins before closing	
May close due to corporate or private hire	

VISIT US

Address: Wellington Arch, Apsley Way, Hyde Park Corner, London

Direction: Hyde Park Corner, W1J

Train: Victoria ½ mile

Bus: From surrounding areas

Tube: Hyde Park Corner, adjacent

Tel: 020 7930 2726

NON-MEMBERS

Adult £6.30 | Concession £5.70
Child £3.80 | Family £16.40

Pre-booked guided tour
Adult £8.50 | Concession £8.20
Child £6.70 | EH Member £3.70

Joint ticket with Apsley House
Adult £15.00 | Concession £13.50
Child £9.10 | Family £39.10

Joint ticket with Apsley House
Pre-booked guided tour
Adult £20.60 | Concession £19.50
Child £16.10 | EH Members £9.10

ACQ.1999 ♿ 🛍 E f 📷 ☕ 📷 ⚠ OVP

MAP PAGE 338 (3E)
OS MAP 176, 161/173: TQ284798

BLUE
PLAQUES

Blue Plaques commemorate famous people and interesting buildings
– and, very often, make the link between the two. They offer an
accessible introduction to the inspiring stories of human endeavour
and achievement that lie behind the front doors of many a street.

London's Blue Plaques scheme, founded in 1866, is believed to be the oldest of its kind in the world – and has inspired many similar programmes across the UK and abroad. English Heritage has run the scheme since 1986, and there are now over 940 official plaques in Greater London.

The London plaques celebrate all areas of human achievement and reflect London's past and present as an international city of great diversity. Plaques put up in recent years have commemorated an exciting range of figures – from sports stars, including football legend Bobby Moore, to the rock stars John Lennon and Freddie Mercury, as well as the suffragettes Emmeline and Christabel Pankhurst, and Maud McCarthy, the army matron-in-chief during the First World War.

Sometimes historical events or groups of people are commemorated, rather than individuals. Examples are the plaque that marks the house in which the Pre-Raphaelite Brotherhood of artists was founded in Gower Street, Bloomsbury, and the blue roundel at Alexandra Palace – from where the world's first regular high-definition television broadcasts were transmitted.

Among the names added to the blue plaque roster in 2018 was the *Mary Poppins* author P. L. Travers, whose plaque graces her old home just off the King's Road in Chelsea. In south London, the film stars Peter Cushing and Margaret Lockwood are commemorated, as is the former workshop of the Formula One-winning Cooper Car Company. Appropriately, perhaps, the botanist Agnes Arber is honoured in Primrose Hill, while the modernist 'Isokon' building in Belsize Park now bears a plaque to the Bauhaus figures Walter Gropius, Marcel Breuer and László Moholy-Nagy.

FIND OUT MORE

An area-by-area walk-around guidebook, *The English Heritage Guide to London's Blue Plaques*, is available at the English Heritage online shop and in all good bookshops. The free Blue Plaques app for Apple and Android features maps and guided walks, and each official London plaque has its own page on the English Heritage website.

GET INVOLVED

The scheme relies entirely on private donations and almost all plaques originate from a proposal from a member of the public. To be considered for a Blue Plaque, a person must have been dead for 20 years, and an authentic building holding strong associations with them must survive in London. If you would like to nominate someone for a Blue Plaque in London, go to **www.english-heritage.org.uk/ propose-a-plaque**

Thirteen new plaques were put up across London over the course of 2018. Help us continue this work by making a donation today: **www.english-heritage.org. uk/support-the-scheme**

King Edward VII

LONDON STATUES

Explore central London to discover 48 statues and monuments which honour famous historical figures. They also include some outstanding 20th-century war memorials.

Central London's statues reflect the priorities of the periods when they were erected. Some commemorate monarchs and aristocrats, and others the heroes of empire. More are associated with wars, from the Napoleonic Wars to the Second World War. Outstanding among these are the famous Cenotaph and the Royal Artillery Memorial. Wartime allies are also remembered, including De Gaulle and Eisenhower. Explorers include Columbus, Scott, Raleigh and Sir John Franklin. Only four women are commemorated – two queens and the nurses Florence Nightingale and Edith Cavell.

THE CAPITAL'S MONUMENTS

Baron Lawrence
Waterloo Place, SW1

Belgian War Memorial
Victoria Embankment, WC2N

Captain Scott
Waterloo Place, SW1

Carabiniers Memorial
Chelsea Embankment, SW3

Cenotaph
Whitehall, SW1

Chindit Memorial
Victoria Embankment, SW1

Christopher Columbus
Belgrave Square, SW1

Clive of India
King Charles St, SW1

Colin Campbell
Waterloo Place, SW1

Crimea Memorial
Waterloo Place, SW1

Duke of Cambridge
Whitehall, SW1

Duke of Devonshire
Whitehall, SW1

Duke of Kent
Crescent Gardens
(locked), Portland Place, W1

Duke of Wellington
Apsley Way, W1

Earl Haig
Whitehall, SW1

Edith Cavell
St Martin's Place, WC2

Florence Nightingale
Waterloo Place, SW1

General de Gaulle
Carlton Gardens, SW1

General de San Martin
Belgrave Square, SW1

General Eisenhower
Grosvenor Square, W1

General Gordon
Victoria Embankment, SW1

George Washington
Trafalgar Square, WC2

King Charles I
Whitehall, SW1

King Edward VII
Waterloo Place, SW1

King George II
Golden Square, W1

King George III
Cockspur St, SW1

King James II
National Gallery,
Trafalgar Square, WC2

King William III
St James's Square, SW1

Lord Curzon
Carlton House Terrace, SW1

Lord Herbert
Waterloo Place, SW1

Lord Napier of Magdala
Queen's Gate, SW7

Lord Portal
Victoria Embankment, SW1

Lord Trenchard
Victoria Embankment, SW1

Machine Gun Corps
Apsley Way, W1

Marble Arch W1

Montgomery
Whitehall, SW1

Queen Anne
Queen Anne's Gate, SW1

Queen Charlotte
Queen Square, WC1

Royal Artillery Memorial
Apsley Way, W1

Samuel Plimsoll
Victoria Embankment, SW1

Simon Bolivar
Belgrave Square, SW1

Sir Arthur Harris
St Clement Danes, WC2

Sir John Franklin
Waterloo Place, SW1

Sir Walter Raleigh
Old Royal Naval College,
Greenwich, SE10

Thomas Cubitt
St George's Drive, Pimlico, SW1

Viscount Alanbrooke
Whitehall, SW1

Viscount Slim
Whitehall, SW1

Wellington Arch and Quadriga
Apsley Way, W1

Clive of India

Cenotaph

Florence Nightingale

ESTIC

Osborne

TELLING TALES:
THE MYTHS,
LEGENDS AND
FOLKLORE OF
ENGLAND

DID HAROLD SURVIVE?

Harold, the last Saxon king of England, was killed at the Battle of Hastings. Or was he? By the 12th century there were several legends about Harold surviving Hastings. According to one, he was actually smuggled from the battlefield and taken to Winchester, where a Muslim woman healed his wounds – although she didn't replace his missing eye. Afterwards, he wandered through Germany and England for 50 years as an anonymous pilgrim. It was said that he died in Chester, aged over 100, only revealing his identity on his deathbed.

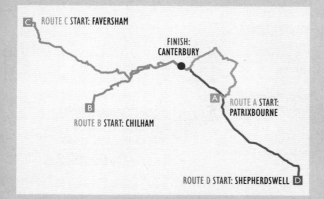

Discover English Heritage sites along the pilgrimage route

Route A
The Old Way to Canterbury
(Patrixbourne start, 8 miles)
See St Augustine's Abbey & Conduit

Route B
North Downs Pilgrims Way
(Chilham start, 7 miles)
See St Augustine's Abbey & Conduit

Route C
Augustine Camino
(Faversham start, 12 miles)
See Faversham Stone Chapel, Maison Dieu, St Augustine's Abbey & Conduit

Route D
Via Francigena in England
(Shepherdswell start, 11 miles)
See St Augustine's Abbey & Conduit

CANTERBURY

4 x 1-day routes
(an extra day is recommended to enjoy Canterbury).

Canterbury was where St Augustine first settled, on a mission from Rome to convert England to Christianity, and where Thomas Becket, the 12th-century Archbishop, was murdered in the Cathedral. The city has welcomed pilgrims for over a thousand years, attracted by St Augustine's Abbey, Canterbury Cathedral and St Martin's Church – the oldest church in the English-speaking world – and its many other ancient churches, saints, holy springs, and, latterly, Chaucer's tales. Give yourself an extra day to explore the city and hear the cathedral choir sing evensong.

View more details and a downloadable version of this route at
www.english-heritage.org.uk/pilgrimage

In partnership with

the **British Pilgrimage Trust**

DONNINGTON CASTLE

WEST BERKSHIRE – RG14 2LE

The striking, twin-towered, 14th-century gatehouse of this castle, later the focus of a Civil War siege and battle, survives amid impressive earthworks.

OPENING TIMES

Any reasonable daylight hours, exterior viewing only

Car park open daily	7am-7pm

VISIT US

Direction: 1 mile N of Newbury, off B4494

Train: Newbury 1¼ miles

Bus: Kennections service 6A & West Berkshire Council Transport 5, 5A, 5C

 ACQ.1952 🚻 ♿ 🐕 P

Disabled access (steep slopes within grounds).

MAP PAGE 338 (4C)
OS MAP 174, 158: SU461692

BISHOP'S WALTHAM PALACE

HAMPSHIRE – SO32 1DH

The ruins of a medieval palace used by the bishops of Winchester. Much of what survives is the work of William Wykeham, bishop from 1367. The ground floor of the farmhouse, adapted from the palace's lodging range, houses the Bishop's Waltham Town Museum.

BISHOP'S WALTHAM PALACE

OPENING TIMES

Grounds

1 Apr-30 Sep, daily	10am-6pm
1 Oct-31 Mar, Sat-Sun	10am-4pm

Farmhouse Museum

4 May-30 Sep, Sat-Sun	12pm-4pm

VISIT US

Direction: In Bishop's Waltham

Train: Botley 3½ miles

Bus: Xelabus X9, X10 & X17 (Wed); Stagecoach Bus 69

ACQ.1952 ♿ 🐕 P 🏕 ⚠

Disabled access (grounds only).

Dogs on leads (restricted areas only).

MAP PAGE 338 (5C)
OS MAP 185, 119: SU552174

CALSHOT CASTLE

HAMPSHIRE – SO45 1BR

This Tudor artillery fort, built to defend the approaches to Southampton, later saw service in both World Wars.

Managed by Hampshire County Council.

OPENING TIMES

1 Apr-29 Sep, daily	10.30am-4.30pm
Castle closed 1.00pm-1.30pm daily	
30 Sep-31 Mar	Closed
Last entry 30 mins before closing	

VISIT US

Direction: On spit, 2 miles SE of Fawley, off B3053

CALSHOT CASTLE

Train: Beaulieu Road 10 miles, Southampton 15 miles

Bus: Solent Blue Line Bluestar 8 passes within 1 mile

Tel: 023 8089 2023; when castle is closed, please call 023 8089 2077

NON-MEMBERS

Adult **£4.00** | Concession **£3.50**
Child **£2.80** | Family **£10.80**

ACQ.1964 ♿ 🧍 🧍 🐕 P 📷 ⚠

Disabled access
(Keep: ground floor only; toilets).

Parking charges apply.

MAP PAGE 338 (6C)
OS MAP 196, OL22/OL29/119: SU489025

FLOWERDOWN BARROWS

HAMPSHIRE – SO22 6PS

Three Bronze Age burial mounds, including two bowl barrows and the largest and finest disc barrow in Hampshire.

OPENING TIMES

Any reasonable daylight hours

VISIT US

Direction: Off B3049, out of Winchester to Littleton; at crossroads in centre of village

Train: Winchester 2 miles

Bus: Stagecoach in Hampshire 7; Wheelers Travel 16

ACQ.1972 🐕

MAP PAGE 338 (5C)
OS MAP 185, 132: SU459320

FORT BROCKHURST

HAMPSHIRE – PO12 4DS

One of the best surviving of the artillery forts built to protect Portsmouth's vital harbour during the 1850s-60s, when invasion by Napoleon III's France was expected. It's largely unaltered, and you can still see the moated keep, parade ground and emplacements for formidable heavy guns.

The fort stores a treasure trove of objects from English Heritage's extensive reserve collections, including stonework, textiles, jewellery and furniture. Pre-booked group tours available.

OPENING TIMES

Exterior:
Any reasonable daylight hours

Interior: May-Sep, 2nd Sat of the month	11am-3pm

Due to occasional operational changes, we advise visitors to call in advance to check opening times

Additional opening times during Gosport Heritage Open Days – please check website

VISIT US

Direction: Off A32, in Gunner's Way, Elson; on N side of Gosport

Train: Fareham 3 miles

Bus: First E1, E2, 9A, 10 & 11 – Gosport Ferry links with ⊠ Portsmouth & Southsea

Tel: 023 9258 1059

[ACQ.1963] 🚻 ♿ 🐕 🏛 🚶 🅿 ⚠

Disabled access (grounds and ground floor only).

Dogs on leads (restricted areas only).

> MAP PAGE 338 (6C)
> OS MAP 196, OL29/119:
> SU596021

THE GRANGE AT NORTHINGTON

HAMPSHIRE – SO24 9TG

Set like a lakeside temple in a landscaped park, the Grange at Northington is among the foremost examples of the Greek Revival style in England, remodelled after 1808.

🎬 *Onegin*, with Ralph Fiennes.

OPENING TIMES

Exterior only:

1 Apr-31 May, daily	10am-6pm
1 Jun-31 Jul, daily	9am-2pm*
1 Aug-30 Sep, daily	10am-6pm
1 Oct-31 Mar, daily	10am-4pm

*Closes early for Opera evenings in June and July

24-26 Dec & 1 Jan	Closed

VISIT US

Direction: Located 4 miles N of New Alresford, off B3046 along a farm track – 450 metres (493 yards)

Train: Winchester 8 miles

Bus: Cresta Coaches C41 to Northington then ½ mile walk

Tel: 0370 333 1181

[ACQ.1975] ♿ 🐕 🛡 🍽 🅿 🏛 ⚠

Disabled access (with assistance, steep steps to terrace).

> MAP PAGE 338 (5C)
> OS MAP 185, 132: SU562362

HURST CASTLE

HAMPSHIRE – SO41 0TP

Among the most advanced of Henry VIII's artillery fortresses, guarding the Solent entrance. It was later strengthened by immense 19th-century gun emplacements and a Second World War lookout tower and searchlight positions. We're currently carrying out a £1 million conservation project on the castle.

Managed by Hurst Marine.
www.hurstcastle.co.uk

OPENING TIMES

1 Apr-30 Sep, daily	10.30am-5.30pm
1-31 Oct, daily	10.30am-4pm
1 Nov-31 Mar	Closed

Occasionally open in winter at weekends – please ring 01590 642500

VISIT US

Direction: 1½ mile walk on shingle spit from Milford-on-Sea. Best approached by ferry from Keyhaven – call 01590 642344 for ferry details and fares

Train: Lymington Town 6½ miles

Bus: End of June to mid-Sep New Forest Tour 'Blue Route' daily to Keyhaven. Or, catch the More X1 to Milford-on-Sea to within 2½ miles, or 1 mile to ferry

Tel: 01590 642500 (office), 01590 642344 (Castle)

NON-MEMBERS

Adult **£5.00** | Concession **£4.50**
Child (5-15) **£3.00** | Family (2+3) **£15.00**

[ACQ.1933] 🎧 🐕 ♿ f 🏛 🚶 🍽 ⚠

Dogs on leads (restricted areas only).

Tearoom (Castle Café, not managed by EH). Open daily Easter-October.

Parking (charge payable, at Milford seafront or Keyhaven).

> MAP PAGE 338 (6B)
> OS MAP 196, OL22/OL29:
> SZ318897

KING JAMES'S AND LANDPORT GATES, PORTSMOUTH

HAMPSHIRE – PO1 2EJ

Two ornamental gateways, formerly part of Portsmouth's defences. King James's Gate (1687) has been moved, but Georgian Landport Gate (1760), once the principal entrance to Portsmouth, remains in its original position.

OPENING TIMES

Any reasonable daylight hours, exterior viewing only

VISIT US

Direction: King James's Gate forms the entrance to United Services Recreation Ground (officers), Burnaby Rd; Landport Gate as above, men's entrance on St George's Road

Train: Portsmouth Harbour ¼ mile

Bus: First services 1, X4, 15, 16 and Stagecoach service 23 pass Landport Gate. First services 7 & 15 pass within a short walk of the King James's Gate

ACQ.1930

MAP PAGE 338 (6C)
OS MAP 196, OL29/119
KING JAMES'S GATE: SZ636999
LANDPORT GATE: SZ634998

MEDIEVAL MERCHANT'S HOUSE, SOUTHAMPTON

HAMPSHIRE – SO14 2AT

Among the oldest surviving merchant's houses in England, this partly timber-framed combination of home, shop and warehouse was originally built in about 1290. Now vividly recreated as it looked in the mid-14th century, with replica furnishings.

OPENING TIMES

1 Apr-30 Sep, Sat-Sun	11am-4pm
1 Oct-31 Mar	Closed

VISIT US

Direction: 58 French St, ¼ mile S of city centre, just off Castle Way (between High St and Bugle St)

Train: Southampton ¾ mile

Bus: Unilink U1, U6 & First 1, 2, 3, 6 all stop very close by

Tel: 023 8022 1503

Local Tourist Information: Southampton: 023 8083 3333

NON-MEMBERS

Adult **£4.50** | Concession **£4.10**
Child **£2.70** | Family **£11.70**

ACQ.1973 OVP

Disabled access (two steps). Ground floor only.

MAP PAGE 338 (6B)
OS MAP 196, OL22: SU419112

NETLEY ABBEY

HAMPSHIRE – SO31 5FB

The most complete surviving Cistercian monastery in southern England, with much of its big 13th-century church, cloister and monastic buildings still standing. Later converted into a Tudor mansion, now largely vanished. The abbey's Romantic Gothic ruins inspired many artists and writers, including Constable, Turner and Jane Austen. Download a free audio tour from our website.

OPENING TIMES

1 Apr-30 Sep, daily	10am-4.30pm
1 Oct-31 Mar, Sat-Sun	10am-4pm
24-26, 31 Dec & 1 Jan	Closed

VISIT US

Direction: In Netley; 4 miles SE of Southampton, facing Southampton Water

Train: Netley 1 mile

Bus: First service 6 & Xelabus X15

ACQ.1922 P

Gravel car park, limited spaces.

MAP PAGE 338 (6C)
OS MAP 196, OL22: SU453090

ROYAL GARRISON CHURCH, PORTSMOUTH

HAMPSHIRE – PO1 2NJ

The roofed and furnished chancel of a church constructed c. 1212 and damaged by 1941 bombing.

Managed by the Friends of the Royal Garrison Church.

OPENING TIMES

2 Apr-28 Sep, Tue-Sat	11am-4pm
29 Sep-31 Mar & Bank Hols	Closed

The chapel may be closed from May until late summer for conservation work – please check website before visiting

VISIT US

Direction: In Portsmouth; on Grand Parade S of High St

Train: Portsmouth Harbour ¾ mile

Bus: First services 1, 16 & X4

ACQ.1970 ♿ P ʭ

Parking (nearby).

MAP PAGE 338 (6C)
OS MAP 196, OL29/119: SZ633992

SILCHESTER ROMAN TOWN WALLS AND AMPHITHEATRE

HAMPSHIRE – RG7 2HP

An Iron Age tribal centre, Silchester became the important Roman town of Calleva Atrebatum. The complete circuit of its walls, 1½ miles long, can be traced, although no buildings within survive. Outside are remains of a Roman amphitheatre. Download a free audio tour from our website.

OPENING TIMES

Any reasonable daylight hours

Car park	
1 Apr-30 Sep, daily	8am-7pm
1 Oct-31 Mar, daily	8.30am-4pm

VISIT US

Direction: On a minor road, 1 mile E of Silchester

Train: Bramley or Mortimer, both 2¾ miles

Bus: Stagecoach Hampshire 14 to Silchester (within ½ mile)

ACQ.1965 ʭ ⎙ P

There is no parking at the Amphitheatre, visitors should park at the main car park for the Roman Town. Prior notice of tall vehicles (i.e. coaches and minibuses) wishing to park in the car park is needed. Car park operated by Hampshire County Council – please contact 0118 970 0132 to open height barrier.

MAP PAGE 338 (4C)
OS MAP 175, 159: SU639624

SOUTHWICK PRIORY

HAMPSHIRE – PO17 6EB

Remains of a wealthy Augustinian priory, originally founded at Portchester: once a famous place of pilgrimage. Only part of the refectory wall survives.

OPENING TIMES

Any reasonable daylight hours

SOUTHWICK PRIORY

VISIT US

Direction: Access via footpath from Priory Road, opposite village car park

Bus: The only public transport is the Southwick demand responsive service 38 (to register Tel: 01962 846786) operated by Hughes Travel (Tel: 01329 283283)

ACQ.1970

MAP PAGE 338 (6C)
OS MAP 196, 119: SU629084

TITCHFIELD ABBEY

HAMPSHIRE – PO15 5RA

The ruins of a 13th-century abbey of Premonstratensian canons, later converted into a Tudor mansion. The church was rebuilt as a grand turreted gatehouse. Download a free audio tour from our website.

OPENING TIMES

1 Apr-30 Sep, daily	10am-5pm
1 Oct-31 Mar, daily	10am-4pm
24-26 Dec & 1 Jan	Closed

VISIT US

Direction: Located ½ mile N of Titchfield, off A27, along Mill Lane, opposite Fisherman's Rest pub

Train: Fareham 2 miles

Bus: First services X4, X5, 28 & 28A. Alight Titchfield by-pass and then use public footpath

ACQ.1923 ♿ ʭ P

Car park accessed via narrow entrance through high wall.

MAP PAGE 338 (6C)
OS MAP 196, 119: SU542067

PORTCHESTER CASTLE

HAMPSHIRE PO16 9QW

Set within the most magnificently complete Roman fort walls in northern Europe, this medieval castle became a crowded prisoner of war camp. Our dramatic displays immerse you in the story of the African-Caribbean soldiers held here during the Napoleonic wars.

Much the best-preserved of the Roman 'Saxon Shore' forts, Portchester retains most of its Roman defences, including sixteen towers. During the 12th century a Norman castle with a powerful keep was built in one corner, developing into a 14th-century royal palace.

Later, the castle was transformed into a vast prisoner of war camp. During the Napoleonic Wars up to 8,000 captives were held here. Our displays witness how they fought poverty and boredom and retained their national identity.

CLIMB TO THE KEEP ROOF FOR BREATHTAKING VIEWS OF THE ROMAN FORT

On the keep's ground floor, you'll find a representation of the theatre where French prisoners performed plays. On the upper floors, wrap-around sound-effects evoke the prisoners' sea journey to Britain.

Another arresting installation highlights Portchester's most surprising prisoners, around 2,000 African-Caribbean soldiers captured while fighting for the French on St Lucia in the Caribbean. You'll discover how they encountered kindness as well as cruelty and prejudice. Find more about them at www.english-heritage.org.uk/portchestercastle

Climb to the roof of the 30 metre (100 feet) high keep for breathtaking views of the Roman fort, with the great sweep of Portsmouth harbour beyond.

OPENING TIMES

1 Apr-30 Sep, daily	10am-6pm
1 Oct-3 Nov, daily	10am-5pm
4 Nov-16 Feb, Sat-Sun	10am-4pm
17-23 Feb, daily	10am-4pm
24 Feb-31 Mar, Sat-Sun	10am-4pm

VISIT US

Direction: On the S side of Portchester off A27; Junction 11 on M27

Train: Portchester 1 mile

Bus: First service 3 to within ¼ mile. Alternatively First X4 to Portchester Precinct and ¼ mile walk

Tel: 023 9237 8291

NON-MEMBERS

Adult **£8.00** | Concession **£7.20**
Child **£4.80** | Family **£20.80**

ACQ.1926 🎧 ♿ 🎁 🗡 E f 🛍 💻 🚶 🚶

P 🏕 📷 OVP

Warning: Relatively steep stairs to the exhibitions on upper floors of the keep.

Disabled access (grounds and lower levels only).

Dogs on leads (outer grounds only).

Toilets (facilities are in the car park, operated by Fareham District Council).

MAP PAGE 338 (6C)
OS MAP 196, OL29/119: SU625046

WOLVESEY CASTLE (OLD BISHOP'S PALACE)

HAMPSHIRE – SO23 9NB

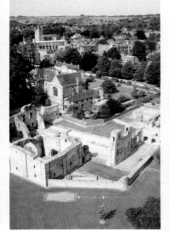

An important residence of the wealthy bishops of Winchester since Anglo-Saxon times, standing near to Winchester Cathedral. The extensive surviving ruins date largely from the 12th century. Download a free audio tour from our website.

OPENING TIMES

1 Apr-31 Oct, daily	10am-5pm
1 Nov-31 Mar	Closed

VISIT US

Direction: 600 metres SE of Winchester Cathedral, next to the Bishop's Palace; access from College St

Train: Winchester ¾ mile

Bus: Bus services to Winchester are operated by Stagecoach Hampshire, Mervyn's Coaches &, Wheelers. Alight at the Broadway, which is within walking distance of Wolvesey Castle and the Old Bishop's Palace

MAP PAGE 338 (5C)
OS MAP 185, 132: SU484291

BAYHAM OLD ABBEY   KENT – TN3 8LP

One of southern England's finest monastic ruins, Bayham Abbey was founded in the early 13th century by Robert de Thurnham for the Premonstratensian 'white canons'. Renowned for the quality and richness of its architecture, these impressive ruins include much of the church, chapter house and picturesque 14th-century gatehouse. The secluded nature of the site is enhanced by views of the picturesque landscape designed by Humphry Repton, creating a beautiful and tranquil experience.

OPENING TIMES

1 Apr-31 Oct, daily	10am-5pm
1 Nov-31 Mar	Closed

VISIT US

Direction: 1¾ miles W of Lamberhurst, off B2169

Train: Frant 4 miles then bus 256

Bus: Autocar 256

Tel: 01892 890381

Local Tourist Information: Tunbridge Wells: 01892 515675

MAP PAGE 339 (5G)
OS MAP 188, 136: TQ650365

DEAL CASTLE

Lively storytelling, displays and activities help you explore every corner of Deal Castle, the biggest and most elaborate of all Henry VIII's coastal artillery forts.

KENT CT14 7BA

As you enter this formidable fortress, you'll be faced by a replica Tudor cannon. It's a reminder that Deal was one of the revolutionary new-style artillery castles built from 1539 by Henry VIII to counter a threatened invasion by European Catholic powers. Flanked by neighbouring Walmer Castle and now-vanished Sandown Castle, it was the crucial centrepiece of three forts whose heavy guns commanded the vital sheltered anchorage between the hazardous Goodwin Sands and the shore. Its distinctive multi-lobed design provided all-round firepower from a total of over 140 guns, arranged in five tiers.

On its squat rounded bastions – intended to minimise the effect of incoming cannonballs – you'll find 'Guarding the Downs', one of the displays which vividly illustrate how the castle worked.

Within the round keep, the core of the fortress, you'll find 'Henry VIII's Castle of War', opening windows on the world of 1539 and how Deal fitted into it. A huge illustrated jigsaw-style map of Europe lays out the international situation when the castle was built. Sit on the thrones of Henry, his nervous fourth wife, Anne of Cleves, or his opponents the Pope, the Emperor and the King of France; pick up the earphones and you'll hear each one's thoughts. Nearby, there's a 3D jigsaw model of the castle to assemble. In neighbouring rooms you'll discover site-finds of Tudor weaponry from Camber Castle, another of Henry's forts, including pike heads, armour-piercing arrows, and equipment for cannons and muskets.

If you want to try defending the castle yourself, go down to the castle basement to 'Explore and Defend the Rounds'. This dark, narrow and winding passage encircles the whole castle, and is equipped with 53 ports for handguns to mow down close-quarter attackers who'd got into the dry moat. If you dare to venture into the Rounds, you can borrow wellies (the passage floor can be wet after rain) and a replica musket from racks near the entrances. Look out for the wind-up listening devices, which let you eavesdrop on two soldiers during the Civil War siege of 1648, when the castle saw hard fighting. Don't get lost!

VENTURE INTO THE ROUNDS, THE DARK AND WINDING PASSAGE ENCIRCLING THE CASTLE

To find out more about the fort's later history, climb the spiral stairs to the Georgian panelled rooms of the keep's upper floor. Here the 'Captains of Deal' display tells you about the commanders and garrison soldiers of the castle from Tudor times until the 20th century. You can read 'conversations' between contrasting captains, and hear the thoughts of others. Don't miss the room highlighting the graffiti written or scratched on the castle roof over the centuries, where you can leave your own mark on paper to add to Deal Castle's fascinating history.

The castle stands right next to Deal's attractive beach, and there are fine sea views from the ramparts. A cycle path links Deal and Walmer Castles along the beachfront.

OPENING TIMES

1 Apr-30 Sep, daily	10am-6pm
1 Oct-3 Nov, daily	10am-5pm
4 Nov-23 Dec, Sat-Sun	10am-4pm
2 Jan-16 Feb, Sat-Sun	10am-4pm
17-23 Feb, daily	10am-4pm
24 Feb-31 Mar, Wed-Sun	10am-4pm
Christmas Opening 24-25 Dec	Closed
26 Dec-1 Jan, daily	10am-4pm

VISIT US

Direction: SW of Deal town centre

Train: Deal ½ mile

Bus: Stagecoach East Kent services 12, 80/80A, 81, 81A, 81B, 82 & 82A; Regent Coaches 93, 541, 542, 544

Tel: 01304 372762

NON-MEMBERS

Adult **£8.40** | Concession **£7.60**
Child **£5.10** | Family **£21.90**

ACQ.1904 🎧 ♿ 🍴 📺 🚹 ♿ ✖ 📷 ⚠ OVP

Disabled access (courtyards and ground floor only, parking available).

Parking charges apply to non-members.
Parking free for Members.

MAP PAGE 339 (4J)
OS MAP 179, 150: TR378522

DOVER CASTLE

Crowning the White Cliffs high above the Channel, Dover's majestic fortress offers visitors an unparalleled journey into the past. Over 2,000 years this famous place has housed a Roman lighthouse, a medieval royal castle-palace of immense strength, and labyrinthine tunnels where, in 1940, Vice Admiral Ramsay planned the miraculous rescue of the British Army from Dunkirk.

KENT CT16 1HU

Renowned as 'the Key to England', Dover Castle boasts a long and immensely eventful history. Its spectacular site still displays a Roman lighthouse and an Anglo-Saxon church. Established soon after 1066 as a Norman earthwork castle, the fortress was garrisoned uninterruptedly until 1958, and between the 1960s and 1980s concealed a secret Cold War Regional Seat of Government.

Medieval Royal Palace

Dover Castle is first and foremost the strongest medieval fortress in England, created by King Henry II and his Plantagenet successors. At its heart stands the mighty Great Tower. Built between 1180 and 1185, this symbol of kingly power was also a palace designed for royal ceremony.

The interior of Henry's Great Tower palace has been recreated as it might have appeared when newly completed. Follow the dramatic story of Henry II and his turbulent brood in an introductory exhibition, 'A Family at War'. Both children and adults can enjoy the interactive displays, and a virtual tour reveals the Great Tower to those unable to explore it.

JOURNEY ROUND THE VIBRANTLY RECREATED ROOMS

Entering the Great Tower, you'll find projected figures, which bring to life your journey round the vibrantly recreated rooms of the palace. On selected days, you might also meet costumed live interpreters – including Henry himself. See our website for dates.

Epic Sieges

Climb to the Great Tower's roof for panoramic views over the castle's immense complex of medieval fortifications. These saw desperate fighting during the epic sieges of 1216-17, when the castle resisted ten months of attack by a French army aiding rebellious English barons. By steadfastly holding out, almost alone, Dover literally saved southern England from French domination. Intrepid visitors can descend into the Medieval Tunnels, burrowed beneath the castle during and after the siege.

STAY WITH US

Peverell's Tower was at one time a prison. Today it makes a perfect romantic castle tower for two.

The **Sergeant Major's House** is surrounded by hundreds of years of history. This spacious four-storey Georgian residence sleeps six. Great for families, it even has its own secret games room.

See p.332 for details on staying at **Dover** and our other holiday cottages.

The First World War

The Fire Command Post highlights one of the many dramatic chapters in Dover Castle's later story. During the First World War, Dover was officially designated as a Fortress, with a garrison of over 10,000 men. The naval headquarters in Dover town also directed the vital defence of the Straits of Dover, attracting, on 21 December 1914, the first recorded bombing raid on Britain by a German aeroplane.

Defences against this new type of warfare included one of the earliest purpose-built anti-aircraft guns, which in 1915 scored the first successful hit on a German Zeppelin. An identical type of British 3-inch gun, the only working example of just six in the world, has been restored to firing condition and installed in a recreated gun-emplacement. You can experience regular gun-firing drills on selected weekends throughout the summer, given by a specially trained team of authentically costumed English Heritage volunteers.

We have also conserved and re-presented Dover Castle's First World War Fire Command Post and Port War Signal Station. So you can explore what it was like to work here via a range of replica and original artefacts. Try communicating in Morse code, learn semaphore and discover how to spot enemy or friendly ships.

Operation Dynamo: Rescue from Dunkirk

Dover Castle's defences were even more sorely tested in the darkest days of the Second World War, when part of an existing network of tunnels deep beneath the castle became Vice Admiral Bertram Ramsay's bomb-proof naval headquarters.

On 26 May 1940, Ramsay began the rescue of the British Army and its allies, trapped at Dunkirk and fighting for their lives. The task of rescuing them – 'Operation Dynamo' – demanded sending a huge improvised fleet of ships across the Channel, under attack from air, sea and land. The British Army in France depended upon it.

OPENING TIMES

1 Apr-31 Jul, daily	10am-6pm
1-31 Aug, daily	9.30am-6pm
1-30 Sep, daily	10am-6pm
1 Oct-3 Nov, daily	10am-5pm
4 Nov-23 Dec, Sat-Sun	10am-4pm
2 Jan-16 Feb, Sat-Sun	10am-4pm
17-23 Feb, daily	10am-4pm
24 Feb-31 Mar, Wed-Sun	10am-4pm
Christmas Opening	
24-25 Dec	Closed
26 Dec-1 Jan, daily	10am-4pm
Last entry one hour before closing	

The Great Tower is free-flow and self-guided. Costumed live interpreters welcome you at the Great Tower on selected days. Stewards in the tower are always on hand to answer any questions. Access to the Operation Dynamo experience in the Secret Wartime Tunnels is by guided tour only. Due to the immersive nature of these visits, no independent guiding is allowed in these areas. However, tour leaders of groups of younger visitors must stay with their parties at all times. Access to the Underground Hospital (separate access from Operation Dynamo) is by guided tour only (limited to 30 people and lasting approximately 20 minutes). At peak times, there may be queues at the popular tunnel experiences. Groups of 11+ can call and book ahead for a group discount on admission. Car parks open at site opening time. Last tunnel tours depart one hour before closing

VISIT US

Address: Dover Castle, Castle Hill, Dover, Kent

Direction: E of Dover town centre

Train: Dover Priory 1½ miles

Bus: Stagecoach in East Kent 80, 80A, 80B, 81; Regent Coaches 93

Tel: 01304 211067

Local Tourist Information: Dover: 01304 205108

NON-MEMBERS

Adult **£23.00** | Concession **£20.70**
Child **£13.80** | Family **£59.80**

Additional charges for members and non-members may apply on event days

Please refer to the Dover Castle web page or ring the site directly for information on accessibility. Mobility scooters are available and should be booked in advance. Wheelchair routes and guides are available on site.

Dogs are welcome on a lead at all times, although not permitted in the Great Tower and Secret Wartime Tunnels (apart from assistance dogs).

We advise you to wear comfortable shoes.

MAP PAGE 339 (5J)
OS MAP 179, 138: TR325419

Make the adventurous journey into the Wartime Tunnels and immerse yourself in the drama of the daring evacuation that followed. Film presentations vividly recreate the run-up to Dunkirk. Then, in the very place where Operation Dynamo was planned, witness the astounding rescue from the eastern breakwater and beaches happening all around you.

You can also take a fascinating guided tour of the Underground Hospital within the tunnels, re-living the tension as a surgeon battles to save an injured pilot. Find out more about the 'Miracle of Dunkirk' in the 'Wartime Tunnels Uncovered' exhibition, featuring the recorded voices of many who actually took part.

All this, and very much more, makes it well worth enjoying a whole day of discovery at Dover Castle.

The Crown; Disney's Into the Woods; Avengers: Age of Ultron; The Other Boleyn Girl; Zeffirelli's Hamlet; BBC series Wolf Hall and King Lear.

HOME OF
CHARLES DARWIN,
DOWN HOUSE

Experience the Victorian country house where the world was
changed. Explore the home of Charles Darwin and his family at
your own pace, using Down House's innovative, handheld guides.

KENT BR6 7JT

A delightful place in itself to visit, Down House is a site of outstanding international significance. Here the famous naturalist Charles Darwin lived with his family for 40 years, worked on his revolutionary theories, and wrote *On the Origin of Species by Means of Natural Selection* – the book which shook the Victorian world and has influenced thinking ever since.

You'll find Darwin's work and personality vividly reflected throughout the house and grounds. The hand-held tour, narrated by Sir David Attenborough and Andrew Marr, guides you round the family rooms as well as the garden. It includes commentaries by experts, animations, film footage and games for all the family.

The ground floor rooms have been recreated as they appeared when he lived here with his indefatigably supportive wife, Emma, and their many children. They include the 'Old Study' where Darwin wrote his most famous books, still displaying his chair, writing board and many personal items. You can also visit the family's drawing room – with Emma's grand piano – billiard room and dining room. Upstairs his bedroom has been recently recreated as when he rested there. It gives a detailed insight into Darwin's personal side – from the non-scientific books he enjoyed reading to his taste for Old Master prints. A refuge for when he was suffering from poor health, it also enabled him to keep an eye on his garden experiments from the room's large bay windows. A soundscape lets you listen in on Emma reading to her husband, and both children and adults can step into the dressing closet to dress up as Charles and Emma.

'Uncovering Origin' Exhibition

The award-winning exhibition on the house's first floor covers Darwin's life, his scientific work, and the controversy that it provoked. Beginning with an introduction to Darwin and the impact of his theories, the displays continue with his famous five-year voyage aboard the *Beagle* in 1831-36, including a full-scale recreation of his onboard cabin. Further displays highlight *On the Origin of Species*, which immediately sold out its first edition.

The Darwin children's schoolroom celebrates family life at Down House. There's also an education room available for family learning, and a resources room for those interested in delving deeper.

Experiments in the Gardens

By no means the stereotypically stern Victorian father, Darwin involved his children in his practical experiments in the extensive gardens of Down House. This was his 'outdoor laboratory' and the place where he made many of his discoveries. You can now follow these via the multimedia guide, beginning with Darwin's 'weed garden' illustrating the struggle for existence in nature.

The sundial amid pretty flowerbeds highlights Emma Darwin's role as a gardener, a surviving mulberry tree recalls family traditions, and a 'lawn experiment' investigates proliferation of plant species. Visit the nearby hot-house to see some of Darwin's most fascinating experiments, involving carnivorous plants and exotic orchids. There is a working observation beehive in the laboratory.

After a tour of the extensive kitchen gardens, you reach what is for many a place of pilgrimage: the wooded Sandwalk. This was Darwin's famous 'thinking path', which he paced for five laps a day while working out his theories.

Stop off at the tearoom, in Darwin's kitchen area, for a refreshing break before exploring the grounds.

Please note: No photography is allowed inside the house.

OPENING TIMES

1 Apr-30 Sep, daily & Bank Hols	10am-6pm
1 Oct-3 Nov, daily	10am-5pm
4 Nov-23 Dec, Sat-Sun	10am-4pm
2 Jan-16 Feb, Sat-Sun	10am-4pm
17-23 Feb, daily	10am-4pm
24 Feb-31 Mar, Wed-Sun	10am-4pm
Christmas Opening	
24-25 Dec	Closed
26 Dec-1 Jan, daily	10am-4pm

VISIT US

Address: Down House, Luxted Road, Downe, Kent

Direction: Luxted Rd, Downe; off A21 or A233

Train: Orpington 3¾ miles, Bromley South 5½ miles

Bus: TfL bus R8 from Orpington passes (except Sun); TfL bus 146 from Bromley North & South terminates in Downe village ½ mile from property on unpaved road. Services run approx. every 70 mins

Tel: 01689 859119

NON-MEMBERS

Adult £14.00 | Concession £12.60
Child £8.40 | Family £36.40

Audio tour is the multimedia tour.

Parking, no booking required (plus 1 coach bay, which must be pre-booked).

MAP PAGE 339 (4F)
OS MAP 177/187,147: TQ431611

DYMCHURCH MARTELLO TOWER

KENT – TN29 0NU

One of 103 ingeniously-designed artillery towers built between 1805 and 1812 at vulnerable points around the south and east coasts, to resist threatened Napoleonic invasion. It's been re-equipped with its single roof-mounted cannon, which could be rotated to fire in any direction. The small garrison occupied 'bomb-proofed' rooms within.

Open in partnership with the Friends of Martello 24.

OPENING TIMES

Exterior only:
Any reasonable daylight hours

Interior:
6 Apr-27 Oct, Sat-Sun
& Bank Hols   2pm-4pm

Visits for groups of 10 or more by appointment between November and Easter

The tower may be closed from May to August for conservation work – please check website or phone 01797 212507 before visiting

VISIT US

Direction: Access from Dymchurch High Street

Train: Sandling 7 miles; Dymchurch (Romney, Hythe and Dymchurch Railway) ¾ mile

Bus: Stagecoach in East Kent 'The Wave' services 100, 101 & 102

ACQ.1959

MAP PAGE 339 (5H)
OS MAP 189, 138: TR102292

EYNSFORD CASTLE

KENT – DA4 0AA

The substantial walls of a very early Norman 'enclosure castle', begun c. 1085-87 and unusually little altered. In an attractive village setting.

OPENING TIMES

1 Apr-30 Sep, daily	10am-6pm
1 Oct-31 Mar, daily	10am-4pm
24-26 Dec & 1 Jan	Closed

VISIT US

Direction: In Eynsford, off A225

Train: Eynsford 1 mile

Bus: Go-Coach 421 & 429

ACQ.1948

MAP PAGE 339 (4F)
OS MAP 177, 162: TQ542658

FAVERSHAM STONE CHAPEL (OUR LADY OF ELVERTON)

KENT

Ruins of a small Anglo-Saxon and medieval chapel, incorporating the remains of a pagan Romano-British mausoleum. Near the probable site of the Roman town of Durolevum.

Managed by The Faversham Society and the Maison Dieu Trustees.

OPENING TIMES

Any reasonable daylight hours

VISIT US

Direction: In field immediately N of A2 just W of Ospringe and opposite Faversham Road

Train: Faversham 1½ miles

Bus: Arriva 333; Chalkwell 324 (Wed & Fri); Stagecoach The Hop services 3, 3A, 3B, 3X

Tel: 01795 534542

Email: ticfaversham@btconnect.com

ACQ.1972

MAP PAGE 339 (4H)
OS MAP 178, 149: TQ992613

HORNE'S PLACE CHAPEL

KENT – TN26 2AL

Rare survival of a domestic chapel, built for William Horne in 1366 and attached to his manor house, which was attacked during the Peasants' Revolt of 1381. (House and chapel are privately owned.)

OPENING TIMES

By appointment only; please call the regional office at Dover on 01304 211067 option 4

VISIT US

Direction: 1½ miles N of Appledore

Train: Appledore 2½ miles

Bus: Stagecoach East Kent service 11B (one return weekday journey) & Kent Coach Tours 293 (Mon & Fri); Arriva 293 (Thu)

Tel: 01304 211067

ACQ.1950

MAP PAGE 339 (5H)
OS MAP 189, 125: TQ958309

LULLINGSTONE ROMAN VILLA

KENT DA4 0JA

Among the most exciting Roman villa survivals in Britain, Lullingstone Roman Villa's vivid displays and interpretation give you a unique insight into Roman domestic life over three centuries.

The villa was begun in about AD 100, and developed to suit successive wealthy owners. These may have included the family of Pertinax, Roman Emperor for just 87 days in AD 193. Additions included a heated bath-suite and a remarkable underground pagan 'cult-room', including a wall-painting of water-nymphs, by far the oldest painting in English Heritage's care.

The villa reached its luxurious zenith in the mid-4th century, when a big new dining room was added. This displays spectacular mosaics, including Europa and the Bull, and Bellerophon Killing the Chimera. By now Christians, the owners also created a 'house-church' above the pagan cult-room: wall-paintings discovered here are among the earliest evidence of Christianity in Britain, but pagan worship may also have continued, suggesting a relaxed relationship between the old and new faiths.

All this is clearly interpreted in the galleries overlooking the excavated remains, where you'll find a fascinating collection of Roman artefacts. Children and adults can play Roman board games, handle original building materials and try on Roman costumes. See the villa come to life in a film and light show that illuminates excavated areas and reveals how they were once used.

OPENING TIMES

1 Apr-30 Sep, daily	10am-6pm
1 Oct-3 Nov, daily	10am-5pm
4 Nov-16 Feb, Sat-Sun	10am-4pm
17-23 Feb, daily	10am-4pm
24 Feb-31 Mar, Sat-Sun	10am-4pm
24-26 Dec & 1 Jan	Closed

VISIT US

Direction: ½ mile SW of Eynsford, off J3 of M25, A20 towards West Kingsdown, A225 to Eynsford

Train: Eynsford 2 miles

Bus: Go-Coach 403, 421 & 429 then 1 mile walk via footpath from Shoreham Road

Tel: 01322 863467

NON-MEMBERS

Adult **£9.00** | Concession **£8.10**
Child **£5.40** | Family **£23.40**

ACQ.1958

Parking charges apply to non-members.
Parking free for Members.

MAP PAGE 339 (4F)
OS MAP 177/188, 147/162: TQ530651

KIT'S COTY HOUSE AND LITTLE KIT'S COTY HOUSE

KENT – ME20 7EZ

The remains of two megalithic burial chambers. Impressive Kit's Coty has three uprights and a massive capstone. Little Kit's Coty, alias the Countless Stones, is now a jumble of sarsens.

OPENING TIMES

Any reasonable daylight hours

VISIT US

Direction: W of A229, 2 miles N of Maidstone

Train: Aylesford 2½ miles

Bus: Arriva 101; Arriva/Nu-Venture 142; Farleigh Coaches service 150

ACQ.1883

MAP PAGE 339 (4G)
OS MAP 178/188, 148
KIT'S COTY HOUSE: TQ745608
LITTLE KIT'S COTY HOUSE: TQ744604

KNIGHTS TEMPLAR CHURCH, DOVER

KENT – CT17 9DP

The foundations of a small medieval church, traditionally the site of King John's submission to the Papal Legate in 1213.

OPENING TIMES

Any reasonable daylight hours

VISIT US

Direction: On the Western Heights above Dover

KNIGHTS TEMPLAR CHURCH

Train: Dover Priory ¾ mile

Bus: Regent Coaches service 93 from Dover town centre

Tel: 01304 211067

ACQ.1968

Dogs on leads (restricted areas only).

MAP PAGE 339 (5J)
OS MAP 179, 138: TR313407

MAISON DIEU

KENT – ME13 8TS

This attractive flint and timber-framed medieval building was part of a much larger complex, including a Canterbury pilgrims' hostel, a royal lodging and a school. It houses a museum including archaeological finds made here and at a nearby Roman cemetery.

Managed by the Maison Dieu Trustees.

OPENING TIMES

| 6 Apr-27 Oct, Sat-Sun & Bank Hols | 2pm-5pm |
| 28 Oct-31 Mar | Closed |

Group visits at other times by appointment between Apr & Oct

VISIT US

Direction: On main A2 on W corner of Water Lane in village of Ospringe. Public car park 300yds W

Train: Faversham ¾ mile

Bus: Arriva 333; Chalkwell 324 pass nearby

Tel: 01795 531131

NON-MEMBERS

Adult £3.00 | Concession £1.50
Child **Free if accompanied by adult**

ACQ.1947

MAP PAGE 339 (4H)
OS MAP 178, 149: TR003609

MILTON CHANTRY

KENT – DA12 2BH

Retaining its 14th-century timber roof, this was in turn a hospital, chantry chapel, pub, barracks and Second World War gas decontamination chamber.

Managed by Gravesham Borough Council.

OPENING TIMES

| 6 Apr-29 Sep, Sat-Sun & Bank Hols | 12pm-5pm* |
| 30 Sep-31 Mar | Closed |

*Admission outside these times by appointment

VISIT US

Direction: In New Tavern Fort Gardens; E of central Gravesend, off A226

Train: Gravesend ¾ mile

Bus: Arriva pass through the town and most close to Milton Chantry

Tel: 01474 337600

ACQ.1972

MAP PAGE 339 (4G)
OS MAP 177/178, 162/163: TQ653743

OLD SOAR MANOR

KENT – TN15 0QX

A small but complete portion of a stone manor house built c. 1290.

Managed by the National Trust on behalf of English Heritage.

OPENING TIMES

| 1 Apr-30 Sep, Sat-Thu | 10am-6pm |
| 1 Oct-31 Mar | Closed |

VISIT US

Direction: 1 mile E of Plaxtol

Train: Borough Green and Wrotham 2½ miles

Bus: Autocar 222 Tonbridge – Borough Green; Go-Coach 404 from Sevenoaks. Alight E end of Plaxtol, then ¾ mile by footpath

Tel: 01732 810378

ACQ.1948 Parking (limited).

MAP PAGE 339 (4G)
OS MAP 188, 147/148: TQ619541

RICHBOROUGH ROMAN FORT AND AMPHITHEATRE

KENT CT13 9JW

Evocatively sited amid the East Kent marshes, Richborough Roman Fort is the most symbolically important of all Roman sites in Britain, witnessing both the beginning and almost the end of Roman rule here.

Now two miles inland, in AD 43 it overlooked a sheltered channel where the invading Roman forces first came ashore.

A mighty triumphal arch, whose foundations still survive, commemorated the landing. The arch also provided an impressive gateway for arrivals at what became the port of 'Rutupiae', the province's main point of entry.

By the mid-3rd century seaborne raiders threatened Roman Britain. A fort was therefore hastily created within the port. At first defended by the triple ditches still visible, but soon after by stone walls, this became one of the most important of the 'Saxon Shore' forts. Long sections of its walls still stand high, giving you an idea of its strength. It was also among the last forts to be regularly occupied: there was still a large Roman population here in the early 5th century.

The small site museum offers interpretation, site finds and handling samples of Roman artefacts.

You can choose to reach the fort as the Romans would have done, by boat. Boats sail from Sandwich, but pre-booking is advisable. Ring 07958 376183 for details.

OPENING TIMES

Fort:

1 Apr-30 Sep, daily	10am-6pm
1 Oct-3 Nov, daily	10am-5pm
4 Nov-31 Mar, Sat-Sun	10am-4pm
24-26 Dec & 1 Jan	Closed

Amphitheatre: Any reasonable time in daylight hours, access across grazed land from footpath; please call 01304 612013 for details

VISIT US

Direction: At the A256/A257 roundabout, head for Sandwich then turn left onto Richborough Road and proceed for approx. 1 mile

Train: Sandwich 2 miles

Bus: Stagecoach East Kent 87, 88 then walk using Stour Valley Walk/Saxon Shore Way

Tel: 01304 612013

NON-MEMBERS

Adult **£7.50** | Concession **£6.80**
Child **£4.60** | Family **£19.60**

ACQ.1912
Dogs on leads (restricted areas only).

MAP PAGE 339 (4J) OS MAP 179, 150
FORT: TR324602
AMPHITHEATRE: TR321598

RECULVER TOWERS AND ROMAN FORT

KENT – CT6 6SS

Twin 12th-century towers of an atmospheric ruined seaside church, enclosing traces of a Saxon monastery. Within the partly visible walls of one of the first Roman 'Saxon Shore' forts. Download a free audio tour from our website.

Managed by Canterbury City Council.

OPENING TIMES

Exterior only: Any reasonable daylight hours

VISIT US

Direction: At Reculver, 3 miles E of Herne Bay; signed off Thanet Way A299

Train: Herne Bay 4 miles

Bus: Stagecoach in East Kent 7; Regent Coaches service 36

Tel: 01227 740676

Disabled access (grounds only – long slope up from car park).

Parking (pay and display), toilets and a café are available at nearby Reculver Visitor Centre (not managed by English Heritage).

MAP PAGE 339 (4J)
OS MAP 179, 150: TR228693

ST AUGUSTINE'S ABBEY CONDUIT HOUSE

KENT

The Conduit House is part of the monastic waterworks that supplied nearby St Augustine's Abbey.

OPENING TIMES

Exterior only: Any reasonable daylight hours

VISIT US

Direction: In King's Park. Approx. 5-10 min walk from St Augustine's Abbey. Please call or ask at the Abbey for directions

Train: Canterbury East and West, both ¾ mile

Bus: Regent Coaches 649 from George's Street city centre stops at law courts, then short walk

ACQ.1977

MAP PAGE 339 (4H)
OS MAP 179, 150: TR159580

ST AUGUSTINE'S CROSS

KENT – CT12 5JB

This Anglo-Saxon style Victorian cross marks what is traditionally believed to be the site of St Augustine's landing in England in AD 597. Nearby was the stream where he allegedly baptised his first English convert.

ST AUGUSTINE'S CROSS

OPENING TIMES

Any reasonable daylight hours

VISIT US

Direction: Cliffs End, Thanet, 2 miles E of Minster off B29048

Train: Minster 2 miles

Bus: Stagecoach 43 from Ramsgate

ACQ.1912

MAP PAGE 339 (4J)
OS MAP 179, 150: TR340642

ST JOHN'S COMMANDERY

KENT – CT15 7HG

The 13th-century chapel and hall of a 'Commandery' of Knights Hospitallers, later converted into a farmhouse. Features a medieval crown-post roof and 16th-century ceilings.

OPENING TIMES

By appointment only; please call the regional office at Dover on 01304 211067 option 4

VISIT US

Direction: 2 miles NE of Densole, off A260

Train: Kearsney 4 miles; Folkestone Central 6 miles

Bus: Stagecoach in East Kent Gold 16 from ▨ Folkestone Central to within 1 mile

ACQ.1978

MAP PAGE 339 (5J)
OS MAP 179/189, 138: TR232440

ROCHESTER CASTLE

KENT ME1 1SW

Discover the tallest Norman keep in England, the target of famous medieval sieges.

Dominating the bridge where the road from London to Dover crossed the river Medway, Rochester Castle was among the most strategically important fortresses in medieval England. In 1136 William of Corbeil, Archbishop of Canterbury, completed the great stone keep at the command of Henry I. At 37.7 metres (125 feet) high, it was probably the tallest castle keep ever built.

In 1215, garrisoned by rebel barons, the castle endured an epic siege by King John. He used 'the fat of 40 pigs' to fire a mine burrowed beneath the keep, bringing its south-east corner crashing down. Even then the defenders held out behind a stout wall within the building, living on water and horsemeat until finally starved out.

You can still see how the demolished corner tower was rebuilt – it's rounded, not square like the rest – before the keep endured a second siege in 1264, when it beat off an assault by Simon de Montfort's rebel army.

Exploring Rochester's keep shows you why it was so hard to take. After entering the forebuilding at first floor level, you can climb some 200 spiralling steps, winding from the basement cesspit up to the battlements. On the way you'll pass the chapel, displaying a model of the whole castle and a cutaway of the keep. Next comes the vast galleried great hall with its round-headed Norman arches, one of the most impressive spaces in any English castle. Then you climb past the third floor to the keep roof. Enjoy breathtaking views over the nearby cathedral, the historic core of Rochester and the broad sweep of the Medway whose crossing this noble fortress once guarded.

Managed by Medway Council.

OPENING TIMES

1 Apr-30 Sep, daily	10am-6pm
1 Oct-31 Mar, daily	10am-4pm
24-26 Dec & 1 Jan	Closed
Last entry 45 mins before closing	

Due to the concert series that takes place in July adjacent to the castle, it may be necessary to close early. Please check the website for details

VISIT US

Direction: By Rochester Bridge (A2): Junction 1 of M2 and Junction 2 of M25. Signposted from A228 Rochester by-pass

Train: Combined train/bus station, 5 minutes' walk from castle

Bus: Services are operated by Arriva, ASD Buses and Nu-Venture. Alight in Corporation Street a short distance from the castle

Tel: 01634 332901

NON-MEMBERS

Adult **£6.40** | Concession **£4.00**
Child **£4.00** | Family **£16.80**
Groups of 10+ **15% discount**

ACQ 1965 🎧 ♿ E 📷 🧍 🧍 ✕ 📷 ⚠ OVP

Audio tours (small charge).

Toilets (in castle grounds).

No disabled access to keep.

MAP PAGE 339 (4G)
OS MAP 178, 148/163: TQ741686

ST AUGUSTINE'S ABBEY

KENT CT1 1PF

Virtual reality technology helps you explore this ancient monastery, an outstandingly important landmark in English history.

Founded in AD 598 by St Augustine himself, this once-great abbey proclaims the rebirth of Christianity in southern England. The pagan King Aethelberht of Kent, then most powerful of the Anglo-Saxon monarchs, married a Christian princess from France. Soon afterwards he accepted baptism by Augustine, a missionary from Rome. He thus became the first Anglo-Saxon Christian ruler.

To mark his conversion, Aethelberht gave Augustine land to build this very first monastery in Anglo-Saxon England. Displaying a wonderful variety of site finds – including personal possessions and intriguing artefacts from graves – the big site museum traces how the Saxon monastery was magnificently rebuilt by the Normans before becoming a Tudor royal palace and Stuart garden.

Adults as well as children can try on monks' habits and enjoy varied interactives. Using award-winning state-of-the-art technology, you can also take a personal virtual reality tour of the abbey as it looked in about 1500; a fascinating and absorbing experience.

Be sure to explore the extensive and atmospheric abbey ruins in person, too. They're set against a backdrop of Canterbury's medieval buildings, with the cathedral towers soaring in the distance. Guided by the audio tour, you'll discover excavated remains of the oldest Anglo-Saxon churches in England. These were overlaid after 1072 by the huge Norman monastery with its cathedral-sized church, whose crypt and other features you can still clearly see.

The cradle of revived English Christianity, this tranquil but immensely significant place shouldn't be missed by visitors to the Canterbury World Heritage Site.

OPENING TIMES

1 Apr-30 Sep, daily	10am-6pm
1 Oct-3 Nov, daily	10am-5pm
4 Nov-31 Mar, Sat-Sun	10am-4pm
24-26 Dec & 1 Jan	Closed

VISIT US

Direction: In Canterbury, ¼ mile E of Cathedral Close

Train: Canterbury East and West, both ¾ mile

Bus: Stagecoach East Kent 4, 5, 6, 7, 8, 9, 21, 21A (alight in Lower Bridge Street) or Stagecoach East Kent 13, 14, 23, 23A (alight in Longport)

Tel: 01227 767345

Local Tourist Information: Canterbury: 01227 378100

NON-MEMBERS

Adult £8.00 | Concession £7.20
Child £4.80 | Family £20.80

ACQ.1938

Audio tours.

Disabled access (all site can be viewed, but some steps).

Parking (nearby).

MAP PAGE 339 (4H)
OS MAP 179, 150: TR155578

WALMER CASTLE AND GARDENS

Surround yourself with colourful stories from the history of Walmer Castle, a Tudor fort which became an elegant country house. It stands amid delightful gardens, with a lot more to enjoy this year. Recreated rooms highlight Walmer's famous residents and visitors, notably the 'Iron Duke' of Wellington.

KENT CT14 7LJ

Originally built as a vital link in Henry VIII's chain of coastal artillery fortresses – hence its distinctive 'clover-leaf' form – Walmer Castle evolved over the centuries into a comfortable and fashionable home. For over three centuries, it has been the official residence of the Lord Warden of the Cinque Ports, an office granted to some of Britain's most honoured people.

Among the most famous was the Duke of Wellington, Lord Warden for 23 years until his death here, aged 83, in 1852. You can see an original pair of his 'Wellington boots' and his death mask. His spartan bedroom has also been carefully re-presented, including the original armchair in which he died. Adjacent rooms highlight Wellington's celebrity status, and tell the story of his funeral, the grandest ever yet seen.

Re-imagined rooms also highlight the castle's other stories. Prime Minister and Lord Warden William Pitt the Younger planned England's coastal defences against Napoleon here, and in 1915 Winston Churchill, then First Lord of the Admiralty and later Lord Warden, was at Walmer Castle when he devised the disastrous Dardanelles campaign, during which the soldier-poet Rupert Brooke (another Walmer guest) lost his life.

NEW FOR 2019

From April, you'll find much more to enjoy in Walmer Castle's gardens. We're restoring and opening up the Paddock wild flower meadow and the Glen, a former planted chalk quarry. They're both part of the gardens created by William Pitt and his niece Lady Hester Stanhope, but have long been overgrown and inaccessible. We've also opened a new Glasshouse Café in the Kitchen Garden.

The multimedia guide includes a programme designed for children, and families can enjoy entertaining special activities as you tour the recreated rooms.

Recent Lords Warden still use private apartments above the gatehouse. They have included Queen Elizabeth the Queen Mother, and a magnificent garden created for her 95th birthday is among the highlights of Walmer's delightful grounds, a joy to wander and admire. These also encompass the Broadwalk, with its famous Cloud Yew Hedge. Don't miss the re-created Pleasure Garden, or the working kitchen gardens, orchard and greenhouses. Further afield you'll find wild gardens and woodlands, with new nature trails and a play trail.

Enjoy homemade refreshments, including produce from Walmer's own kitchen garden, in the Lord Warden's Tearoom or the new Glasshouse Café.

OPENING TIMES

1 Apr-30 Sep, daily*	10am-6pm
1 Oct-3 Nov, daily	10am-5pm
4 Nov-23 Dec, Sat-Sun	10am-4pm
2 Jan-16 Feb, Sat-Sun	10am-4pm
17-23 Feb, daily	10am-4pm
24 Feb-31 Mar, Wed-Sun	10am-4pm
Christmas Opening 24-25 Dec	Closed
26 Dec-1 Jan, daily	10am-4pm

*Closed from 12-14 July when Lord Warden is in residence

VISIT US

Address: Walmer Castle, Kingsdown Road, Deal, Kent

Direction: On coast S of Walmer, on A258; Junction 13 of M20 or from M2 to Deal

Train: Walmer 1 mile

Bus: Stagecoach East Kent service 82/82A

Tel: 01304 364288

Local Tourist Information:
Deal: 01304 369576 and Dover: 01304 205108

NON-MEMBERS

Adult £13.50 | Concession £12.20
Child £8.10 | Family £35.10

New guidebook.

Multimedia guides for adults (available in Dutch, French and German). Children's version also available.

Disabled access (three ground floor display rooms, tearooms, shop courtyard and garden only; parking available near approach to castle).

Parking charges apply to non-members. Parking free for Members.

No coach parking at the site.

MAP PAGE 339 (4J)
OS MAP 179, 138: TR378501

STAY WITH US

Walmer Castle's holiday cottages, the **Greenhouse Apartment** and the **Garden Cottage**, both offer great views over the kitchen garden and are only a few minutes' walk from the beach.

See p.332 for details on staying at **Walmer** and our other holiday cottages.

ST LEONARD'S TOWER

KENT – ME19 6PD

An early and well-preserved example of a small free-standing Norman tower-keep, surviving almost to its original height. Probably built c. 1080 by Gundulf, Bishop of Rochester.

OPENING TIMES

Exterior only: Any reasonable daylight hours

VISIT US

Direction: Nr West Malling, on unclassified road W of A228

Train: West Malling 1 mile

Bus: Nu-Venture 70, 123, 151; Arriva Kent & Surrey 72, 77

ACQ.1937 🐾 ♿

Disabled access (grounds only).

> MAP PAGE 339 (4G)
> OS MAP 178/188, 148: TQ676571

SUTTON VALENCE CASTLE

KENT – ME17 3LW

The ruins of a small 12th-century Norman keep, with panoramic views over the Weald.

OPENING TIMES

Any reasonable daylight hours

VISIT US

Direction: 5 miles SE of Maidstone, in Sutton Valence village, on A274

Train: Headcorn 4 miles, Hollingbourne 5 miles

Bus: Arriva 12 Maidstone – Tenterden (passes ⭐ Headcorn)

ACQ.1976 🐾

> MAP PAGE 339 (4G)
> OS MAP 188, 137: TQ815491

TEMPLE MANOR

KENT – ME2 2AH

Part of a Knights Templar manor house, built c. 1240, with a first floor hall displaying traces of wall-paintings.

Managed by Medway Council.

www.visitmedway.org

TEMPLE MANOR

OPENING TIMES

6 Apr-27 Oct, Sat-Sun	11am-4pm
28 Oct-31 Mar	Closed

For group visits call 01634 332901

VISIT US

Direction: Located in Strood (Rochester), off A228

Train: Strood ¾ mile

Bus: Arriva, ASD and Nu-Venture operate services in Strood. Alight in Knight Road Strood and then short walk

ACQ.1950 🐾 P ♿

Disabled access (grounds only).

> MAP PAGE 339 (4G)
> OS MAP 178, 148/163: TQ733685

UPNOR CASTLE

KENT – ME2 4XG

Set in a riverside village, this Elizabethan artillery fort was built to protect warships in Chatham dockyard. Its furious cannonade failed to stop the Dutch severely damaging the anchored English fleet in 1667. An exhibition highlights the raid.

Managed by Medway Council.

OPENING TIMES

1 Apr-30 Sep, daily	10am-6pm
1-31 Oct, daily	10am-4pm
1 Nov-31 Mar	Closed

Last entry 45 mins before closing

VISIT US

Direction: At Upnor, on unclassified road off A228

Train: Strood 2 miles

Bus: ASD service 197 from Chatham

Tel: 01634 332902 or when castle is closed 01634 332901

UPNOR CASTLE

NON-MEMBERS

Adult £6.40 | Concession £4.00
Child £4.00 | Family £16.80
Groups of 10+ 15% discount

Members also get discounted entry to the Historic Dockyard Chatham (p.297)

ACQ.1961 🎧 E 🖼 ⛺ 🛗 🚶 🐾 P
📷 ♿ ⚠ OVP

Audio guide (small charge).

Disabled access (grounds only).

Parking (at a slight distance from castle – park before village).

> MAP PAGE 339 (4G)
> OS MAP 178, 163: TQ759706

WESTERN HEIGHTS, DOVER

KENT – CT17 9DZ

A huge fortification constructed during the Napoleonic Wars and completed in the 1860s, designed to protect Dover from French invasion.

Operated by Western Heights Preservation Society.

OPENING TIMES

Exterior only: Any reasonable daylight hours

Tours of the Drop Redoubt: Guided tours are held on the 3rd Sunday of the month from April to September, 11am and 2pm. Places must be pre-booked. Visit www.doverwesternheights.org for details and additional opening times

VISIT US

Direction: Above Dover town on W side of harbour

Train: Dover Priory ¾ mile

Bus: Regent Coaches 93 from Dover town centre

Tel: 01304 211067

ACQ.1968 🐾 P ⚠

Unsuitable for visitors who use wheelchairs or have limited mobility.

> MAP PAGE 339 (5J)
> OS MAP 179, 138: TR312408

ABINGDON COUNTY HALL MUSEUM

OXFORDSHIRE – OX14 3HG

Designed by colleagues of Sir Christopher Wren, this delightful 17th-century 'English Baroque' building houses the Abingdon Museum, and has fine rooftop views.

Managed by Abingdon Town Council, maintained by English Heritage.

OPENING TIMES

1 Apr-23 Dec, Tue-Sun & Bank Hols	10am-4pm
24 Dec-2 Jan	Closed
3 Jan-31 Mar, Tue-Sun	10am-4pm

Roof open all year, weather permitting (charges apply)

VISIT US

Direction: In Abingdon, 7 miles south of Oxford; in Market Place

Train: Radley 2½ miles

Bus: Oxford Bus Co X3, 4, 4B, X13, 35; Stagecoach X15, 34; Thames Travel X2

Tel: 01235 523703

ENTRY

Museum entry free. Small charge for admission to roof

Adult	£2
EH Members and Children	£1

ACQ.1952

MAP PAGE 338 (3C)
OS MAP 164, 170: SU498971

DEDDINGTON CASTLE

OXFORDSHIRE – OX15 0TE

Extensive earthwork remains of an 11th-century castle, associated with Odo, Bishop of Bayeux, half-brother of William the Conqueror.

Managed by Deddington Parish Council.

OPENING TIMES

Any reasonable daylight hours

VISIT US

Direction: S of B4031 on E side of Deddington; 17 miles N of Oxford

Train: King's Sutton 5 miles

Bus: OurBus Bartons 4A, 4B, 6, 7; Stagecoach in Oxfordshire S4 to within ½ mile

ACQ.1951

MAP PAGE 338 (2C)
OS MAP 151, 191: SP472316

MINSTER LOVELL HALL AND DOVECOTE

OXFORDSHIRE – OX29 0RR

The extensive and picturesque ruins of a 15th-century riverside manor house, including a fine hall,

south-west tower and complete nearby dovecote. The home of Richard III's henchman Lord Lovell.

OPENING TIMES

Any reasonable daylight hours

Dovecote exterior viewing only

VISIT US

Direction: Adjacent to Minster Lovell Church; 3 miles W of Witney, off A40

Train: Charlbury 7 miles

Bus: Stagecoach in Oxford 233. Swanbrook 853. Also Villager Community Bus V20 & V25. Then short walk

| ACQ.1935 | Minster Lovell Hall |
| ACQ.1957 | Dovecote |

Please do not climb on the walls.

MAP PAGE 338 (2B)
OS MAP 164, 180: SP325113

NORTH HINKSEY CONDUIT HOUSE

OXFORDSHIRE – OX2 9AS

Roofed conduit for Oxford's first water mains, constructed during the early 17th century.

OPENING TIMES

Apr-Oct, Thu-Sun & Bank Hols	10am-4pm

VISIT US

Direction: In North Hinksey off A34; 1½ miles W of Oxford. Located off track leading from Harcourt Hill

Train: Oxford (1½ miles)

Bus: Stagecoach Brookes Bus service U1 terminates within ¾ mile of the site

ACQ.1973

No nearby parking, pedestrian access only.

MAP PAGE 338 (3C)
OS MAP 164, 180: SP495050

NORTH LEIGH ROMAN VILLA

OXFORDSHIRE – OX29 6QE

The remains of a large, well-built Roman courtyard villa, with a nearly complete mosaic tile floor, patterned in reds and browns.

OPENING TIMES

Grounds – any reasonable daylight hours. There is no internal access to the mosaic building

VISIT US

Direction: 2 miles N of North Leigh; 10 miles W of Oxford, off A4095

Train: Hanborough 3½ miles

Bus: Stagecoach in Oxford 11 & 233 to within 1½ miles

 ᴀᴄQ.1952

Pedestrian access only from main road – 550 metres (600 yards).

Parking (lay-by, not in access lane).

> **MAP PAGE 338 (2B)**
> **OS MAP 164, 180: SP397154**

ROLLRIGHT STONES

OXFORDSHIRE – OX7 5QB

Traditionally a petrified monarch and his courtiers, the Rollright Stones include the King's Men stone circle, the Whispering Knights burial chamber and the King Stone. They span nearly 2,000 years of Neolithic and Bronze Age development.

Managed and owned by the Rollright Trust.

ROLLRIGHT STONES

OPENING TIMES

Entry at any reasonable time all year by permission of The Rollright Trust and English Heritage

VISIT US

Direction: Off unclassified road between A44 and A3400, 3 miles NW of Chipping Norton, near villages of Little Rollright and Long Compton

Train: Moreton-in-Marsh 6½ miles

Bus: Stagecoach 50 (Chipping Norton – Stratford Upon Avon) passes within ½ mile. Also Shipston Link service 3 (Wed) and 5 (Thu) pass close to the site

Contact: sitemanager@rollrightstones.co.uk

ENTRY

Admission charges apply to EH members and non-members

Adults/Concessions	£1
Children	50p

ᴀᴄQ.1883

Parking (in lay-by).

Dogs welcome on leads except inside the stone circle.

Refreshments, toilet, guidebook and postcards available at Wyatts Farm Shop: approx. 1 mile east towards Great Rollright.

> **MAP PAGE 338 (2B)**
> **OS MAP 151, OL45/191: SP297309**

UFFINGTON CASTLE, WHITE HORSE AND DRAGON HILL

OXFORDSHIRE – SN7 7QJ

Atmospheric sites along the Ridgeway. Uffington 'Castle' is a large Iron Age hillfort, Dragon Hill a natural mound. The famous White Horse is the oldest chalk-

---

UFFINGTON CASTLE

cut hill figure in Britain, perhaps over 3,000 years old.

Managed by the National Trust on behalf of English Heritage.

OPENING TIMES

Any reasonable daylight hours

VISIT US

Direction: S of B4507, 7 miles W of Wantage. Ridgeway National Trail runs directly past the site

Bus: Closest public transport is West Berks Council Transport service 47 to Ashbury then a 2 mile walk along the Ridgeway path

Tel: 01793 762209

 ᴀᴄQ.1936

Parking in NT White Horse car park. Pay and display or free to EH members displaying car sticker or with current membership card.

> **MAP PAGE 338 (3B)**
> **OS MAP 174, 170: SU301866**

WAYLAND'S SMITHY

OXFORDSHIRE – SN7 7QJ

An atmospheric Neolithic long barrow on the Ridgeway, named after the Saxon smith-god Wayland.

Managed by the National Trust on behalf of English Heritage.

OPENING TIMES

Any reasonable daylight hours

VISIT US

Direction: On the Ridgeway (closed to vehicles); ¾ mile NE of B4000, Ashbury – Lambourn Road

Bus: West Berks Council Transport service 47 then a short walk along the Ridgeway path

ᴀᴄQ.1922

Parking in NT White Horse car park. Pay and display or free to EH members displaying car sticker or with current membership card.

> **MAP PAGE 338 (3B)**
> **OS MAP 174, 170: SU281854**

FARNHAM CASTLE KEEP
SURREY – GU9 0AG

WAVERLEY ABBEY
SURREY – GU9 8EP

CAMBER CASTLE
EAST SUSSEX – TN31 7TD

Ruins of an unusually unaltered artillery fort, built by Henry VIII to guard Rye. Limited opening times, but regular guided walks around Rye Harbour Nature Reserve include the castle.

Managed by Rye Harbour Nature Reserve.

The impressive motte and shell keep of a castle founded in 1138 by Henry of Blois, Bishop of Winchester. A viewing platform reveals the buried remains of an earlier tower.

Managed by Farnham Castle.

OPENING TIMES

1 Apr-24 Dec, Mon-Fri	9am-5pm
Sat-Sun & Bank Hols	10am-4pm
25 Dec-31 Jan	Closed
1 Feb-31 Mar, Mon-Fri	9am-5pm
Sat-Sun & Bank Hols	10am-4pm
Last entry 30 mins before closing	

Tours of the Bishop's Palace are available on Wednesday afternoons for an additional fee. Please phone 01252 721194 to book

VISIT US
Direction: ½ mile north of Farnham off A287

Train: Farnham ¾ mile

Bus: Stagecoach services 4, 5, 16, 17, 18, 19, 46 and 65 stop in the town centre, which is a ¾ mile walk uphill

Tel: 01252 721194

ACQ.1933 E ✗ P ▢

MAP PAGE 338 (4D)
OS MAP 186, 145: SU837473

Remains of the monastic buildings and church of the very first abbey of Cistercian monks to be built in Britain, founded in 1128 and largely rebuilt in the 13th century. Set by a peaceful loop of the River Wey.

Download a free audio tour from our website.

Elizabeth; Disney's Into the Woods (2014); The Mummy (2017); Midsomer Murders; BBC Series, Howards End.

OPENING TIMES
Any reasonable daylight hours

VISIT US
Direction: 2 miles SE of Farnham, off B3001; off Junction 10 of M25

Train: Farnham 2 miles

Bus: Stagecoach in Hants & Surrey 46 Guildford – Aldershot (passing ▣ Farnham)

ACQ.1961 ✗ P

Parking (limited).

MAP PAGE 338 (5D)
OS MAP 186, 145: SU868453

OPENING TIMES
Aug-Oct open on the first Sat of the month for guided tour starting at 2pm prompt. Meet at the castle, but please be aware there is no vehicular access to the site and the nearest parking is a 1 mile walk away. In addition there are regular guided walks around the Rye Harbour Nature Reserve that include the castle. Please check website or visit www.sussexwildlifetrust.org.uk/visit/ryeharbour/

VISIT US
Direction: 1 mile walk across fields, off the A259; 1 mile S of Rye, off Harbour Road. No vehicle access. Follow the public footpath from Brede Lock

Train: Rye 1¼ miles

Bus: Stagecoach in Hastings service 100 Hastings – Lydd then walk from Winchelsea or Rye (1½ miles) or Stagecoach service 101 and walk from Winchelsea Sea Road (¾ mile)

Tel: Nature reserve office number 01797 227784 (Mon-Fri, 9am-5pm only)

NON-MEMBERS
Adult £3.00 | Concession £1.50
Child Free

ACQ.1967 ✗

MAP PAGE 339 (5H)
OS MAP 189, 125: TQ922185

1066 BATTLE OF HASTINGS, ABBEY AND BATTLEFIELD

There are so many ways to enjoy the scene of England's most renowned and crucial battle. Alongside the battlefield you can also explore abbey ruins and the intriguing traces of a country house, as well as interactive displays in the beautiful abbey gatehouse. An all-round great experience, this vast and varied site provides a unique day out for the whole family.

EAST SUSSEX TN33 0AE

Its history began on the fateful 14th of October 1066, when after many hours of hard fighting William the Conqueror's Norman invaders finally defeated King Harold Godwinson's English army in this very place. You can discover the dramatic story of the epic conflict in the visitor centre, where a host of interactives, displays of Norman and Anglo-Saxon weaponry, and a compelling film recount the background to the battle, the fighting, and how the Norman victory transformed the nation's history.

Accompanied by an audio tour, which recreates the sounds of battle and 'interviews' key figures of the time, you can stand on the abbey terrace to view the slope where the Normans advanced against the hilltop English shield wall. Or you can choose to walk more of the battlefield, using the 'Battlefield 1066' family trails to hunt out dramatic wooden figures including a Norman mounted knight and archer as well as a Saxon axeman and standard bearer.

DON'T MISS OUR DISPLAYS IN THE SPLENDIDLY RECREATED GATEHOUSE CHAMBERS

The turning point of the battle came when Harold Godwinson was killed, perhaps struck in the eye by an arrow. You can stand by the spot where he fell, later marked by the high altar of Battle Abbey, the great monastery William founded as a penance for the terrible bloodshed of the battle and a memorial to the dead. All around, the abbey's ruins stand ready to explore, notably the great dormitory range with its atmospheric pillared and vaulted undercrofts, built just below the place where the English army awaited attack.

As the symbol of Norman triumph, Battle Abbey enjoyed enormous wealth and influence, symbolised by the Great Gatehouse. Built in about 1338, it's among the finest medieval monastic portals in Britain. You can climb to its rooftop for astonishing views over the pretty town of Battle, the abbey ruins, and the landscape of the fighting. Don't miss our displays in the splendidly recreated gatehouse chambers. They vividly illustrate how the abbey operated and ruled its wide estates, and how its monks lived from day to day.

STAY WITH US

South Lodge is a former gatehouse, which sleeps four and comes with its own fully enclosed garden. There is so much to see and experience here, but nothing beats soaking up the atmosphere as the evening sun lights up the mellow stone of the beautiful abbey ruins.

See p.332 for details on staying at **Battle** and our other holiday cottages.

Site-finds, handling replicas and imaginative interactives share stories of monastic health, worship, finance, manuscript production, writing and much more. You can listen to part of a monastic service, hear a specially recorded carol found in an early 16th-century Battle manuscript, design your own coat of arms to add to the abbey's roll of knights, look down a monks' garderobe loo, try your hand at reassembling a stained glass window and open drawers and boxes to make discoveries of your own.

The displays also trace how, after its suppression by Henry VIII, the abbey became a grand country house. You'll find intriguing survivors of this later life as you wander the extensive grounds, including a thatched ornamental Regency dairy, an underground icehouse, and the Duchess of Cleveland's tranquil, hidden Walled Garden, now replanted with local species of fruit trees and equipped with beehives.

With so much to see, do and experience throughout the site, you'll need a break in our big café, with indoor and outdoor seating among the trees near the gatehouse. There's an imaginative children's playground nearby, with timber play stations inspired by the site's history to climb and swing on – just one of the many activities that children can enjoy as part of their day out.

OPENING TIMES

1 Apr-30 Sep, daily	10am-6pm
1 Oct-3 Nov, daily	10am-5pm
4 Nov-23 Dec, Sat-Sun	10am-4pm
2 Jan-16 Feb, Sat-Sun	10am-4pm
17-23 Feb, daily	10am-4pm
24 Feb-31 Mar, Wed-Sun	10am-4pm
Christmas Opening 24-25 Dec	Closed
26 Dec-1 Jan, daily	10am-4pm

VISIT US

Address: Battle Abbey, High Street, Battle, East Sussex

Direction: In Battle, at south end of High St. Take the A2100 off the A21

Train: Battle ½ mile

Bus: Renown Coaches 95 & 384; Rambler/ Stagecoach 304; Stagecoach 305; Battle Community Transport B67, B72, B73, B74, B75, B79; Wealdlink CT 225 (Tue & Thu)

Tel: 01424 775705/776787 (shop)

Local Tourist Information: Battle and Bexhill Tourist information: 01797 229049/01424 451111

NON-MEMBERS

Adult **£13.60** | Concession **£12.30**
Child **£8.20** | Family **£35.40**

Audio tours (suitable for families, the visually impaired and for those in wheelchairs or with learning difficulties. Also available in Dutch, French, German, Japanese and Spanish). Audio tours are complimentary but will not be issued on special events days.

Disabled access (grounds and visitor centre).

Dogs on leads (restricted areas only).

Parking charges apply to non-members. Parking free for Members.

MAP PAGE 339 (6G)
OS MAP 199, 124: TQ749157

NEW FOR 2019

From July 2019, new interpretation will include external panels, a refurbished museum and a dungeon viewing platform. We're also revealing a new medieval basement room, and fresh Second World War interpretation in the east tower.

PEVENSEY CASTLE

EAST SUSSEX BN24 5LE

With a history stretching back over 16 centuries, Pevensey Castle chronicles better than any other fortress the story of Britain's south coast defences.

Begun in the late 3rd century as one of the last and strongest of the Roman 'Saxon Shore' forts, Pevensey was the landing place of William the Conqueror in 1066.

During the century after the Conquest, a Norman castle with a great square keep and powerful gatehouse was built within one corner of the fort. In the 1250s the towered bailey wall was added, and tested during the great siege of 1264. Later still the castle was strengthened against the Spanish Armada in 1588. Finally, Second World War pillboxes and machine gun posts were cunningly camouflaged among its ancient walls.

OPENING TIMES

1 Apr-30 Sep, daily	10am-6pm
1 Oct-3 Nov, daily	10am-5pm
4 Nov-31 Mar, Sat-Sun	10am-4pm
24-26 Dec & 1 Jan	Closed

VISIT US

Direction: In Pevensey off A259

Train: Pevensey & Westham or Pevensey Bay, both ½ mile

Bus: Stagecoach 55 & 55A pass the site. Frequent Stagecoach service 99 also runs within ½ mile. Alight at Pevensey, Church Lane

Tel: 01323 762604

NON-MEMBERS

Adult £7.50 | Concession £6.80
Child £4.60 | Family £19.60

ACQ.1925 OVP

New guidebook.

Dogs on leads (restricted areas only).

Parking (charge payable). Car park managed by Pevensey Town Trust.

Toilets (near car park).

MAP PAGE 339 (6G)
OS MAP 199, 123/124: TQ645048

BOXGROVE PRIORY   WEST SUSSEX

In a beautiful setting at the foot of the South Downs, the small Benedictine priory of Boxgrove was founded in about 1117.

Its principal remains are the lodging house for guests and travellers, roofless but standing to full height at the gable ends, and the priory church. This lovely building (not in the guardianship of English Heritage) became Boxgrove's parish church at the Dissolution of the Monasteries.

Today you can explore the church's splendid 12th-century chancel, central tower and unusual transepts, which survive complete, along with an early Tudor chantry chapel with fine Renaissance carvings. There's a model of the monastic buildings in the church.

Nearby, in Boxgrove gravel pit, archaeological excavation (funded by English Heritage) produced much the oldest human bones yet discovered in England: dating from around 500,000 years ago, they belonged to a 1.8-metre (6-foot) tall man.

OPENING TIMES

Any reasonable daylight hours

VISIT US

Direction: N of Boxgrove; 4 miles E of Chichester, on minor road off A27

Train: Chichester 4 miles

Bus: Stagecoach Bus 55; Compass Bus 99

ACQ.1977 ✕ P

MAP PAGE 338 (6D)
OS MAP 197, 121: SU908076

BRAMBER CASTLE
WEST SUSSEX

The remains of a Norman motte-and-bailey castle on the banks of the River Adur, founded by William de Braose c. 1073. The earthworks are dominated by a towering wall of the keep-gatehouse.

OPENING TIMES

Any reasonable daylight hours

VISIT US

Direction: On W side of Bramber village, off A283

Train: Shoreham-by-Sea 4½ miles

Bus: Brighton & Hove 2, 60; Compass Bus 100 & 106

ACQ.1975 ✕ P

Parking (limited).

MAP PAGE 338 (6E)
OS MAP 198, 122: TQ185107

STAY WITH US

Each one of our luxurious self-catering holiday cottages is in a unique historic setting.

See p.332 for details.

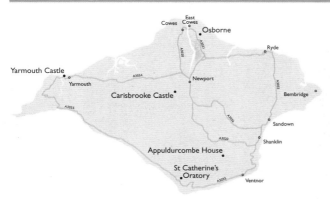

ST CATHERINE'S ORATORY

ISLE OF WIGHT – PO38 2JB

This medieval octagonal lighthouse tower was built in 1328 as penance for plundering church property – casks of wine – from a ship wrecked nearby.

Managed by the National Trust on behalf of English Heritage.

OPENING TIMES

Any reasonable daylight hours

VISIT US

Direction: E of Blackgang roundabout, off A3055. Approx. ¼ mile ascent across fields

Train: Shanklin 9 miles

Bus: Southern Vectis service 6 or Island Coaster (summer) to Blackgang Chine and then ½ mile walk

Ferry: West Cowes 14 miles, East Cowes 14 miles (both Red Funnel – Tel: 0844 844 9988); Yarmouth 15 miles (Wightlink – Tel: 0333 999 7333)

ACQ.1952

MAP PAGE 338 (7C)
OS MAP 196, OL29: SZ494773

APPULDURCOMBE HOUSE

ISLE OF WIGHT – PO38 3EW

The imposing partly-restored shell of Appuldurcombe, once the grandest mansion on the Isle of Wight. Still an outstanding example of English Baroque architecture, it stands amid 11 acres of Capability Brown-designed ornamental grounds. The 1701 east wing has been re-roofed. Sir Richard Worsley, whose marital antics deliciously outraged Georgian England, extended the house in the 1770s.

OPENING TIMES

| 1 Apr-30 Sep, daily except Sat | 10am-4pm |
| 1 Oct-31 Mar | Closed |

VISIT US

Direction: Wroxall ½ mile, off B3327

Train: Shanklin 3½ miles then bus 3

Bus: Southern Vectis 3

Ferry: Ryde 11 miles (Wightlink 0333 999 7333; Hovercraft 01983 811000); West Cowes 12 miles, East Cowes 12 miles (Red Funnel 0844 844 9988)

ACQ.1952

No facilities at the house.

MAP PAGE 338 (7C)
OS MAP 196, OL29: SZ543800

OSBORNE

Osborne opens a window on the private family life of Queen Victoria and Prince Albert, away from the public eye. Here you can see the monarch as wife and mother. Revealing how royal meals were prepared, how the queen relaxed, and how her children entertained themselves, Victoria's 'palace-by-the-sea' also offers a beach, acres of grounds and gardens, and the lavishly restored lower terrace. There's lots of entertainment for visitors of all ages, and this year you can witness how the royal couple celebrated their birthdays at Osborne.

ISLE OF WIGHT PO32 6JX

Shared with the couple's nine children, Osborne originated with the queen's desire for a 'place of one's own – quiet and retired'. Knowing and liking the Isle of Wight from childhood visits, she and Albert were determined to buy a property there. In 1845 they bought Osborne, and plans for a new mansion began at once. Eventually a pair of Italianate towers dominated the landscape, looking out on the Solent. Reminded by the view of youthful stays on the Bay of Naples, Albert lavished tremendous care on designing the surrounding gardens.

The lower terrace has intimate links with the young royal couple, still in their early thirties when they created it. Victoria bought the bronze statue of Andromeda at the Great Exhibition of 1851, and commissioned the eight figures of children riding sea monsters which surround it. She loved to relax in the Shell Alcove, returned to its original colour scheme, with motifs of cherubs and dolphins and a frieze of seashells. We've also restored the terrace's 'Osborne yellow' rendered walls, while carefully preserving its magnolia and myrtle, offspring of original plantings by the royal pair.

NEW FOR 2019

The royal couple were exact contemporaries; Victoria was born on 24 May and Albert on 26 August 1819. From 1847 until Albert's death in 1861, they always made sure they celebrated their birthdays here at Osborne.

The day usually started with the giving of flowers and nosegays and then the entire family would make their way to an elaborately decorated room where all the birthday gifts were displayed.

This year we are celebrating their bicentenary with royal birthday displays highlighting the birthday gifts they gave to each other.

Inside, Osborne's state rooms abound in opulent design and decoration. Marble sculptures line the Grand Corridor, and portraits and frescos are reminders of the family's links to the crowned heads of Europe, and of the worldwide extent of the British Empire. Most artefacts at Osborne are on loan from H.M. Queen Elizabeth II.

STAY WITH US

No 1 & No 2 Sovereign's Gate both sleep four. The stunning building was built for Queen Victoria and Prince Albert as the ceremonial entrance to Osborne for visiting heads of state. Pavilion Cottage (pictured above) sleeps four. Built in the early 1900s, this former Cricket Pavilion brims with period character. After the public leave, explore the tranquil grounds and enjoy the spectacular views across the Solent.

See p.332 for details on staying at Osborne and our other holiday cottages.

Most lavish of all, the Durbar Room reflects Queen Victoria's pride in her title Empress of India, granted in 1877. Much less prejudiced than many British people of her time, Victoria had a particular respect for her Indian 'subjects', so in 1890 she ordered a new banqueting chamber to be built in the 16th-century North Indian style. Symbols of India appear everywhere, with a splendid peacock standing proudly over the chimneypiece. You can also admire an outstanding collection of Indian treasures. Displays help you understand Victoria's relationship with the Empire, and give children the chance to get hands-on.

Elsewhere in the house, you can go behind the scenes to visit more intimate royal family apartments and bedrooms. And you can take a further step into the Victorian royal family's private life by exploring Osborne's vast and beautiful grounds.

Family visitors shouldn't miss the Swiss Cottage Quarter, domain of the royal children. A purpose-built playhouse where they learnt 'normal' life-skills, the Swiss Cottage includes a room dressed as on 11 July 1861, when the children prepared afternoon tea for their parents, not long before Prince Albert's tragically premature death.

In the once private royal museum, full of strange objects from all over the world, look out for the clothes worn by two Romanian orphans, rescued by the Royal Navy from a massacre and brought up on Osborne estate. There's a child-sized toy fort, and a trail reveals more clues to the personalities of the nine royal children and their pets.

During the summer a courtesy minibus, with wheelchair access, runs to the Swiss Cottage Quarter, from where you can make your way to the queen's once strictly private beach. Its attractions include the restored royal bathing machine, with its plumbed-in toilet.

Take time to recreate a Victorian beach holiday; relax in deckchairs and enjoy traditional seaside refreshments from the beach café. In summer there are beach games, Punch and Judy shows, and other events to entertain all ages. The beach is a ¾ mile walk from the house and minibus transfers are available in the summer.

There's a children's play area and picnic tables near the visitors' car park. You can also picnic in the grounds, or enjoy a light lunch in the stylish café in the Petty Officers Quarters.

For a treat, sample a delicious served lunch or afternoon tea in the Terrace Restaurant, where a contemporary interior complements restored original features. Please note, non-Members will need to buy an admission ticket to the house to visit the restaurant.

🎬 *Mrs Brown* (1997); *Victoria and Abdul* (2017).

🍸 Available for corporate and private hire
🍾 Licensed for civil wedding ceremonies

VICTORIAN CHRISTMAS 2019

On the weekend of Saturday 30 November and Sunday 1 December, Osborne celebrates the festive season with its popular annual Victorian Christmas event. From mid-November and through December, the ground floor of the house is dressed festively for the season, and expert guides describe how the Victorian Royal family celebrated Christmas.

OPENING TIMES

House and Grounds

1 Apr-30 Sep, daily	10am-6pm
	(House closes 5pm)
1 Oct-3 Nov, daily	10am-5pm
Last entry 4.30pm	

Ground Floor House and Grounds
(tours also available) (excluding Swiss Cottage & Museum)

4-11 Nov, Sat-Sun	10am-4pm
12 Nov-23 Dec, Wed-Sun	10am-4pm
2 Jan-16 Feb, Sat-Sun	10am-4pm

Property and Grounds Fully Open
(excluding Swiss Cottage & Museum)

17-23 Feb, daily	10am-4pm
24 Feb-31 Mar, Wed-Sun	10am-4pm

Victorian Christmas Event

30 Nov, Sat & 1 Dec, Sun	11am-7pm

Christmas Opening

24-25 Dec	Closed
26 Dec-1 Jan, daily	10am-4pm

Horse Trials
23-24 Jul, Tue-Wed – check website for details

VISIT US

Address: York Avenue, East Cowes, Isle of Wight

Direction: 1 mile SE of East Cowes. For satnav use postcode PO32 6JT

Train: Ryde Esplanade 7 miles; Wootton 3 miles

Bus: Southern Vectis services 4 & 5

Ferry: East Cowes 1½ miles (Red Funnel – Tel: 0844 844 9988); Fishbourne 4 miles; Ryde 7 miles (Wightlink – Tel: 0333 999 7333)

Hovertravel: 08434 878887

Tel: 01983 200022

Local Tourist Information:
Visit Isle of Wight: 01983 813813
www.visitisleofwight.co.uk

NON-MEMBERS

House and Garden
Adult £20.40 | Concession £18.40
Child £12.30 | Family £53.10

Winter Opening: Ground Floor House Tours and Grounds Only (excluding Swiss Cottage Quarter)
Adult £14.30 | Concession £12.90
Child £8.60 | Family £37.20

Baby carriers are available at the house entrance, as pushchairs are not permitted within the house but are welcome in the garden.

Disabled access – access for wheelchairs to the first floor is by an existing lift. Manual wheelchairs are available to borrow on a first come, first served basis. Mobility scooters are not permitted inside the house, but they can be used in the gardens.

MAP PAGE 338 (6C)
OS MAP 196, OL29: SZ516948

CARISBROOKE CASTLE

Medieval fortress and guardian of the Isle of Wight, Carisbrooke Castle was later in turn an Elizabethan artillery fortress, a king's prison and an Edwardian royal residence. It's also the home of the famous Carisbrooke donkeys.

ISLE OF WIGHT PO30 IXY

A fascinatingly varied site to visit, Carisbrooke Castle has been the key to the Isle of Wight's security for more than nine centuries. This great hilltop-crowning fortress has a keep to climb for panoramic views and a colourful history to explore.

There has been a fortress here since Saxon times, but the present castle was begun in c. 1100, when the Isle of Wight was granted to the Norman family of de Redvers. They raised the great Norman shell-keep on its towering mound, and after 1262 the formidable Countess Isabella de Redvers rebuilt the principal accommodation and service buildings. In 1377, following the addition of its double-towered 14th-century gatehouse, Carisbrooke Castle experienced its only siege, beating off a French raiding force. After the Spanish Armada passed alarmingly close in 1588, the castle was updated as an artillery fortification by surrounding it with 'bastioned' earthworks, still impressively visible.

DON'T MISS THE AWARD-WINNING EDWARDIAN-STYLE PRINCESS BEATRICE GARDEN

Most famous among the castle's varied cast of past residents was Charles I, imprisoned here in 1647-48 after his defeat in the Civil War. At first comfortably accommodated in the Constable's Lodging, he later became a closely guarded captive. An attempt to escape was foiled only when he became wedged in the window bars.

Much later, Princess Beatrice, Queen Victoria's youngest and favourite daughter and Governor of the Isle of Wight between 1896-1944, made Carisbrooke Castle her summer home. She also commissioned the altar painting in the castle chapel, in memory of a son killed in action in 1914. The award-winning Edwardian-style Princess Beatrice Garden, designed by Chris Beardshaw, was inspired by the princess, and includes a fountain and plantings in the rich colours of the royal arms. We are grateful to the late Mrs Dorothy Frazer, whose generous bequest and devotion to the island made the creation of this garden possible.

STAY WITH US

The **Bowling Green Apartment** sleeps a family of four in contemporary comfort. Enjoy the excitement of staying in a castle after dark.

See p.332 for details on staying at **Carisbrooke** and our other holiday cottages.

MEET THE FAMOUS CARISBROOKE DONKEYS, THE CASTLE'S MOST BELOVED RESIDENTS

The castle's most beloved modern residents are undoubtedly the renowned Carisbrooke donkeys. These happy animals still demonstrate the tread wheel, which originally raised water 49 metres (160 feet) from the castle well. Today's donkeys have to work much less hard, and you can hear their story in a film hosted by Jupiter the cartoon donkey, voiced by locally raised comedian Phill Jupitus.

Don't miss the changing exhibitions at the Carisbrooke Castle Museum.

OPENING TIMES

1 Apr-30 Sep, daily	10am-6pm
1 Oct-3 Nov, daily	10am-5pm
4 Nov-23 Dec, Sat-Sun	10am-4pm
2 Jan-16 Feb, Sat-Sun	10am-4pm
17-23 Feb, daily	10am-4pm
24 Feb-31 Mar, Wed-Sun	10am-4pm
Christmas Opening	
24-25 Dec	Closed
26 Dec-1 Jan, daily	10am-4pm

Last entry one hour before closing

VISIT US

Address: Carisbrooke Castle, Castle Hill, Newport, Isle of Wight

Direction: 1¼ miles SW of Newport. Follow signs to Carisbrooke village, then castle

Train: Ryde Esplanade 9 miles; Wootton 5 miles

Bus: Southern Vectis 6, 7, 12, 38 pass nearby to within ¼ mile

Ferry: West Cowes 5 miles, East Cowes 6 miles (Red Funnel – 0844 844 9988); Fishbourne 6 miles, Ryde 8 miles, Yarmouth 9 miles (Wightlink – Tel: 0333 999 7333)

Tel: 01983 522107

Local Tourist Information: 01983 813813

NON-MEMBERS

Adult £11.60 | Concession £10.50
Child £7.00 | Family £30.20

ACQ.1856

Disabled access (grounds and lower levels only).

Tearooms open daily Apr-Oct and weekends during winter (close 1 hour before site closes). 27-31 Dec & 1 Jan, 11am-3pm.

Parking charges apply to non-members. Parking free for Members.

MAP PAGE 338 (6C)
OS MAP 196, OL29: SZ486878

YARMOUTH CASTLE

ISLE OF WIGHT PO41 OPB

Built following a French raid on the Isle of Wight, Yarmouth Castle was designed to protect strategic Yarmouth harbour and (in conjunction with Hurst Castle – see p.53 – on the mainland) to defend the western end of the Solent against invasion fleets.

The last and most advanced addition to Henry VIII's chain of coastal artillery forts, it was completed after his death in 1547. Unlike Henry's earlier circular forts – such as Deal and Pendennis Castles – Yarmouth Castle is a square blockhouse. It has a heavy-gun battery to the front and the first new-style 'arrowhead' bastion built in England protecting its most exposed angle against land attack. In the 1560s its central courtyard was filled in to provide a solid gun platform. Again altered during the 17th century, it was garrisoned until 1885 and re-used during both World Wars.

Inside, you can discover atmospheric recreations of how rooms were used in the 16th century, and an exhibition about the many wrecks in 'Yarmouth Roads', the treacherous stretch of sea which the castle overlooks. Also a magnificent picnic site, with views over the Solent.

OPENING TIMES

1 Apr-30 Sep, daily	11am-5pm
1 Oct-31 Mar	Closed

VISIT US

Direction: In Yarmouth town centre, adjacent to car ferry terminal. Located just off Quay Street, up the short walkway and through the main gates into the castle

Train: Lymington Pier 🚆 adjoins the ferry berth for the Wightlink service to Yarmouth

Bus: Southern Vectis 7 & Needles Breezer & Island Coaster (summer only)

Ferry: Yarmouth, adjacent (Wightlink – Tel: 0333 999 7333)

Tel: 01983 760678

NON-MEMBERS

Adult £6.30 | Concession £5.70
Child £3.80 | Family £16.40

ACQ.1913 ♿ 🐕 📷 🅿 📷 ⚠ OVP

Disabled access (part of ground floor only).

Parking (coaches and cars 200 metres (220 yards). Charges payable).

MAP PAGE 338 (6B)
OS MAP 196, OL29: SZ354898

UNMIS

SABLE

Worcestershire Warwickshire

Herefordshire

•59 •55 47 •52
57 Cheltenham •50 •51
49 •50 •51 Gloucestershire
58 54 Stroud 61 48
•56 60 Cirencester
53 Swindon
South Gloucestershire Bristol Wiltshire
Bristol Chippenham Marlborough
North Somerset 4 1 Bath 74 Devizes 77 76
Bath & North East Somerset 2 3 67 75 79 78
Weston-super-Mare 69 71 Warminster
Wells 68
Ilfracombe 64 66 63 Somerset 70 80
65 62 Glastonbury 81 Salisbury
Barnstaple Taunton 70
Bideford Yeovil 45
Devon Tiverton 38 41
Bude Dorset
14 31 Okehampton Exeter 23 46 43 Dorchester Poole 37
19 29 26 27 Lyme Regis 40 42 39 Bournemouth
12 30 Exmouth 35 44
Launceston Teignmouth 36 Weymouth Swanage
Cornwall Padstow 10 8 34
16 11 21 33 22 Torquay
Newquay 15 28
St Austell 17 Totnes
Truro Plymouth 32 Dartmouth 24
18 25
St Ives Falmouth 13
5 6 Penzance 9
20
Isles of Scilly

■ 72, 73, 82, 83, 84, 85, 86, 87, 88
see Stonehenge and Avebury
page 127

Hugh Town: see Isles of Scilly page 136
89-96: see Isles of Scilly page 136

TELLING TALES: THE MYTHS, LEGENDS AND FOLKLORE OF ENGLAND

INSPIRED BY LEGEND

Many of our castles have inspired legends, but at **Tintagel Castle** it was a legend which inspired the castle. Richard, Earl of Cornwall, the wealthy and ambitious younger brother of Henry III, built the castle during the 1230s, exchanging three prosperous manors for the remote and rocky headland on which it stands. His motive can only have been to claim a link with King Arthur, the greatest hero of the middle ages whose legends cluster round this magical site.

SOUTH DORSET OLD STONES WAY

10 miles | 1 day
Littlebredy village to Abbotsbury

Make pilgrimage through South Dorset's historic landscape, which has an unusually high concentration of prehistoric sites. From the start at Littlebredy Church walk through the 'Valley of Stones' towards the 'Grey Mare and her Colts' – a long barrow guarded by three great stones – and the Kingston Russell Stone Circle overlooking the coastline a few miles away. Delve down into the woods to find a secret ruined chapel with simply an arch, altar and a few gravestones. Ascend to Abbotsbury Hill Fort, before walking the Ridgeway and descending into the village of Abbotsbury, with the remains of its Abbey and the unforgettable finish at St Catherine's Chapel.

View more details and a downloadable version of this route at www.english-heritage.org.uk/pilgrimage

Discover English Heritage sites along the pilgrimage route

A Kingston Russell Stone Circle *(p.112)*

B Abbotsbury Abbey Remains *(p.111)*

C St Catherine's Chapel *(p.111)*

In partnership with

the **British Pilgrimage Trust**

Kingston Russell Stone Circle

St Catherine's Chapel

SIR BEVIL GRENVILLE'S MONUMENT

BATH & NE SOMERSET – BA1 9DD

Erected to commemorate the heroism of a Royalist commander and his Cornish pikemen at the Battle of Lansdown, 1643.

OPENING TIMES

Any reasonable daylight hours

VISIT US

Direction: Located 4 miles NW of Bath on the N edge of Lansdown Hill, near the road to Wick

Train: Bath Spa 4½ miles

Bus: Stagecoach West service 620 Bath Spa – Tetbury

ACQ.1953

Parking (in lay-by).

MAP PAGE 337 (3H)
OS MAP 172, 155: ST722703

STANTON DREW CIRCLES AND COVE

BATH & NE SOMERSET – BS14 0BU

The third largest collection of prehistoric standing stones in England. It includes the Great Circle – among the biggest in the country – two smaller circles and a three-stone 'cove'. Recent surveys prove they were part of a much more elaborate ritual site.

STANTON DREW CIRCLES AND COVE

OPENING TIMES

Cove: Any reasonable daylight hours

Two main stone circles: admission fee of £1.00 charged by landowner

25 Dec   Closed

VISIT US

Direction: Cove: in the garden of the Druid's Arms public house. Circles: E of Stanton Drew village

Train: Bristol Temple Meads 7 miles

Bus: Somerbus 640 (Fri), 683 (Tue), 754 (Mon); Citistar 134 (Tue); ABus/Bugler service 672 all serve the village of Stanton Drew

ACQ.1883

Cove: parking. Stones: limited parking at entrance to Stones field. Cattle on site.

MAP PAGE 337 (3H)
OS MAP 172/182, 154/155
COVE: ST597631
CIRCLES: ST601633

STONEY LITTLETON LONG BARROW

BATH & NE SOMERSET – BA2 8NR

One of the finest accessible examples of a Neolithic chambered tomb, with its multiple burial chambers open to view.

OPENING TIMES

Any reasonable daylight hours

VISIT US

Direction: 1 mile S of Wellow off A367. Narrow lane west of village leads to small parking area (1 mile)

Train: Bath Spa 6 miles

Bus: Somerbus service 757 (Wed) to Wellow then 1 mile walk from village. Otherwise take First 171, 172, 173 or 174 to Peasdown St John and walk 2½ miles

ACQ.1884

Parking (limited). ¼ mile walk uphill from parking area. Sheep may be grazing on site.

Note: visitors are advised to bring a torch.

MAP PAGE 337 (3H)
OS MAP 172, 142: ST735572

TEMPLE CHURCH

BRISTOL – BS1 6HS

The 'leaning tower' and walls of a large late-medieval church – originally founded by the Knights Templar – which survived Second World War bombing.

OPENING TIMES

Exterior only: Any reasonable daylight hours

VISIT US

Direction: Located in Temple St, off Victoria St

Train: Bristol Temple Meads ¼ mile

Bus: From surrounding areas

ACQ.1958

MAP PAGE 337 (3H)
OS MAP 172, 154/155: ST593727

BALLOWALL BARROW

CORNWALL – TR19 7NP

In a spectacular position, this large Bronze Age burial mound was reconstructed by Victorian Cornish antiquarian William Borlase.

Managed by the National Trust.

OPENING TIMES

Any reasonable daylight hours

VISIT US

Direction: 1 mile W of St Just

Train: Penzance 8 miles

Bus: First Kernow 18C, A17 & 240; Travel Cornwall 409; West Penwith Community Bus 7

ACQ.1954

Parking limited.

MAP PAGE 336 (7A)
OS MAP 203, 102: SW355312

CARN EUNY ANCIENT VILLAGE

CORNWALL – TR20 8RB

Among the best-preserved ancient villages in the South West, occupied from Iron Age until late Roman times.

Managed by the Cornwall Heritage Trust.

OPENING TIMES

Any reasonable daylight hours

VISIT US

Direction: 1½ miles W of Sancreed along narrow but signed lanes

Train: Penzance 6 miles

Bus: Travel Cornwall service 409 to Grumbla then ½ mile walk

ACQ.1957 ⛩ **P** ⚠

Parking (limited) in Brane, 600 metres (660 yards) walk to site.

Unguarded sheer drops on site.

MAP PAGE 336 (7A)
OS MAP 203, 102: SW402288

DUPATH WELL

CORNWALL – PL17 8AD

A charming well-house of c. 1500, standing over an ancient spring believed to cure whooping cough.

Managed by the Cornwall Heritage Trust.

OPENING TIMES

Any reasonable daylight hours

VISIT US

Direction: 1 mile E of Callington off A388

Train: Gunnislake 4½ miles

Bus: Go Cornwall services 12 & 12A. Alight in Saltash Road and then ½ mile walk via footpath

ACQ.1937 ⛩ **P**

Parking at farmyard entrance.

MAP PAGE 336 (6D)
OS MAP 201, 108: SX375692

CHYSAUSTER ANCIENT VILLAGE

CORNWALL – TR20 8XA

A new elevated viewing platform offers you a bird's-eye view of Chysauster, one of the finest examples of a Romano-British village in Britain. Set in beautiful countryside rich in wildlife, the village probably originated as an Iron Age settlement in about 400 BC. Some 50 to 70 people may have lived here in Roman times, before Chysauster was abandoned for unknown reasons during the 3rd century AD. A site model gives you more insights into this ancient settlement and its unique prehistoric landscape.

The village includes substantial remains of nine stone-walled 'courtyard houses', a type found only on the Land's End peninsula and the Isles of Scilly. Lining a 'village street', each had an open central courtyard surrounded by thatched rooms. There's also the entrance to a 'fogou', an underground passage distinctive to west Cornwall sites. Their purpose remains a mystery.

OPENING TIMES

1 Apr-30 Jun, daily	10am-5pm
1 Jul-31 Aug, daily	10am-6pm
1-30 Sep, daily	10am-5pm
1 Oct-3 Nov, daily	10am-4pm
4 Nov-31 Mar	Closed

Last entry 30 mins before closing

VISIT US

Direction: Located 2½ miles NW of Gulval, off B3311

Train: Penzance 3½ miles

Bus: On First Kernow service 16A alight New Mill, then 1½ mile walk. Alternatively First Kernow 16 to Castle Gate and then about 2½ mile walk

Tel: 07831 757934

Local Tourist Information: Penzance: 01736 335530

NON-MEMBERS

Adult £5.00 I Concession £4.50
Child £3.00 I Family £13.00

ACQ.1931 ♿ ⛩ 🍴 🏛 🧍 ⚑ **P** 🏠
📷 OVP

MAP PAGE 336 (7B)
OS MAP 203, 102: SW472350

HALLIGGYE FOGOU

CORNWALL – TR12 6AF

The largest of the mysterious underground passages or 'fogous' associated with Cornish Iron Age settlements. Whether they were refuges, storage chambers or shrines is uncertain.

Managed by the Trelowarren Estate.

OPENING TIMES

Any reasonable daylight hours May-Sep. No access inside fogou Oct-Apr inclusive

VISIT US

Direction: 5 miles SE of Helston off B3293. Follow signs for Trelowarren Estate. Turn right at Mawgan Cross roundabout. Turn left onto estate at Double Lodges

Train: Penryn 14 miles

Bus: First Kernow 36 or 235 to Garras and then c. 1 mile walk. Alternatively OTS service 323 to Rosevear Mawgan Cross then c. 1 mile walk

ACQ.1979 🎟 🚶 ⚓ P 🍴 ⚠

Limited parking.

Steps down into the fogou can be slippery: take care when descending.

Visitors are strongly advised to bring a torch.

> MAP PAGE 336 (7B)
> OS MAP 203, 103: SW713239

THE HURLERS STONE CIRCLES

CORNWALL – PL14 5LE

Three late Neolithic or early Bronze Age stone circles arranged in a line, a grouping unique in England.

Managed by the Cornwall Heritage Trust.

OPENING TIMES

Any reasonable daylight hours

VISIT US

Direction: Located ½ mile NW of Minions, off B3254

Train: Liskeard 7 miles

THE HURLERS STONE CIRCLES

Bus: Go Cornwall service 74 to Darite and 1 mile walk. Alternatively Group Travel service 236 to Upton Cross and 1 mile walk

ACQ.1935 🎟 P

Parking ¼ mile walk. Livestock grazing on the moor.

> MAP PAGE 336 (6D)
> OS MAP 201, 109: SX258714

LAUNCESTON CASTLE

CORNWALL – PL15 7DR

Set on a large natural mound, with an unusual keep consisting of a 13th-century round tower inside an earlier shell-keep. George Fox, founder of the Quakers, suffered harsh imprisonment here in 1656.

OPENING TIMES

1 Apr-30 Sep, daily	10am-6pm
1 Oct-3 Nov, daily	10am-5pm
4 Nov-31 Mar	Closed

Last entry 30 mins before closing

VISIT US

Direction: In Launceston town centre

Bus: Stagecoach SW 6/6A; Go Cornwall 12, 12B & 179; Group Travel 223, 231 & 236; Travel Cornwall 410, 420, 425 & 480

Tel: 01566 772365

Local Tourist Information: Launceston: 01566 772321

NON-MEMBERS

Adult **£5.50** | Concession **£5.00** Child **£3.30** | Family **£14.30**

ACQ.1952 ♿ 🎟 E ⛺ 📷 🅿 ⚠ OVP

Disabled access (outer bailey, exhibition and shop).

Refreshments available.

> MAP PAGE 336 (5D)
> OS MAP 201, 112: SX331846

KING DONIERT'S STONE

CORNWALL – PL14 6EG

Two richly carved pieces of a 9th-century cross, commemorating Dumgarth, British King of Dumnonia, died c. AD 875.

Managed by the Cornwall Heritage Trust.

OPENING TIMES

Any reasonable daylight hours

VISIT US

Direction: 1 mile NW of St Cleer, off B3254

Train: Liskeard 7 miles

Bus: Go Cornwall service 74

ACQ.1933 🎟 P

Parking (in lay-by).

> MAP PAGE 336 (6D)
> OS MAP 201, 109: SX236688

PENHALLAM MANOR

CORNWALL – EX22 6XW

The low, grass-covered, complete ground-plan of a moated 13th-century manor house, in a delightful woodland setting.

OPENING TIMES

Any reasonable daylight hours

Car park open   10am-dusk

VISIT US

Direction: Signposted from Week St Mary, off a minor road. From A39 heading north turn right at Treskinnick Cross

Bus: First Kernow service 95 stops at Treskinnick Cross (2 miles). Travel Cornwall services 420 (Tue) & 480 (Mon, Wed, Thu, Fri) to the nearby village of Week St Mary (c. 1 mile walk)

ACQ.1981 🎟 P ⚠

Limited parking. (15 minute walk from the car park along a forest track).

Deep water.

> MAP PAGE 336 (5D)
> OS MAP 190, 111: SX224974

RESTORMEL CASTLE

CORNWALL – PL22 0EE

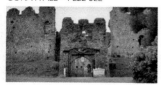

Restormel's great 13th-century circular keep stands on an earlier Norman mound, on top of a high spur beside the River Fowey. Twice visited by the Black Prince, it finally saw action during the Civil War. Commanding fantastic views, it makes an excellent picnic spot. A trail leads to the Duchy of Cornwall Nursery across the valley.

OPENING TIMES

1 Apr-30 Jun, daily	10am-5pm
1 Jul-31 Aug, daily	10am-6pm
1-30 Sep, daily	10am-5pm
1 Oct-3 Nov, daily	10am-4pm
4 Nov-31 Mar	Closed

Last entry 30 mins before closing

VISIT US

Direction: Located 1½ miles N of Lostwithiel, off A390

Train: Lostwithiel 1½ miles

Bus: Travel Cornwall 482 (Wed); Roselyn 296 (Tue); Infrequent Gorran & District Community Bus G4 to Lostwithiel then 1½ mile walk

Tel: 01208 872687

Local Tourist Information
Lostwithiel: 01208 872207

NON-MEMBERS

Adult £5.50 | Concession £5.00
Child £3.30 | Family £14.30

ACQ.1925 ⚐ ⚑ ▢ ⚑ ⚑ ⚑ P ⚑ ⚑
⚠ OVP

New guidebook.

Access via a stock grazing area, appropriate footwear is advisable. There are steps on the entrance path. Disabled visitors may wish to call the site in advance to arrange alternative access.

Refreshments available.

MAP PAGE 336 (6C)
OS MAP 200, 107: SX104614

ST BREOCK DOWNS MONOLITH

CORNWALL – PL30 5PN

Cornwall's largest prehistoric standing stone, originally weighing nearly 17 tonnes, on the summit of St Breock Downs. Managed by the Cornwall Heritage Trust.

OPENING TIMES

Any reasonable daylight hours

VISIT US

Direction: 3½ miles SW of Wadebridge. 2 miles SW of Burlawn, on road to Rosenannon. Follow finger post, then turn right for approx. 500 metres

Train: Roche 5½ miles

Bus: First Kernow services 94/95 to St Jidgey, then walk along the Saints Way (2½ miles)

ACQ.1965 ⚑ P

Parking (in lay-by), track to monument directly opposite.

MAP PAGE 336 (6C)
OS MAP 200, 106: SW968683

ST CATHERINE'S CASTLE

CORNWALL – PL23 4JH

One of two small artillery forts built by Henry VIII to defend Fowey Harbour, consisting of two storeys with gun ports at ground level.

OPENING TIMES

Any reasonable daylight hours

VISIT US

Direction: 1½ miles SW of Fowey along a woodland path off Readymoney Road

Train: Par 4 miles

Bus: First Kernow 24, 25; Yeo's Contracts Fowey Town Service 724 & 725 to within ¾ mile walk of castle

ACQ.1909 ⚑ P ⚠

Parking (Readymoney Cove Car Park, Fowey, ¾ mile walk). Charged (not EH).

Steep drops within castle; keep children under close control. Please do not climb on the walls.

MAP PAGE 336 (6C)
OS MAP 200/204, 107: SX119509

TREGIFFIAN BURIAL CHAMBER

CORNWALL – TR19 6BG

Remains of a Neolithic chambered tomb, with a stone-lined entrance passage leading into the central chamber. Managed by the Cornwall Heritage Trust.

OPENING TIMES

Any reasonable daylight hours

VISIT US

Direction: Located 2 miles SE of St Buryan, on B3315

Train: Penzance 5½ miles

Bus: First Kernow A1 or West Coast Taxi 347 to Lamorna or Lamorna Turn then c. 1 mile walk

ACQ.1971 ⚑ P

Parking (in lay-by).

MAP PAGE 336 (7A)
OS MAP 203, 102: SW431244

TRETHEVY QUOIT

CORNWALL – PL14 5JY

An impressive Neolithic burial chamber, 2.7 metres (8ft 11in) high. Five standing stones are surmounted by a huge capstone. Managed by the Cornwall Heritage Trust.

OPENING TIMES

Any reasonable daylight hours

VISIT US

Direction: 1 mile NE of St Cleer, near Darite; off B3254

Train: Liskeard 3½ miles

Bus: Go Cornwall 74

ACQ.1931 P ⚑

Sheep may be grazing in field.

Limited parking.

MAP PAGE 336 (6D)
OS MAP 201, 109: SX259688

PENDENNIS CASTLE

'Enemies on the Horizon' is our brand-new re-imagining of Pendennis Castle. Exciting displays help you experience first-hand how this picturesquely sited fortress countered England's foes for more than four centuries.

CORNWALL TR11 4NQ

Set on a rocky headland, Pendennis Castle offers you breathtaking views over Falmouth, the Fal estuary and the sea. It was originally built in the 1540s by Henry VIII, at a time when Cornwall was in the front line of the Tudor conflict between England, France and Spain. Along with its sister castle, St Mawes, on the far side of the estuary, it guarded the vital anchorage of Carrick Roads. You'll witness how it was developed, re-armed and updated again and again to face new threats over the centuries, right up to the Second World War and after.

In the Tudor keep or 'gun tower', the core and oldest part of the fortress, you'll be immersed in an alarm as a possible enemy ship is sighted and the gunners rush to their stations. You can even load and fire a Tudor replica cannon, adding a resounding boom to the audio-visual displays. Climb to the top of the round keep for panoramic views.

Threatened again by Spanish landings in Elizabethan times, Henry VIII's fort was strengthened and expanded to defend the whole headland, producing the extensive fortress you see today.

During the First World War Pendennis became the headquarters of 'Fortress Falmouth'. Hands-on displays vividly recreate parts of the fortress as they were in 1914-18. Exhibits include the letters of Battery Quartermaster Sergeant, 'Tommy' Thomas, who died of wounds in France, aged 27. They're now back in the very room where some were written.

Highlighting original Tudor, Napoleonic, Victorian and 20th-century guns, a brand-new display traces how the artillery of Pendennis developed to meet the changing threat of ever more deadly enemy weapons. Between April and October, it's hard to miss the thunderous daily live firing of a noonday gun, using one of the guns in the castle's collection. Often this will be a rare quick-firing 12 pounder, operated by a volunteer crew in Edwardian uniform.

Follow the tunnel down to the Half Moon Battery, and more new interactive presentations transport you back to the most recent crisis in Pendennis's history, the Second World War. In the underground magazine, you'll discover the dangers of working with high explosives, and might even get recruited into a gun-firing team. In the meticulously re-created Battery Observation Post bunker, 1940s 'donkey ear' binoculars help you scan the horizon for close-up three-dimensional views of enemy ships. You can also eavesdrop on telephone conversations between the commander and the crews who fired guns with a range of up to 14 miles.

Take a break from watching out for enemies on the horizon in the café, offering delicious meals and snacks with recipes inspired by the castle's heritage.

Pendennis has plenty of space for families to explore together. The picturesque fortress can also serve as a spectacular venue – from a dramatic coastal wedding to a memorable corporate event. The pre-bookable education suite fits up to 35 children.

Double up on your castle adventures and combine your trip to Pendennis with a visit to her sister fortress at St Mawes (p.106), which also has new stories to share this year.

🖵 Available for corporate and private hire
🔔 Licensed for civil wedding ceremonies

STAY WITH US

Enjoy the grounds and be in the heart of the action on event days when you stay in the **Custodian's House** or **Callie's Cottage** on the castle lawns.

See p.332 for details on staying at **Pendennis** and our other holiday cottages.

OPENING TIMES

1 Apr-30 Sep, daily	10am-6pm
1 Oct-3 Nov, daily	10am-5pm
4 Nov-23 Dec, Sat-Sun	10am-4pm
2 Jan-16 Feb, Sat-Sun	10am-4pm
17-23 Feb, daily	10am-4pm
24 Feb-31 Mar, Wed-Sun	10am-4pm
Christmas Opening 24-25 Dec	Closed
26 Dec-1 Jan, daily	10am-4pm
Last entry 1 hour before closing	

The castle may close at 4pm on Saturdays if an event is booked. Please check with the property in advance

The castle keep may close for 1 hour if an event is booked

Free guided tours of the Half Moon Battery and the gun collection are regularly available

VISIT US

Address: Pendennis Castle, Falmouth, Cornwall

Direction: Follow the A39 through Falmouth and then follow the signs for 'scenic route'. For satnav to main car park use TR11 4NQ or for disabled parking use TR11 4LP

Train: Falmouth Docks ½ mile

Bus: OTS Falmouth town service 366A & 367; First Kernow U3

Tel: 01326 316594

Local Tourist Information: 01326 741194

NON-MEMBERS

Adult £12.00 | Concession £10.80
Child £7.20 | Family £31.20

Wheelchair access to the grounds, but steep slopes or drops in places. There is also full wheelchair access to the shop, tearoom, weapons of war display and barracks.
Tearoom closes ½ hour before the castle.

MAP PAGE 336 (7C)
OS MAP 204, 103/105: SW824318

TINTAGEL CASTLE

Among the most spectacular and intriguing historic sites in Britain, Tintagel Castle is inextricably linked with the story of King Arthur.

CORNWALL PL34 0HE

A dramatic rocky headland once joined to the mainland by a slender neck of rock – its Cornish name 'Din Tagell' means 'the fortress with the narrow entrance' – Tintagel was an important power centre and trading port for Early Medieval Cornish rulers. Recent excavations, including the discovery of an early medieval stone inscribed with Latin and Greek letters, add to the growing archaeological evidence that Tintagel was then the home of a literate, high status Christian community with strong links to Atlantic Europe and the Mediterranean.

A DRAMATIC ROCKY HEADLAND

Tintagel's link with a legendary 'King Arthur', however, is first recorded in the 12th century. Geoffrey of Monmouth then wrote that Duke Gorlois of Cornwall shut his wife Ygraine away here to protect her from the lusts of Uther Pendragon, King of Britain. But Merlin magically transformed Uther into the likeness of Ygraine's husband: he slept with her here, and fathered Arthur.

Richard, Earl of Cornwall, Henry III's ambitious younger brother, built the castle here during the 1230s, almost certainly to claim a link with King Arthur. The atmospheric ruins of his fortress stand partly on the 'mainland' and partly on the 'island' headland: until Tudor times, they were connected by a fortified bridge. On the windswept island you'll also find the remains of 5th-7th-century houses and a medieval garden with 'story stones' for children to seek out – as well as amazing views along the dramatic rocky coast.

DISCOVER TRACES OF ANCIENT CORNISH SETTLEMENT

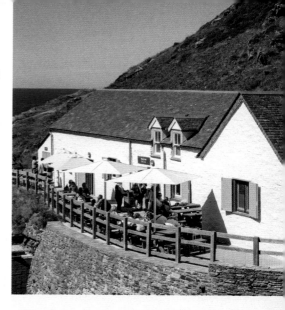

Over the centuries Tintagel's romantic setting and legendary past inspired writers and painters from medieval Malory to Victorian Tennyson and the Pre-Raphaelites. Today outdoor works of art bring to life these connections, including a stone compass highlighting Tintagel's links with other 'Arthurian' sites, a brooding life-sized kingly figure, and a carving of Merlin's face hidden in the rocks on the beach.

The visitor centre exhibition takes a fresh look at how fact and fiction combine at this world-famous landmark.

Another Tintagel highlight is the attractive Beach Café, looking out to the island, the beautiful cove and 'Merlin's Cave'. Our varied menu focusses on seasonal and local food.

COMING SOON

Over the past two years, we have been working on the plans and designs for a new footbridge at Tintagel Castle. Recreating the historic link between the mainland and the island, the spectacular bridge is now in production. When it opens it will add a thrilling new experience to your visit. A walk across the 72-metre long bridge will open up new vistas, and give you the chance to follow in the footsteps of Tintagel's Medieval inhabitants. The footbridge is generously funded by Julia and Hans Rausing.

OPENING TIMES

Please check website for the latest opening times.
www.english-heritage.org.uk/tintagel

VISIT US

Address: Tintagel Castle, Castle Road, Tintagel, Cornwall

Direction: On Tintagel Head, 600 metres (660 yards) along uneven track from Tintagel; no vehicles except Land Rover service (not managed by EH and extra charge payable)

Bus: First Kernow 95 (with connections available at Wadebridge, Camelford and Boscastle)

Tel: 01840 770328

Local Tourist Information:
Tintagel: 01840 779084

NON-MEMBERS

Please check website for the latest admission prices

Access to the castle and island (due to more than 100 steep steps) is severely limited for disabled visitors. However, access is possible to the exhibition, Beach Café and shop, plus viewing points of the island.

New guidebook.

Parking (600 metres (660 yards) in the village) – not managed by EH.

MAP PAGE 336 (5C)
OS MAP 200, 111: SX049891

ST MAWES CASTLE

CORNWALL TR2 5DE

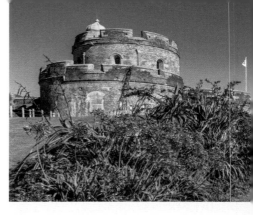

Beautifully sited overlooking the Fal estuary, St Mawes Castle is the best-preserved and most elaborately decorated of Henry VIII's Tudor artillery forts. Updated presentation and a new children's trail now highlight its stories for family explorers.

Along with Pendennis Castle on the other side of the estuary, St Mawes guarded the important anchorage of Carrick Roads. Mounting heavy ship-sinking guns, it was one of the chain of forts Henry VIII commissioned to counter an invasion threat from Catholic Europe. New displays reveal for the first time how the wealthy and ambitious Cornish merchant Thomas Treffry of Fowey masterminded its building, bedecking it with carvings praising the Tudor dynasty and becoming its first captain.

A new model introduces the castle's charming clover-leaf design, hands-on games help families discover its ornate heraldic sculptures, and audio tracks bring Tudor characters to life. Young visitors can become Castle Explorers, following the new children's trail through the grounds stretching down to the estuary.

The castle's collection of historic guns has also been re-presented. They tell the story of how St Mawes guarded the Cornish coast for over 450 years, through the Napoleonic wars, the Victorian period and the two World Wars, right up to 1956.

There are wonderful views of the sea and ships from the battlements, and you can add to your adventures by travelling to the castle by ferry.

STAY WITH US

Fort House sleeps four. Ideal for families with young children due to the fenced and sheltered garden.

See p.332 for details.

OPENING TIMES

1 Apr-30 Sep, daily	10am-6pm
1 Oct-3 Nov, daily	10am-5pm
4 Nov-23 Dec, Sat-Sun	10am-4pm
2 Jan-16 Feb, Sat-Sun	10am-4pm
17-23 Feb, daily	10am-4pm
24 Feb-31 Mar, Wed-Sun	10am-4pm
Christmas Opening 24-26 Dec	Closed
27 Dec-1 Jan, daily	10am-4pm
Last entry 30 mins before closing	

The castle may be closed on a Saturday if an event is booked. Please check with the property in advance

VISIT US

Direction: In St Mawes on A3078

Train: Penmere (Falmouth), 4 miles via Prince of Wales Pier and ferry

Bus: First Kernow service 50 (½ mile), but better to catch ferry from Falmouth

Ferry: St Mawes passenger ferry from Falmouth or King Harry Car Ferry from Feock

Tel: 01326 270526

Local Tourist Information: St Mawes: 01326 270440

NON-MEMBERS

Adult £7.00 | Concession £6.30
Child £4.20 | Family £18.20

ACQ.1961 🎧 ♿ 🐕 🖥 🏠 🚶 👶 P 🖼 📷 ⚠ OVP

Parking charges apply to non-members. Parking free for Members.

MAP PAGE 336 (7C)
OS MAP 204, 105: SW841328

BERRY POMEROY CASTLE

DEVON – TQ9 6LJ

The perfect romantic ruin, tucked away in woodland. Within the 15th-century walls of the Pomeroy family castle looms the dramatic ruined shell of the great Elizabethan and Jacobean mansion of the Seymours, never completed.

OPENING TIMES

1 Apr-30 Sep, daily	10am-6pm
1 Oct-3 Nov, daily	10am-4pm
4 Nov-31 Mar, Sat-Sun	10am-4pm
24-26 Dec & 1 Jan	Closed
Last entry 30 mins before closing	

VISIT US

Direction: 2½ miles E of Totnes off A385

Train: Totnes 3½ miles

Bus: Country Bus 149 to Berry Lodge Cross then 1 mile walk

Tel: 01803 866618

NON-MEMBERS

Adult £7.50 | Concession £6.80
Child £4.60 | Family £19.60

ACQ.1977 🎧 🖼 ♿ ✝ 🖥 🚶 🚻 P
🎪 📷 ⬛ ♿ OVP

Wheelchair and rugged mobility scooter access (grounds and ground floor only).

Parking (no coach access) at end of long drive (approx. ¾ mile).

Tearooms (not managed by EH)
Tel: 01803 849473 for opening times.

MAP PAGE 337 (6F)
OS MAP 202, OL20/110:
SX839623

BLACKBURY CAMP

DEVON – EX24 6JE

An Iron Age hillfort with impressive ramparts and defended single entrance. Now a picturesque spot for a picnic, surrounded by woodland.

OPENING TIMES

Any reasonable daylight hours

VISIT US

Direction: Off B3174/A3052

Train: Honiton 6½ miles

Bus: Stagecoach Devon 9A; First X52 and Axe Valley 899. Alight at Three Horseshoes on A3052 between Sidford & Seaton and then public footpath (steep climb c. 1 mile)

ACQ.1930 ✝ P

MAP PAGE 337 (5G)
OS MAP 192/193, 115: SY187924

DARTMOUTH, BAYARD'S COVE FORT

DEVON – TQ6 9AX

Small Tudor artillery fort guarding Dartmouth's inner harbour, picturesquely sited on the quayside.

OPENING TIMES

Any reasonable daylight hours

VISIT US

Direction: Located in Dartmouth, on the riverside

Train: Kingswear Station on the Torbay & Paignton Railway and then catch the Dart lower or passenger ferry

Bus: Stagecoach SW service 3, X64, 90. Alternatively Stagecoach bus 18, 18A, 18E or 120 to Kingswear Banjo then cross the River Dart by lower or passenger ferry

ACQ.1954 ♿ ✝

Disabled access via town quay but cobbles very uneven.

Please do not climb on the walls.

MAP PAGE 337 (6F)
OS MAP 202, OL20: SX879509

GRIMSPOUND

DEVON – PL20 6TB

The best-known prehistoric Dartmoor settlement. Remains of 24 Bronze Age houses survive within a massive boundary wall.

Managed by the Dartmoor National Park Authority.

OPENING TIMES

Any reasonable daylight hours

VISIT US

Direction: 6 miles SW of Moretonhampstead, off B3212

Bus: Tavistock Country Bus 123 first Saturday of the month. Alight at Challacombe Cross then walk 1¼ miles. There is also a year round service 98 operated by Target Travel between Tavistock and Bellever (Postbridge) which is a 5 miles walk from Grimspound

ACQ.1977 ✝ P

Parking in lay-by.

MAP PAGE 336 (5E)
OS MAP 191, OL28: SX701809

DARTMOUTH CASTLE

———— DEVON TQ6 0JN ————

Multimedia interpretation now brings Dartmouth Castle to life. Imaginative panels, sound and video installations reveal how this picturesquely-sited fortress defended the approach to the busy port of Dartmouth for over 550 years.

Begun in the 1380s by John Hawley, privateering mayor of Dartmouth, about a century later the castle became probably the very first fortification in Britain purpose-built to mount 'ship-sinking' heavy cannon. It was also equipped with a massive 250-metre long iron chain spanning the Dart estuary, which could be drawn up to stop incoming enemy ships, making them an easy target for gunfire. An animated film, projected on the walls, explores how this feat of medieval engineering worked, combining a winding mechanism in the castle with supporting bearer-boats in mid-stream.

EXPLORE HANDS-ON THE WEAPONS AND ARMOUR USED TO DEFEND THE FORTRESS

More installations bring the castle's story right up to its last call to action in the Second World War, and a dramatic audio and light installation in the 19th-century gun battery shows a crew preparing to fire a heavy gun. Families can explore hands-on the weapons and armour used to defend the fortress, trying on helmets and handling cannonballs. You're also introduced to characters from Dartmouth's history, and young history hunters can embark on *John Hawley's Explorer Trail*, a child-friendly activity trail throughout the castle.

Take the scenic boat trip to the castle from the bustling town quay. The best views of the castle are from the water, so be sure to have your camera ready.

OPENING TIMES

1 Apr-30 Sep, daily	10am-6pm
1 Oct-3 Nov, daily	10am-5pm
4 Nov-31 Mar, Sat-Sun	10am-4pm
24-26 Dec & 1 Jan	Closed

Last entry 30 mins before closing

VISIT US

Direction: 1 mile SE of Dartmouth off B3205, narrow approach road. No coach access

Train: Paignton 8 miles via ferry

Bus: Stagecoach SW service 3, X64, 90. Alternatively Stagecoach bus 18, 18A, 18E or 120 to Kingswear Banjo then cross the River Dart by lower or passenger ferry

Ferry: Dartmouth Steam Railway and River Boat Company, and Castle Passenger Ferry service to the castle

Tel: 01803 834445

Local Tourist Information:
Dartmouth: 01803 834224

NON-MEMBERS

Adult £8.00 | Concession £7.20
Child £4.80 | Family £20.80

ACQ.1909 🖼️🛡️📷f♿🔲🏃🚹P🎋🏠🍽️
⚠️ OVP

Parking (not owned by EH, charged).

Tearooms and toilets (not managed by EH).

MAP PAGE 337 (6F)
OS MAP 202, OL20: SX887503

HOUND TOR DESERTED MEDIEVAL VILLAGE

DEVON – TQ13 9XG

The remains of four 13th-century Dartmoor longhouses built of granite boulders, with their barns and garden plots. People lived at one end of the longhouse, their livestock at the other, divided by a passage. Set in an area originally farmed in the Bronze Age, this isolated moorland hamlet was probably abandoned by the early 15th century. A free downloadable audio tour is available from our website.

Managed by the Dartmoor National Park Authority.

OPENING TIMES

Any reasonable daylight hours

VISIT US

Direction: 2½ miles west of Haytor Vale on B3387, right turn to Hound Tor and Manaton, continue for 1½ miles

Bus: Country Bus (summer, Sat) 'Haytor Hoppa' service 271 to Swallerton Gate; Country Bus 193 (Wed & Fri) or 672 (Thu) to Widecombe In The Moor (3 miles) or the Turners Tours service 671 (Wed) to Manaton (2¼ miles)

ACQ.1972 ⌂ ⚐ P

Parking at Swallerton Gate (½ mile walk south east across moor to monument).

MAP PAGE 336 (5E)
OS MAP 191, OL28: SX746788

KIRKHAM HOUSE, PAIGNTON

DEVON – TQ3 3AX

Late medieval house, restored in the 1960s. Furnished with modern furniture, illustrating traditional craftsmanship.

Managed in association with the Paignton Heritage Society.

OPENING TIMES

19, 22 Apr, 6, 27 May,
7, 14, 21, 28 Jul,
4, 11, 18, 25-26 Aug   2pm-5pm
14-15 Sep   11am-4pm

VISIT US

Direction: Located in Kirkham St, off Cecil Rd, Paignton

Train: Paignton ½ mile

Bus: From surrounding areas

ACQ.1948 ⚐

MAP PAGE 337 (6F)
OS MAP 202, OL20/110: SX885610

LYDFORD CASTLE, TOWN BANKS AND SAXON TOWN

DEVON – EX20 4BH

A Norman earthwork castle and a later Norman stone keep, built as a prison and notorious for harsh punishments. Beautifully sited on the fringe of Dartmoor, it stands within the defences of a Saxon fortified 'borough'.

Download a free audio tour from our website.

OPENING TIMES

Any reasonable daylight hours

VISIT US

Direction: In Lydford off A386; 8½ miles S of Okehampton

Bus: Plymouth Citybus 46

ACQ.1934	Castle
ACQ.1965	North of Town Banks
ACQ.1968	South of Town Banks
ACQ.1972	Norman Fort

⌂ ⚐ P

Sheep may be grazing on site.

MAP PAGE 336 (5E)
OS MAP 191/201, OL28: SX509848

MERRIVALE PREHISTORIC SETTLEMENT

DEVON – PL20 6ST

Bronze Age settlement remains, along with ritual sites including Bronze Age cairns and cists, late Neolithic stone rows and a stone circle. Constructed c. 3000-1000 BC.

Managed by the Dartmoor National Park Authority.

OPENING TIMES

Any reasonable daylight hours

VISIT US

Direction: South of B3357 W of Princetown

Train: Gunnislake 10 miles

Bus: Target service 98 Yelverton – Tavistock (with connections from Plymouth)

ACQ.1973 ⚐ P

Parking at Four Winds car park. Five minute walk west across moor.

MAP PAGE 336 (6E)
OS MAP 191, OL28: SX554748

OKEHAMPTON CASTLE

DEVON – EX20 1JA

The remains of the largest castle in Devon. Begun soon after the Norman Conquest, it was converted into a sumptuous residence in the 14th century by Hugh Courtenay, Earl of Devon. Riverside picnic area and woodland walks.

OPENING TIMES

1 Apr-30 Jun, daily	10am-5pm
1 Jul-31 Aug, daily	10am-6pm
1 Sep-3 Nov, daily	10am-5pm
4 Nov-31 Mar	Closed

Last entry 30 mins before closing

VISIT US

Direction: Located ½ mile SW of Okehampton town centre (signposted). Turn into Castle Road by Post Office. Close to A30

Train: Dartmoor Railway, Okehampton (summer, Sun) ½ mile

Bus: Stagecoach SW service 5A, 6, 6A, 75A, 75B; Plymouth Citybus service 46; Country Bus service 178

Tel: 01837 52844

Local Tourist Information: Okehampton: 01837 52295

NON-MEMBERS

Adult £6.00 | Concession £5.40
Child £3.60 | Family £15.60

ACQ.1967 📷🐾🏛🚶🚻🐕‍🦺📷Ⓟ🅿

📷♿🌡⚠OVP

Woodland Walk Guide available from kiosk.

> MAP PAGE 336 (5E)
> OS MAP 191, OL28/113:
> SX583942

ROYAL CITADEL, PLYMOUTH

DEVON – PL1 2PD

Plymouth's most important historic building and one of Britain's finest 17th-century fortresses. Commissioned by Charles II in 1665 to counter a threatened Dutch invasion, it's still in military use today.

OPENING TIMES

By guided tour only, 2 Apr-31 Oct, Bank Hol Mons, Tue, Thu & Sun	2.30pm

Book tours on 07876 402728 and online www.citadel.yapsody.com. Security measures are in force as this is a working military establishment. Please see website for further details. Photography is prohibited

VISIT US

Direction: At E end of Plymouth Hoe

Train: Plymouth 1 mile

Bus: Plymouth Citybus 25

ENTRY

Adult (non-members)	£7
EH Members & Children	£6
Children under 14 years	£4

ACQ.1966 ♿🐾

Parking on Plymouth Hoe. Allow 2 hours for the tour. No large bags. Bags may be searched. No toilets on site.

> MAP PAGE 336 (6D)
> OS MAP 201, OL20/108:
> SX480538

TOTNES CASTLE

DEVON – TQ9 5NU

Classic Norman motte-and-bailey castle, founded soon after the Conquest to overawe the Saxon town. A later shell-keep

crowns its steep mound, offering sweeping views across the rooftops to the River Dart.

OPENING TIMES

1 Apr-30 Sep, daily	10am-6pm
1 Oct-3 Nov, daily	10am-5pm
4 Nov-31 Mar, Sat-Sun	10am-4pm
24-26 Dec & 1 Jan	Closed

Last entry 30 mins before closing

VISIT US

Direction: In centre of Totnes, on Castle Street. By car, follow signs for Historic Town Centre, turn onto Castle Street from Station Road (opposite train station). On foot from town centre, turn north off High Street

Train: Totnes 🚃 ¼ mile and South Devon Railway (Totnes Littlehempston) ½ mile

Bus: From surrounding areas

Tel: 01803 864406

NON-MEMBERS

Adult £5.50 | Concession £5.00
Child £3.30 | Family £14.30

ACQ.1947 🐾🏛Ⓟ📷⚠ OVP

Parking (charged, 64 metres (210 feet); cars only, narrow approach roads).

Keep accessible only via steep steps.

> MAP PAGE 336 (6E)
> OS MAP 202, OL20/110:
> SX800605

UPPER PLYM VALLEY

DEVON – PL7 5EJ

Some 300 Bronze Age and medieval sites, covering 6 square miles of Dartmoor landscape.

OPENING TIMES

Any reasonable daylight hours

VISIT US

Direction: 4 miles E of Yelverton

ACQ.1978 🐾Ⓟ

Parking – ½ mile walk to monuments. Limited parking at Trowlesworthy car park – OS map strongly advised.

> MAP PAGE 336 (6E)
> OS MAP 202, OL20/OL28:
> SX580660

ABBOTSBURY ABBEY REMAINS

DORSET – DT3 4JR

Part of a monastic building, perhaps the abbot's lodging, of the Benedictine Abbey of Abbotsbury. St Catherine's Chapel is within half a mile.

OPENING TIMES

Any reasonable daylight hours

VISIT US

Direction: Located in Abbotsbury, off B3157, near the churchyard

Train: Upwey 7½ miles

Bus: First X53

ACQ.1948 ☒ P

Parking charged (not EH).

MAP PAGE 337 (5H)
OS MAP 194, OL15: SY578852

ABBOTSBURY, ST CATHERINE'S CHAPEL DORSET – DT3 4JH

High on a hilltop overlooking Abbotsbury Abbey, this sturdily buttressed 14th-century chapel was built by the monks as a place of pilgrimage and retreat.

ABBOTSBURY, ST CATHERINE'S CHAPEL

OPENING TIMES

Any reasonable daylight hours

VISIT US

Direction: ½ mile S of Abbotsbury; by steep path from village, off B3157

Train: Upwey 7 miles

Bus: First X53

ACQ.1922 ☒ P

Parking charged (not EH).

MAP PAGE 337 (5H)
OS MAP 194, OL15: SY573848

CHRISTCHURCH CASTLE AND NORMAN HOUSE

DORSET – BH23 1AS

Remains of Christchurch Castle, including parts of the keep and the 12th-century riverside 'Constable's House' – a very early example of domestic architecture with a rare Norman chimney. The important priory church is nearby.

OPENING TIMES

Any reasonable daylight hours

VISIT US

Direction: Located in Christchurch, near the Priory

Train: Christchurch ¾ mile

Bus: More services X2; Yellow Bus P1, P2 & P3

ACQ.1946 ♿ ☒ P ⚠

On-street parking. Please do not climb on the walls.

MAP PAGE 337 (5J)
OS MAP 195, OL22: SZ160927

FIDDLEFORD MANOR

DORSET – DT10 2BX

The principal parts of a small stone manor house, probably begun c. 1370 for William Latimer, Sheriff of Somerset and Dorset. The hall and solar chamber display outstanding timber roofs.

Please note: The adjoining building is a private residence and is not open to visitors.

OPENING TIMES

1 Apr-30 Sep, daily	10am-6pm
1 Oct-31 Mar, daily	10am-4pm
24-26 Dec & 1 Jan	Closed

VISIT US

Direction: 1 mile E of Sturminster Newton off A357

Bus: Only one Mon-Fri return journey on SW Coaches service X10 serves Fiddleford village. Otherwise SW Coaches service X4 and X10 to Sturminster Newton and then 1 mile walk along footpath

ACQ.1961 ☒ P ⛱ ⚠

Disabled access (ground floor only – with 1 step).

Parking (no coach access).

Hazard – deep water.

MAP PAGE 337 (4H)
OS MAP 194, 129: ST801136

JORDAN HILL ROMAN TEMPLE

DORSET – DT3 6PL

The foundations of a 4th-century AD Romano-British temple.

OPENING TIMES

Any reasonable daylight hours

VISIT US

Direction: Located 2 miles NE of Weymouth, off A353

Train: Upwey or Weymouth, 2 miles

Bus: First services 4/4A/5 & X54 and Damory X12 serve Overcombe from where it is a c. ½ mile walk

ACQ.1933 ☒ P

On-street parking.

MAP PAGE 337 (5H)
OS MAP 194, OL15: SY699821

KINGSTON RUSSELL STONE CIRCLE

DORSET – DT3 4JX

A Late Neolithic or Early Bronze Age circle of 18 fallen stones, on a hilltop overlooking Abbotsbury and the sea.

OPENING TIMES

Any reasonable daylight hours

VISIT US

Direction: Turn left off Bishop's Road, approximately 1½ miles NE of Abbotsbury, immediately after the 90° right hand bend

Train: Weymouth (1½ miles) or Dorchester South/West (8 miles)

Bus: First X53 to Abbotsbury then 2 mile walk

ACQ.1887 🐕

Limited parking on road verge at entrance to farm. Access to Stone Circle on foot only via public footpaths, approx. ½ mile. No off-road vehicle access.

MAP PAGE 337 (5H)
OS MAP 194, OL15: SY578878

KNOWLTON CHURCH AND EARTHWORKS

DORSET – BH21 5AE

A ruined medieval church stands at the centre of a large prehistoric henge, part of an important cluster of Neolithic and Early Bronze Age monuments.

KNOWLTON CHURCH AND EARTHWORKS

OPENING TIMES

Any reasonable daylight hours

VISIT US

Direction: SW of Cranborne on B3078

Bus: Dorset Community Transport service 97 to village of Cranborne then c. 1½ mile walk. Alternatively Damory service 20 to Handley Cross Roundabout and then c. 3 mile walk

ACQ.1959 🐕 P

Parking limited.

MAP PAGE 337 (5J)
OS MAP 195, 118: SU024103

MAIDEN CASTLE

DORSET – DT2 9EY

Among the largest Iron Age hillforts in Europe, Maiden Castle's huge multiple ramparts enclose an area equivalent to 50 football pitches. Excavations have revealed the site's 6,000-year history, from Neolithic ritual to late Roman times. Download the free audio experience, 'Echoscape', from our website.

OPENING TIMES

Any reasonable daylight hours

VISIT US

Direction: 2 miles S of Dorchester, off A354, N of bypass

Train: Dorchester South/West (2 miles)

MAIDEN CASTLE

Bus: Damory service 1 to Maiden Castle Lane and then ½ mile walk. Alternatively First service 10, 14, or Damory X12 to Winterbourne Monkton (¾ mile walk) or First service X51 and alight between Martinstown and Poundbury and use footpath 1 mile

ACQ.1908 🎧 🐕 P

Sheep grazing on site.

MAP PAGE 337 (5H)
OS MAP 194, OL15: SY669884

THE NINE STONES

DORSET – DT2 9LX

Small late Neolithic circle of nine standing stones, now in a wooded glade. Winterbourne Poor Lot Barrows (p.114) are nearby.

OPENING TIMES

Any reasonable daylight hours

VISIT US

Direction: 1½ miles SW of Winterbourne Abbas, on A35

Train: Weymouth 4½ miles

Bus: First X51 Weymouth – ▣ Axminster (serves Axminster and Dorchester South ▣)

ACQ.1895 🐕

Use permissive path parallel to A35.

MAP PAGE 337 (5H)
OS MAP 194, OL15/117: SY611904

PORTLAND CASTLE

--------- DORSET DT5 1AZ ---------

Overlooking and defending Portland harbour, this coastal artillery fortress was built by Henry VIII to counter threats from France and Spain. It retains its squat, rounded seaward form, designed to deflect incoming cannon shot.

Much fought over during the Civil War, Portland Castle was taken and retaken several times by both Parliamentarians and Royalists. It later protected shipping against pirates, and vainly tried to control the local smuggling industry, before 'standing-to' again when Napoleonic invasion loomed.

Following a spell as a private home, it became a station for seaplanes flying anti-submarine patrols during the First World War. During the Second World War it served as an ordnance store, and accommodation for British and American soldiers. In 1944 British and American forces carried out top-secret preliminary training for the D-Day landings in nearby bays.

VISIT THE TUDOR KITCHEN, ARMOURY AND GUN DECKS

Experience the fort's long and varied story through presentations, interactive exhibits and an audio tour. Be sure to visit the Tudor kitchen, armoury and gun decks. The Governor's Garden, designed by Christopher Bradley-Hole as part of the Contemporary Heritage Garden series, is a perfectly sheltered spot to enjoy the dramatic sea and harbour views.

Enjoy refreshments in the Captain's House Tearoom, including a range of homemade sandwiches, cakes and snacks made with locally sourced ingredients.

OPENING TIMES

1 Apr–30 Sep, daily	10am–6pm
1 Oct–3 Nov, daily	10am–5pm
4 Nov–31 Mar	Closed

Last entry 30 mins before closing

Audio tours available

Parts of the castle may be closed if an event is booked. Please call the site in advance or check website

VISIT US

Direction: Overlooking Portland Harbour in Castletown, Isle of Portland

Train: Weymouth 4½ miles

Bus: First service 1 passes close by

Tel: 01305 820539

Local Tourist Information: Portland: 01305 821361

NON-MEMBERS

Adult **£7.40** | Concession **£6.70**
Child **£4.40** | Family **£19.20**

[ACQ.1949] [icons]

Disabled access – Captain's House, ground floor of castle and Governor's Garden.

Parking charges apply to non-members. Parking free for Members.

Captain's House Tearoom closes ½ hour before the castle.

MAP PAGE 337 (6H)
OS MAP 194, OL15: SY685744

SHERBORNE OLD CASTLE DORSET – DT9 3SA

WINTERBOURNE POOR LOT BARROWS

DORSET – DT2 9EB

A 'cemetery' of 44 Bronze Age burial mounds of varying types and sizes, by the A35 main road.

OPENING TIMES

Any reasonable daylight hours

VISIT US

Direction: 2 miles W of Winterbourne Abbas, S of junction of A35 with a minor road to Compton Valence. Access via Longlands Lane – 1 mile east of site south of A35

Train: Dorchester West or South, both 7 miles

Bus: First X51 Weymouth – Axminster (serves Axminster & Dorchester South 🚃)

ACQ.1961 🐕 ⚠

Park on roadside approx. 1 mile south along Longlands Lane, follow public right of way, Jubilee Trail for 1 mile (approx.) west over farmland.

Sherborne Old Castle was originally a 12th-century fortified bishop's palace. It was leased to Sir Walter Raleigh and later became a powerful Civil War Royalist base, falling to Parliament after a fierce 11-day siege.

OPENING TIMES

1 Apr-30 Jun, daily	10am-5pm
1 Jul-31 Aug, daily	10am-6pm
1 Sep-3 Nov, daily	10am-5pm
4 Nov-31 Mar	Closed

Last entry 30 mins before closing

VISIT US

Direction: Situated at the end of Castleton Road, off B3145

Train: Sherborne ¾ mile

Bus: Buses of Somerset 58, 58A & 59 and South West Coaches 34, X10 & X11 to Sherborne town centre then ½ mile walk

Tel: 01935 812730

Local Tourist Information: Sherborne: 01935 815341

NON-MEMBERS

Adult **£5.50** | Concession **£5.00**
Child **£3.30** | Family **£14.30**

ACQ.1956 ♿ 🐕 ♿ 🏠 🧍 ↑ P 🏪
📷 ⚠ OVP

Refreshments available.

Parking charges apply to non-members.
Parking free for Members.

Secure cycle parking available.
National network route 26.

MAP PAGE 337 (4H)
OS MAP 183, 129: ST648168

MAP PAGE 337 (5H)
OS MAP 194, OL15/117: SY590907

BELAS KNAP LONG BARROW

GLOUCESTERSHIRE – GL54 5AL

A particularly fine restored example of a Neolithic long barrow: remains of 31 people were found in the chambers.

Managed by Gloucestershire County Council.

OPENING TIMES

Any reasonable daylight hours

VISIT US

Direction: Near Charlton Abbots; ½ mile on Cotswold Way

Train: Cheltenham 9 miles

Bus: Marchants service 606, W1 & W2 & N.N. Cresswell's 656 to Winchcombe then c. 1¾ miles walk

ACQ.1928 🐕 P

Parking with ½ mile steep walk to monument.

MAP PAGE 337 (1J)
OS MAP 163, OL45: SP021254

CIRENCESTER AMPHITHEATRE

GLOUCESTERSHIRE – GL7 1XW

Earthwork remains of one of the largest Roman amphitheatres in Britain, serving the Roman city of Corinium (now Cirencester).

CIRENCESTER AMPHITHEATRE

Managed by Cirencester Town Council.

OPENING TIMES

Any reasonable daylight hours

VISIT US

Direction: Located W of Cirencester, next to the bypass. Access from the town, or along Chesterton Lane from the W end of the bypass, onto Cotswold Ave

Train: Kemble 4 miles

Bus: From surrounding areas

ACQ.1973 🐕 P

MAP PAGE 337 (2J)
OS MAP 163, OL45/169: SP020014

GLOUCESTER, BLACKFRIARS

GLOUCESTERSHIRE – GL1 2HS

Among the most complete surviving friaries of Dominican 'black friars' in England, finished in about 1270. After the Dissolution, it was converted into a Tudor mansion and cloth factory, but its medieval features are now visible again. There's a magnificent 13th-century scissor-braced timber roof over the former friars' library.

Managed by Gloucester City Council.

GLOUCESTER, BLACKFRIARS

OPENING TIMES

| Apr-Sep, Sun-Mon | 10am-3pm |
| Oct-Mar | by appointment only |

VISIT US

Direction: In Blackfriars Lane, off Ladybellegate St, off Southgate St, Gloucester

Train: Gloucester ½ mile

Bus: Short walk from Gloucester Bus Station

Tel: 01452 503050

ACQ.1955 ♿ 🐕 P

Parking adjacent. (Charge applies. Not managed by EH).

MAP PAGE 337 (1H)
OS MAP 162, 179: SO829184

GLOUCESTER, GREYFRIARS

GLOUCESTERSHIRE – GL1 2EZ

Substantial remains of a medieval friary church of Franciscan 'grey friars', rebuilt in the early 16th century.

OPENING TIMES

Any reasonable daylight hours

VISIT US

Direction: On Greyfriars Walk

Train: Gloucester ½ mile

Bus: Gloucester Bus Station ½ mile

ACQ.1969 ♿ 🐕

MAP PAGE 337 (1H)
OS MAP 162, 179: SO832184

HAILES ABBEY

──────── GLOUCESTERSHIRE GL54 5PB ────────

Set amid lovely Cotswold countryside, Hailes Abbey was one of medieval England's most renowned pilgrim shrines. The recently transformed museum displays the abbey's treasures and tells the intriguing story of the 'Holy Blood of Hailes'.

The Cistercian abbey was founded in 1246 by Richard Earl of Cornwall, Henry III's younger brother and among the richest men in Europe. It became a major pilgrimage destination after 1270, when Richard's son Edmund presented it with a sensational relic – allegedly no less than a phial of Christ's own blood. Pilgrims flocking to its shrine financed the rebuilding of the abbey on a magnificent scale. The ruins, picturesquely 'soft-capped' with turf for preservation, include cloister buildings and the footprint of the church, inspired by Westminster Abbey.

A RICH ARRAY OF LAVISH SCULPTURE AND HERALDIC FLOOR TILES, AND EVEN ONE OF THE OLDEST SURVIVING MEDIEVAL SPECTACLE FRAMES

Its relic denounced as a fake, the abbey was suppressed by Henry VIII, and comprehensively looted. Our revamped museum helps you imagine it in all its glory. There's a rich array of lavish sculpture and heraldic floor tiles, and even one of the oldest surviving medieval spectacle frames. More artefacts and interpretation are displayed in a miniature glass 'cloister'.

Nearby, the delightful little parish church houses stained glass and tiles from the abbey, and outstanding medieval wall-paintings.

Owned by the National Trust, managed and maintained by English Heritage.

OPENING TIMES

1 Apr-30 Jun, daily	10am-5pm
1 Jul-31 Aug, daily	10am-6pm
1 Sep-3 Nov, daily	10am-5pm
4 Nov-31 Mar	Closed

Last entry 30 mins before closing

VISIT US

Direction: 2 miles NE of Winchcombe off B4632. On the Cotswold Way National Trail

Train: Cheltenham 10 miles From March to October, Hayles Abbey Halt (600m from site) can be reached from Cheltenham, Winchcombe or Broadway by diesel railcar on the Gloucestershire and Warwickshire Steam Railway. See www.gwsr.com for timetables and prices

Bus: Marchants service 606, W1 or W2 from Cheltenham to Winchcombe and then a 2 mile walk along the Cotswold Way. See www.marchants-coaches.com/Local-Bus-Services

Tel: 01242 602398

NON-MEMBERS

Adult **£6.90** | Concession **£6.20**
Child **£4.10** | Family **£17.90**

National Trust members free, but charged for audio tour (£1) and special events

ACQ.1948 🎧 ♿ ✕ ♨ 🎒 🛒 ✝ ✝ ✉ **P** 🚪 📷 OVP

Disabled access (ramp to museum, disabled toilet).
Refreshments available.

MAP PAGE 337 (1J)
OS MAP 150/163, OL45: SP050300

GREAT WITCOMBE ROMAN VILLA

GLOUCESTERSHIRE – GL3 4TW

Remains of a large and luxurious Roman villa built c. AD 250, with a bath-house and possibly the shrine of a water spirit.

OPENING TIMES

Exterior:

1 Apr-30 Sep, daily	10am-6pm
1 Oct-31 Mar, daily	10am-4pm

There is no access to the building, which houses the mosaics

VISIT US

Direction: Located 5 miles SE of Gloucester off Cirencester Road; 400 metres (440 yards) from Cotswold Way National Trail

Train: Gloucester 6 miles

Bus: Stagecoach 10 to Brockworth

ACQ.1919 🐕 P

Parking (no access for coaches). No parking permitted in the lane. 300 metre walk to site.

MAP PAGE 337 (2J)
OS MAP 163, 179: SO899142

KINGSWOOD ABBEY GATEHOUSE

GLOUCESTERSHIRE – GL12 8RA

This 16th-century gatehouse, sole survivor of a Cistercian abbey, is one of the latest monastic buildings in England. Displays a richly sculpted window.

OPENING TIMES

Exterior: reasonable daylight hours

Interior: key available from 3 Wotton Road, Kingswood 10am-3.30pm weekdays only

VISIT US

Direction: In Kingswood, off B4060; 1 mile SW of Wotton-under-Edge

Train: Yate 8 miles

Bus: Eurotaxis 626; Stagecoach West 60, 84, 85; Mike's Travel 201

ACQ.1950 🐕 P

On-street parking.

MAP PAGE 337 (2H)
OS MAP 162/172, 167: ST747920

NYMPSFIELD LONG BARROW

GLOUCESTERSHIRE – GL11 5AU

Large Neolithic burial mound with spectacular views over the Severn Valley. Its burial chambers are uncovered for viewing.

Managed by Gloucestershire County Council.

OPENING TIMES

Any reasonable daylight hours

VISIT US

Direction: Located 1 mile NW of Nympsfield on B4066

Train: Stroud 5 miles

Bus: Stagecoach West service 65

ACQ.1975 🐕 P

MAP PAGE 337 (2H)
OS MAP 162, 167/168: SO794013

ODDA'S CHAPEL

GLOUCESTERSHIRE – GL19 4BX

Among the most complete Saxon churches in England, built in 1056 by Earl Odda and rediscovered in 1865. Deerhurst's Saxon parish church is nearby.

OPENING TIMES

1 Apr-30 Sep, daily	10am-6pm
1 Oct-31 Mar, daily	10am-4pm
24-26 Dec & 1 Jan	Closed

VISIT US

Direction: Located in Deerhurst off B4213, at Abbots Court; SW of parish church

Train: Cheltenham 8 miles

Bus: Swanbrook service 351 serves Apperley (1½ mile)

ACQ.1962 🐕 P

Parking (not EH, charges apply).

MAP PAGE 337 (1J)
OS MAP 150, 179: SO869298

OFFA'S DYKE

GLOUCESTERSHIRE – GL15 6XD

Three-mile wooded section of the great 8th-century boundary dyke built by Offa, King of Mercia. Includes the Devil's Pulpit, with fine views of Tintern Abbey.

OPENING TIMES

Any reasonable daylight hours

VISIT US

Direction: Located 3 miles NE of Chepstow, off B4228. Via Tidenham Forestry Commission car park. 1 mile walk (waymarked) down to the Devil's Pulpit on Offa's Dyke

Train: Chepstow 7 miles

Bus: Forest Community Transport 707 (Tue, Thu & Fri) passes site. Alternatively Phil Anslow Travel (not Sun)/New Adventure Travel (Sun) service 69 to Tintern then 1 mile walk or James Bevan 755 to Wibdon and then 1 mile walk

ACQ.1973 🐕 P

Strong footwear is recommended.

MAP PAGE 337 (2H)
OS MAP 162, OL14/167
SO546011-ST549975

OVER BRIDGE

GLOUCESTERSHIRE – GL2 8BZ

A single-arch stone bridge spanning the River Severn, built in 1825-30 by the great engineer Thomas Telford.

OPENING TIMES

Any reasonable daylight hours

VISIT US

Direction: 1 mile NW of Gloucester, at junction of A40 (Ross) and A417 (Ledbury)

Train: Gloucester 2 miles

Bus: Stagecoach 23, 24, 24A, 30, 31, 32, 33, 132

ACQ.1978 🐕

MAP PAGE 337 (1H)
OS MAP 162, 179: SO816196

ST BRIAVELS CASTLE

GLOUCESTERSHIRE – GL15 6RG

Well-preserved castle, former hunting lodge of King John, with fine gatehouse built by Edward I in 1292 and late Victorian restoration. Now a Youth Hostel.

OPENING TIMES

Exterior (moat area):
Any reasonable daylight hours

Bailey (interior grounds only):
1 Apr-31 Oct, daily   1pm-4pm

Limited access to interior as working youth hostel (call in advance to check)

VISIT US

Direction: In St Briavels; 7 miles NE of Chepstow off B4228

Train: Lydney 🚉 6 miles; Chepstow 8 miles

Bus: Forest Community Transport service 701 (Tue & Thu) or 707 (Tue, Thu & Fri) and F. R. Willetts Coaches service 787 (Fri)

Tel: 01594 530272

ACQ.1982 🍴 P 🚹 🚻 💼 ⚠

Please do not climb on the walls.

MAP PAGE 337 (2H)
OS MAP 162, OL14: SO559046

ST MARY'S CHURCH, KEMPLEY

GLOUCESTERSHIRE – GL18 2AT

ST MARY'S CHURCH, KEMPLEY

Delightful Norman church, displaying one of the most complete sets of medieval wall-paintings in England, dating from the 12th to 15th centuries.

Download a virtual tour from our website.

Managed in association with the Friends of Kempley Church.

OPENING TIMES

| 1 Apr-30 Oct, daily | 10am-6pm |
| Nov & Feb, Sat-Sun | 10am-4pm |

Dec-Jan by appointment only

VISIT US

Direction: 1 mile N of Kempley off B4024; 6 miles NE of Ross-on-Wye

Train: Ledbury 8 miles

Bus: Newent Community Transport service 676 (Mon & Thu) to Kempley village. 1¼ miles walk to church

Tel: 0117 975 0714/0709 for all group bookings

ACQ.1979 ♿ 🍴 P

Parking (in lay-by). Disabled access (1 step).

MAP PAGE 337 (1H)
OS MAP 149, 189: SO670313

ULEY LONG BARROW (HETTY PEGLER'S TUMP)

GLOUCESTERSHIRE – GL11 5AR

Restored Neolithic chambered mound, 37 metres (121 feet) long, atmospherically sited overlooking the Severn Valley. The internal chambers are accessible through a very low entrance.

Managed by Gloucestershire County Council.

ULEY LONG BARROW

OPENING TIMES

Any reasonable daylight hours

VISIT US

Direction: Located 3½ miles NE of Dursley, on B4066. Take care crossing road

Train: Stroud 6 miles

Bus: Stagecoach West service 65

ACQ.1883 🍴 P ⚠

Parking (in lay-by).

Warning: cross road with care.

Note: visitors are advised to bring a torch.

MAP PAGE 337 (2H)
OS MAP 162, 167/168: SO790000

WINDMILL TUMP LONG BARROW, RODMARTON

GLOUCESTERSHIRE – GL7 6PU

A Neolithic chambered tomb with an enigmatic 'false entrance'.

Managed by Gloucestershire County Council.

OPENING TIMES

Any reasonable daylight hours

VISIT US

Direction: 1 mile SW of Rodmarton

Train: Kemble 5 miles

Bus: Pulhams service 881 Cirencester – Kemble 🚉 Tetbury

ACQ.1979 P

Dogs on leads.

Parking in lay-by.

MAP PAGE 337 (2J)
OS MAP 163, 168: ST933973

CLEEVE ABBEY

——— SOMERSET TA23 OPS ———

Gain a vivid insight into monastic life at Cleeve Abbey and admire its strikingly redisplayed tiled pavement.

Atmospheric Cleeve Abbey boasts the most impressively complete and unaltered set of monastic cloister buildings in England. Standing roofed and two storeys high, they include the gatehouse, the 15th-century refectory with its glorious angel roof, and an unusual 'painted chamber'. The great dormitory is one of the finest in the country. Beneath it are the vaulted warming room, and the sacristy with early 13th-century tilework and decoration.

Cleeve's crowning glory is the magnificent tiled floor of its earliest refectory. Decked from end to end with high-quality heraldic tiles dating from around 1270, it's the only large-scale survival of a decorated medieval monastic refectory floor in Britain. Its royal and baronial heraldry celebrates the abbey's wealthy patrons. Buried in the late 15th century and rediscovered in 1876, it had suffered from exposure to the elements. Now it's redisplayed within a purpose-built timber shelter, complete with seating and viewing platforms.

An exhibition and touchscreen virtual tour tell the story of abbey life. A story bag, 'Brother Cedric and the Missing Sheep', is a fun way for families to explore the abbey.

OPENING TIMES

1 Apr-30 Jun, daily	10am-5pm
1 Jul-31 Aug, daily	10am-6pm
1 Sep-3 Nov, daily	10am-5pm
4 Nov-31 Mar	Closed

Last entry 30 mins before closing

The abbey may be closed if an event is booked. Please call the site in advance or check website

VISIT US

Direction: Located in Washford, ¼ mile S of A39

Train: Washford ½ mile (West Somerset Steam Railway)

Bus: Buses of Somerset 15 & 28

Tel: 01984 640377

Local Tourist Information:
Watchet: 01984 632101

NON-MEMBERS

Adult £6.90 | Concession £6.20
Child £4.10 | Family £17.90

ACQ. 1951 ⛔ ♿ 🐕 🏛 E ♨ ▭ ↑ ⚑ P 🏛 🗄
⚠ OVP

Disabled access (grounds and ground floor only, plus toilet).

Dogs on leads (in grounds only).

Refreshments available.

MAP PAGE 337 (4F)
OS MAP 181, OL9: ST047407

DAWS CASTLE

SOMERSET – TA23 0JP

Clifftop fortress begun by King Alfred to defend the people of Watchet against Viking attacks.

OPENING TIMES

Any reasonable daylight hours

VISIT US

Direction: ½ mile W of Watchet off B3191

Train: Watchet (West Somerset railway) ¾ mile

Bus: Buses of Somerset 15 & 28 serve Watchet station which is about a ¾ mile walk

 ACQ.1983

Sheep may be grazing on site.

Parking in Watchet (paid, not EH) and walk ½ mile via SW Coastal Path.

MAP PAGE 337 (4F)
OS MAP 181, OL9: SS989432

DUNSTER, BUTTER CROSS

SOMERSET – TA24 6RT

The repositioned stump of a medieval stone cross, once a meeting place for butter sellers.

Managed by the National Trust.

OPENING TIMES

Any reasonable daylight hours

VISIT US

Direction: Beside minor road to Alcombe, 350 metres (400 yards) NW of Dunster parish church

Train: Dunster (West Somerset Railway) 1 mile

Bus: Somerset CC service 198 serves Dunster village. In addition Buses of Somerset services 15 & 28 serve Dunster Steep from where it is about a ½ mile walk

ACQ.1951

Parking in village (charged, not EH).

MAP PAGE 337 (4F)
OS MAP 181, OL9: ST823604

DUNSTER, GALLOX BRIDGE

SOMERSET – TA24 6SR

This ancient stone bridge – originally 'gallows bridge' – once carried packhorses bringing fleeces to Dunster market.

Managed by the National Trust.

OPENING TIMES

Any reasonable daylight hours

VISIT US

Direction: Located off A396 at the S end of Dunster village

Train: Dunster ¾ mile (West Somerset Railway)

Bus: Somerset CC service 198 serves Dunster village. In addition Buses of Somerset services 15 & 28 serve Dunster Steep from where it is about a ½ mile walk

ACQ.1951

Parking in village (charged, not EH).

MAP PAGE 337 (4F)
OS MAP 181, OL9: SS989432

DUNSTER, YARN MARKET

SOMERSET – TA24 6SG

This fine 17th-century timber-framed octagonal market hall is a monument to Dunster's once-flourishing cloth trade.

Managed by the National Trust.

OPENING TIMES

Any reasonable daylight hours

VISIT US

Direction: In Dunster High St

Train: Dunster (West Somerset Railway) ½ mile

Bus: Somerset CC service 198 serves Dunster village. In addition Buses of Somerset services 15 & 28 serve Dunster Steep from where it is about a ½ mile walk

ACQ.1951

Parking in village (charged, not EH).

MAP PAGE 337 (4F)
OS MAP 181, OL9: SS992438

While in the region, why not visit **Stonehenge**, one of the wonders of the world and the best-known prehistoric monument in Europe. There's a world-class visitor centre, plus a spacious shop and café.

See **p.132** for details.

FARLEIGH HUNGERFORD CASTLE

SOMERSET – BA2 7RS

Sir Thomas Hungerford, Speaker of the Commons, began this fortified mansion in the 1370s. It was extended in the 15th century by his son Walter, Lord Hungerford, distinguished soldier and statesman. Remains include two tall corner towers and a complete chapel, displaying family monuments and wall-paintings. You can still see many Hungerford coffins in its crypt, some with 'death masks'.

The colourful Hungerford family included two members executed during the Wars of the Roses and another – who imprisoned his wife here for four years – beheaded by Henry VIII. A Tudor Lady Hungerford burnt her murdered husband's body in the kitchen furnace.

Discover Farleigh's story through an audio tour and extensive displays in the Priests' House. There is a virtual tour for disabled visitors, family and educational facilities, and a schools base with historical costumes.

🎬 BBC Series, *The White Princess*.

OPENING TIMES

1 Apr-30 Sep, daily	10am-6pm
1 Oct-3 Nov, daily	10am-5pm
4 Nov-31 Mar, Sat-Sun	10am-4pm
24-26 Dec & 1 Jan	Closed

Last entry 30 mins before closing

VISIT US

Direction: In Farleigh Hungerford, 9 miles SE of Bath; 3½ miles W of Trowbridge on A366

Train: Avoncliffe 2 miles; Trowbridge 3½ miles

Bus: Libra 94 or 96; Frome Minibuses X69 from Trowbridge (pass close Trowbridge 🚃) to Wingfield then 1½ miles walk

Tel: 01225 754026

Local Tourist Information: Trowbridge: 01225 710535

NON-MEMBERS

Adult **£6.30** | Concession **£5.70**
Child **£3.80** | Family **£16.40**

ACQ.1915 🎧 ♿ 🐕 🍴 ♿ E f 🌾
📷 🧗 👶 P 📷 📷 ⚠ OVP

Disabled access (Chapel and Priests' House, ground floor only. Disabled toilet).

Dogs allowed on leads in the grounds only.

Refreshments available.

MAP PAGE 337 (3H)
OS MAP 173, 143/156: ST801576

GLASTONBURY TRIBUNAL

SOMERSET – BA6 9DP

A late 15th-century town house, with early Tudor façade and panelled interiors. Houses the Glastonbury Lake Village Museum (charged).

Managed by Glastonbury Tribunal Ltd.

OPENING TIMES

1 Apr-31 Mar, Tue-Sun	10am-4pm
24-26 Dec & 1 Jan	Closed

VISIT US

Direction: In Glastonbury High St

Bus: Libra service 668 passes site. Buses of Somerset 29, 75 & 77; First West of England 376; Frome Minibuses 669 pass within ½ mile

Tel: 01458 832954

NON-MEMBERS

Museum
Adult **£3.50** | Concession **£3.00**
Child **£2.00**

Admission charges apply for Glastonbury Lake Village Museum

ACQ.1932 🐕 📷 P

Disabled access (ground floor – 2 steps).

Parking (charged, not EH).

MAP PAGE 337 (4H)
OS MAP 182/183, 141: ST499389

MEARE FISH HOUSE

SOMERSET – BA6 9SP

A unique survivor both in function and design, this housed the keeper of medieval Glastonbury Abbey's (then) adjacent fishery lake.

OPENING TIMES

Any reasonable daylight hours.
Key available from Manor House farm

VISIT US

Direction: In Meare village, on B3151

Bus: Libra service 668 Lower Langford – Street

Parking in lay-by.

Livestock may be grazing on site.

MAP PAGE 337 (4G)
OS MAP 182, 141: ST458417

NUNNEY CASTLE

SOMERSET – BA11 4LW

A striking moated tower-house castle, built in the 1370s by Sir John de la Mere. Held by Royalists during the Civil War, it fell to Parliamentarian cannon, the damaged portion finally collapsing on Christmas Day 1910.

OPENING TIMES

Any reasonable daylight hours

VISIT US

Direction: Located in Nunney, 3½ miles SW of Frome, off A361 (no coach access)

Train: Frome 3½ miles

Bus: Frome Minibuses service 162 Frome-Shepton Mallet

ACQ.1926 🕱 P ⚠ Deep water.
Please do not climb on the walls.

MAP PAGE 337 (4H)
OS MAP 183, 142: ST737457

MUCHELNEY ABBEY   SOMERSET – TA10 0DQ

You will find many rewards when visiting the atmospheric 'great island' amid the Somerset Levels. Beside the foundations of the wealthy medieval Benedictine abbey (and its Anglo-Saxon predecessor) stands the abbots' lodgings, a complete early Tudor house. This charming building includes a magnificent great chamber with ornate fireplace and stained glass; rooms with wall-paintings imitating cloth hangings; kitchens with fine timber roofs and parts of the richly decorated cloister walk. Nearby is the thatched two-storey monks' lavatory, unique in Britain.

Exhibitions illustrate monastic life with a fascinating collection of site-finds, and there is a touchscreen tour for disabled visitors. A 'story bag' is a fun way for families to explore the abbey together.

The nearby parish church (with 17th-century painted ceiling) and medieval Priest's House are not managed by English Heritage.

OPENING TIMES

1 Apr-30 Jun, daily	10am-5pm
1 Jul-31 Aug, daily	10am-6pm
1 Sep-3 Nov, daily	10am-5pm
4 Nov-31 Mar	Closed

Last entry 30 mins before closing

VISIT US

Direction: In Muchelney, 2 miles S of Langport via Huish Episcopi

Bus: Isle Valley Transport 850 (Thu); otherwise use Buses of Somerset service 54 and 1 mile walk from Langport

Cycle: Sustrans: National Route 339

Tel: 01458 250664

Local Tourist Information:
Langport: 01458 253527

NON-MEMBERS

Adult **£6.60** | Concession **£6.00**
Child **£4.00** | Family **£17.20**

ACQ.1927 ♿ E 🕱 🕱 🕱 P 🚻 📷
⚠ OVP

Disabled access (grounds and most of ground floor, adapted toilet).

Refreshments available.

MAP PAGE 337 (4G)
OS MAP 193, 129: ST429249

BRADFORD-ON-AVON TITHE BARN

WILTSHIRE – BA15 1LF

A spectacular monastic stone barn, 51 metres (168 feet) long and 10 metres (33 feet) wide. Its magnificent timber-cruck roof supports a hundred tons of stone roof tiles.

Built in the early 14th century as part of a 'grange' or outlying farm belonging to Shaftesbury Abbey, the richest nunnery in England, it continued in use until 1974.

Managed by Bradford-on-Avon Preservation Trust.

OPENING TIMES

1 Apr-31 Mar, daily	10.30am-4pm
24-26 Dec & 1 Jan	Closed

Barn may be closed during local events. Check EH website for details

VISIT US

Direction: Located ½ mile S of town centre off B3109

Train: Bradford-on-Avon ½ mile

Bus: Faresaver service 68/69; First 265; Frome Minibuses service X69 & 98; Libra services 69 & 96

[ACQ.1939] 🚫 ✖ **P**

Parking (adjacent, not managed by EH – charge applies).

MAP PAGE 337 (3H)
OS MAP 173, 156: ST823604

BRATTON CAMP AND WHITE HORSE

WILTSHIRE – BA13 3EP

Bratton Camp is an Iron Age hillfort, which enclosed an earlier Neolithic long barrow and a Bronze Age burial mound as well as a 'town' of huts, stores and workshops. Below it stands the Westbury White Horse. Cut in 1778, this replaced an earlier horse, perhaps made in the late 1600s to commemorate King Alfred's decisive victory over the Vikings at 'Ethandun', probably fought nearby in AD 878.

OPENING TIMES

Any reasonable daylight hours

VISIT US

Direction: 2 miles E of Westbury off B3098, 1 mile SW of Bratton

Train: Westbury 3 miles

Bus: Faresaver/Libra 87/87A Trowbridge – Devizes (passes ▣ Westbury). Also Real Coach Hire X88 (Wed)

[ACQ.1930] ✖ **P**

Sheep may be grazing on site.

MAP PAGE 337 (3J)
OS MAP 184, 143: ST900516

CHISBURY CHAPEL

WILTSHIRE – SN8 3JA

An appealing thatched and flint-walled chapel, with the remains of fine windows and plasterwork and a 'consecration cross' within. It was built by the lord of Chisbury Manor in the 13th century, both as a symbol of his status and to save his tenants the inconvenient journey to Great Bedwyn parish church. In use until 1547, it later served as a barn. Set by the earthwork defences of Iron Age Chisbury Camp.

OPENING TIMES

Any reasonable daylight hours

VISIT US

Direction: 300m walk off unclassified road, ¼ mile E of Chisbury, off A4; 6 miles E of Marlborough

Train: Bedwyn 1 mile

Bus: Thamesdown Transport services 20 & 22 to Great Bedwyn then ¾ mile walk

[ACQ.1982] ✖ **P**

Parking (in lay-by).

MAP PAGE 337 (3K)
OS MAP 174, 157: SU280660

HATFIELD EARTHWORKS (MARDEN HENGE)

WILTSHIRE – SN10 3RQ

The earthworks of one of the largest Neolithic henges in Britain. The outer enclosure, raised in about 2500 BC, is formed on three sides by a bank and ditch, and on the other by a loop in the River Avon. Within is a second Neolithic henge, and the scanty remains of a monumental mound, once allegedly over 64 metres (210 feet) in diameter and a smaller version of Silbury Hill (p.129).

Excavations at the henge in 1969 and 2010 revealed evidence of Neolithic activity here, including a circular timber structure, evidence of feasting and a small late Neolithic building with a substantial hearth. Ongoing research by the University of Reading is continuing to reveal more about this important site, comparable with Durrington Walls (p.131) near Stonehenge, 10 miles away.

OPENING TIMES

Any reasonable daylight hours.
Note: Only a small section of henge accessible, marked with a fingerpost

VISIT US

Direction: 5½ miles SE of Devizes, off A342; NE of village of Marden. Look for the fingerpost

Train: Pewsey 5 miles

Bus: Connect2Wiltshire MF services 101 & 102 and Tourist Coaches 210 (Thu & Sat) pass the site

ACQ.1972

Animals may be grazing on site.

MAP PAGE 337 (3J)
OS MAP 173, 130: SU092583

LUDGERSHALL CASTLE AND CROSS

WILTSHIRE – SP11 9QT

Ruins and extensive earthworks of a mainly 12th to 14th-century royal castle, including a 'strong tower' probably built by King John and a hall and royal apartments added by Henry III. More a palatial hunting lodge than a fortress, Ludgershall was favoured by Plantagenet kings from Henry II to Edward III as a resting place on their travels to the west, and a base for hunting in Savernake Forest.

The remains of a market cross stand at the centre of the village, once an important medieval market town, which elected two MPs.

OPENING TIMES

Any reasonable daylight hours

VISIT US

Direction: Located on the N side of Ludgershall, off A342

Train: Andover 7 miles

Bus: Salisbury Red 'Active 8' service; Stagecoach 8

ACQ.1915 Castle

ACQ.1952 Cross

Parking (limited).

MAP PAGE 337 (3K)
OS MAP 184/185, 131: SU264512

NETHERAVON DOVECOTE

WILTSHIRE – SP4 9RJ

A charming early 18th-century brick dovecote, with a pyramid roof and dormer windows. It still contains most of its 700 or more nesting boxes for doves or pigeons.

Dovecotes were 'living larders', providing fresh meat in winter as well as eggs and fertiliser, but their occupants ravaged surrounding crops, and until 1761 only important landowners could build them.

OPENING TIMES

Exterior viewing from nearby Millenium Park, as there is no access across the field in which dovecote is situated

VISIT US

Direction: In Netheravon, 4½ miles N of Amesbury on A345

Train: Pewsey 9 miles, Grateley 11 miles

Bus: Salisbury Reds service X4/X5 Salisbury – Swindon (pass close Pewsey, Salisbury & Swindon ⊞) and Tourist Coaches 210 (Thu & Sat)

ACQ.1939

MAP PAGE 337 (3J)
OS MAP 184, 130: SU147484

OLD WARDOUR CASTLE

--- WILTSHIRE SP3 6RR ---

John, Lord Lovel, built Old Wardour Castle in the late 14th century as a lightly fortified but luxurious residence.

Beautifully sited beside a lake, it pioneered the inclusion of self-contained suites for noble guests. A hexagonal tower house ranged round a central courtyard, its design is unique in England.

Substantially updated by the staunchly Roman Catholic Arundell family after c. 1570, the castle saw much fighting during the Civil War. In 1643 the 61-year-old Lady Arundell, with a garrison of just 25 soldiers, was forced to surrender it to 1,300 Parliamentarians after a 5-day siege. But the new Parliamentarian garrison was almost immediately besieged in turn by Royalist forces led by her son, Henry, Lord Arundell. After an eventful three months of bombardment and undermining, they finally capitulated in March 1644.

The abandoned castle became a romantic ruin, and was incorporated into the 18th-century landscaped grounds of Lord Arundell's New Wardour House (not managed by English Heritage, no public access). Almost the last addition was the fantasy-Gothic Grotto, an artificial cave built in 1792 using stones from the castle ruins and recycled prehistoric monoliths.

The castle's setting in a Registered Landscape enhances the significance of this hidden jewel.

🔳 Licensed for civil wedding ceremonies

OPENING TIMES

1 Apr-30 Sep, daily	10am-6pm
1 Oct-3 Nov, daily	10am-4pm
4 Nov-31 Mar, Sat-Sun	10am-4pm
24-26 Dec & 1 Jan	Closed

Last entry 30 mins before closing

Parts of the castle may be closed if an event is booked. Please call site or check website for details

VISIT US

Direction: Located off A30 3½ miles SW of Tisbury. Also accessible from A350 (narrow rural roads). Coaches approach with care

Train: Tisbury 3½ miles

Bus: Salisbury Reds service 26 Salisbury – Shaftesbury (passes Tisbury ≥). Short walk to Wardour

Tel: 01747 870487

Local Tourist Information: Shaftesbury: 01747 853514

NON-MEMBERS

Adult £6.30 | Concession £5.70
Child £3.80 | Family £16.40

Disabled access (grounds and ground floor only), disabled toilet.

Refreshments available.

MAP PAGE 337 (4J)
OS MAP 184, 118: ST939263

OLD SARUM

———— WILTSHIRE SP1 3SD ————

Explore the lost city of Old Sarum, crowning a ridge with sweeping views towards Salisbury. Iron Age people raised its mighty prehistoric earthworks in about 500 BC, and within them Saxons and, most importantly, the Normans later settled.

In 1086 William the Conqueror summoned all the great landowners of England here to swear an oath of loyalty. A Norman castle on the inner mound was soon joined by a royal palace. By the mid-12th century a bustling town occupied much of the great earthwork, complete with a noble new Norman cathedral. An original copy of Magna Carta was sent to the cathedral in 1215, and can still be seen in its successor, Salisbury Cathedral.

However, soldiers and priests quarrelled, and life on the almost waterless hilltop became intolerable, so the settlement migrated downhill to what became Salisbury, where a new cathedral was founded in 1220. Thereafter Old Sarum went into steep decline, with its cathedral demolished and its castle abandoned. Though largely uninhabited, it continued to 'elect' two MPs until 1832, becoming the most notorious of the corrupt 'Rotten Boroughs' swept away by the Reform Act.

Today, the remains of the prehistoric fortress and of the Norman palace, castle and cathedral evoke echoes of thousands of years of history.

OPENING TIMES

1 Apr-30 Sep, daily	10am-6pm
1 Oct-3 Nov, daily	10am-5pm
4 Nov-31 Mar, daily	10am-4pm
24-25 Dec	Closed

Last entry 30 mins before closing

VISIT US

Direction: 2 miles N of Salisbury, off A345

Train: Salisbury 2 miles

Bus: Salisbury Reds X4, X5, 8; P&R 11; also Stonehenge Tour service. See www.thestonehengetour.info

Tel: 01722 335398

Local Tourist Information: Salisbury: 01722 342860

NON-MEMBERS

Adult **£6.00** | Concession **£5.40**
Child **£3.60** | Family **£15.60**

Disabled access (outer bailey and grounds only, disabled toilet).

Toilets located in the car park.

Parking charges apply to non-members. Parking free for Members.

Refreshments available.

MAP PAGE 337 (4J)
OS MAP 184, 130: SU138327

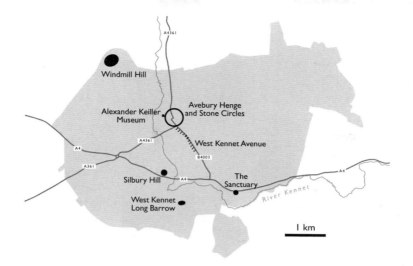

STONEHENGE, AVEBURY
AND ASSOCIATED WORLD HERITAGE SITES

Stonehenge and Avebury and their associated sites were inscribed onto the UNESCO World Heritage List in 1986. They stand alongside over 1,000 other outstanding sites across the world – such as the Great Wall of China and India's Taj Mahal – selected for their 'outstanding universal value' to all people.

Stonehenge and Avebury were chosen for their extraordinary prehistoric monuments. These help us to understand the Neolithic and Bronze Age world, and demonstrate around 2,000 years of continuous use and monument building between 3700 and 1600 BC.

Management Plans for both the Avebury and Stonehenge parts of the World Heritage Site bring a whole range of organisations and individuals together, working in partnership to manage the site and protect its outstanding universal value.

Take time to visit both parts of the World Heritage Site and you will be well rewarded. At Stonehenge, displays in the spectacular visitor centre explore the evocative prehistoric landscape surrounding this iconic monument. View the rich collections in the Wiltshire Museum in Devizes and The Salisbury Museum, and learn more about the people who built the prehistoric monuments of the World Heritage Site. Experience a very different but equally rich visit to the Avebury area, with its prehistoric 'sacred landscape' and the Alexander Keiller Museum, displaying finds from the immediate region.

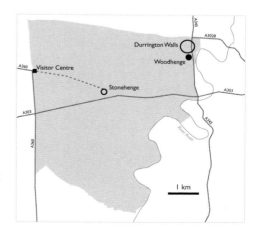

AVEBURY, ALEXANDER KEILLER MUSEUM

WILTSHIRE – SN8 1RF

Set in traditional farm buildings in picturesque Avebury, this displays many notable finds from the World Heritage Site monuments, along with child-friendly interactives and memorabilia of Alexander Keiller's colourful life. There is also a shop and a café.

OPENING TIMES

1 Apr-26 Oct, daily	10am-6pm or dusk if earlier
27 Oct-31 Mar, daily	10am-4pm
24-26 Dec	Closed

VISIT US

Direction: In Avebury, 7 miles W of Marlborough

Train: Pewsey 10 miles; Swindon 11 miles

Bus: Stagecoach 49 from Swindon; Thamesdown 42

NON-MEMBERS

Adult **£5.00** | Family (1+3) **£7.50**
Child **£2.50** | Family (2+3) **£12.50**

ACQ.1944 🔲 E 🔲 🔲 🔲 🔲 P OVP

Parking: S of Avebury off A4361. Free to EH members displaying a current car sticker or presenting current membership cards to National Trust staff on site.

MAP PAGE 337 (3J)
OS MAP 173, 157: SU099700

Avebury henge and stone circles are one of the greatest marvels of prehistoric Britain. Built and altered between 2600-2400 BC, the henge survives as a huge circular bank and ditch. Within it was a circle of originally about 100 great sarsen stones, the largest circle in Britain. This enclosed two smaller stone circles, each enclosing a central stone setting.

Avebury is part of a much wider complex of Neolithic and Bronze Age ceremonial sites, including West Kennet Avenue and The Sanctuary. Older West Kennet Long Barrow and Windmill Hill and later Silbury Hill are nearby. You can reach many of these sites by pleasant walks from Avebury village. This extraordinary assemblage of monuments seemingly formed a huge 'sacred landscape', whose purpose can still only be guessed at.

Avebury and its surroundings, with Stonehenge, are a World Heritage Site.

OPENING TIMES

Any reasonable daylight hours

VISIT US

See Alexander Keiller Museum

ACQ.1944 🔲 🔲 P

Parking (see Alexander Keiller Museum).

MAP PAGE 337 (3J)
OS MAP 173, 157: SU102700

WHILE IN THE AREA, MAKE SURE YOU ALSO VISIT...

The **Wiltshire Museum** in Devizes, and **The Salisbury Museum**, set in Salisbury Cathedral Close. Both are home to stimulating collections, events and exhibitions. See **p.301-302** for details.

USUAL FACILITIES MAY NOT BE AVAILABLE AROUND THE SUMMER SOLSTICE 20-22 JUNE. PLEASE CALL 01672 539250 BEFORE YOU VISIT.

Begun around 2500 BC, The Sanctuary was originally a setting of timber posts arranged in six concentric circles. Subsequently these were replaced or augmented by two stone circles, the outermost twice the diameter of the timber circles. Today concrete slabs and posts indicate these now-vanished components.

Various objects such as animal bones, pottery, flint tools and even human remains were buried at the site, but its function remains a mystery. Like the similar monuments at Woodhenge and Durrington Walls, The Sanctuary complex was probably a free-standing ceremonial site rather than a building. Later, the West Kennet Avenue of standing stones was constructed to connect it with Avebury henge, reinforcing the status of this enigmatic but clearly very important site. Part of the Avebury section of the World Heritage Site.

OPENING TIMES

Any reasonable daylight hours

VISIT US

Direction: ½ mile S of West Kennett, beside S side of A4

Train: Pewsey 9 miles, Bedwyn 12 miles

Bus: Thamesdown service 42. Also AD Rains service X76 serves West Kennett village

 ACQ.1944

Very limited parking in lay-by on S side of A4.

MAP PAGE 337 (3J)
OS MAP 173, 157: SU118680

Dramatically dominating the landscape around Avebury, mysterious Silbury Hill is the largest prehistoric artificial mound in Europe. Approximately 37 metres (120 feet) high and 500 metres (1,640 feet) in diameter, it compares in size with the roughly contemporary Egyptian pyramids. The mound was built in a series of stages over perhaps 100 years around 2400 BC, starting with a small gravel mound. Antiquarians and archaeologists have dug three separate tunnels into its centre, but found no central burial. Though Silbury Hill's position near the source of the River Kennet was clearly important, its purpose and significance remain unknown. Part of the Avebury section of the World Heritage Site.

No access to the hill itself. This is to prevent erosion of archaeological deposits and rare chalk grassland (the hill is a Site of Special Scientific Interest).

OPENING TIMES

Viewing area during reasonable daylight hours. Strictly no access to the hill itself

VISIT US

Direction: 1 mile W of West Kennett on A4

Train: Pewsey 9 miles, Swindon 13 miles

Bus: Stagecoach in Swindon service 49 passes within ¾ mile of the site. Also Thamesdown 42

 ACQ.1883

Disabled access (viewing area).

MAP PAGE 337 (3J)
OS MAP 173, 157: SU100685

USUAL FACILITIES MAY NOT BE AVAILABLE AROUND THE SUMMER SOLSTICE 20-22 JUNE. PLEASE CALL 01672 539250 BEFORE YOU VISIT.

WEST KENNET AVENUE

NEAR AVEBURY, WILTSHIRE
– SN8 1RD

An avenue, originally of around 100 pairs of prehistoric standing stones, forming a winding 1½ mile ritual link between the monuments of Avebury and The Sanctuary. The section nearest Avebury is the only part still visible. Many of the pairs, set around 20-30 metres (approx. 80 feet) from the next pair and around 15 metres (50 feet) apart, seem to follow a set form, with a large diamond-shaped stone matched with a slender straight-sided stone. Part of the Avebury section of the World Heritage Site.

OPENING TIMES

Any reasonable daylight hours

VISIT US

Direction: Runs alongside B4003

Train: Pewsey 9 miles, Swindon 12 miles

Bus: Thamesdown service 42. Also AD Rains service X76 serves West Kennett village

ACQ.1944 P

Parking (in lay-by, or at Avebury).

MAP PAGE 337 (3J)
OS MAP 173, 157: SU105695

WEST KENNET LONG BARROW

NEAR AVEBURY, WILTSHIRE – SN8 1QH

One of the largest, most impressive and most accessible Neolithic long barrow chambered tombs in Britain. It crowns a ridge above the River Kennet, with views across to Silbury Hill. Its now grassed-over chalk mound, over 100 metres (328 feet) long and 3 metres (10 feet) high, is an oasis of wild flowers in summer. You can explore the five atmospheric burial chambers within, constructed of massive boulders and opening off a central passage fronted by a façade of huge sarsens.

Built around 3650 BC, it is among the oldest visible monuments in the Avebury landscape. The dismembered remains of around 50 people were deposited here, over a short period of time and according to a system; children predominate in some chambers, adults in others. Part of the Avebury section of the World Heritage Site.

OPENING TIMES

Any reasonable daylight hours

VISIT US

Direction: ¾ mile SW of West Kennett, along footpath off A4

Train: Pewsey 9 miles, Swindon 13 miles

Bus: Thamesdown service 42. Also AD Rains service X76 serves West Kennett village

ACQ.1883 P

Very limited parking in lay-by, S of A4 10-15 minutes uphill walk, on gravel and then grass track.

MAP PAGE 337 (3J)
OS MAP 173, 157: SU105677

USUAL FACILITIES MAY NOT BE AVAILABLE AROUND THE SUMMER SOLSTICE 20-22 JUNE. PLEASE CALL 01672 539250 BEFORE YOU VISIT.

WINDMILL HILL
NEAR AVEBURY, WILTSHIRE
– SN4 9NW

The classic Neolithic 'causewayed enclosure', constructed around 3675 BC and thus pre-dating the Avebury henge. Its three concentric but intermittent ditches cover an area of approximately 22 acres. Large quantities of animal bones, cereal crops, stone tools, artefacts and pottery were found here, suggesting the communal gathering of people to feast, trade and carry out ritual ceremonies. This site can be reached by a 40-50 minute walk from Avebury village, along footpaths. Part of the Avebury section of the World Heritage Site.

OPENING TIMES

Any reasonable daylight hours

VISIT US

Direction: 1¼ miles NW of Avebury

Train: Swindon 11 miles

Bus: Stagecoach in Swindon service 49 and a couple of journeys on Thamesdown service 42 pass within ¾ mile of the site. Alight between Winterbourne Monkton and Avebury and use footpath

ACQ. 1944 🐕

Dogs on leads. Sheep may be grazing on site.

MAP PAGE 337 (3J)
OS MAP 173, 157: SU087714

WOODHENGE AND DURRINGTON WALLS WILTSHIRE – SP4 7AR

Woodhenge is a late Neolithic monument, where concrete markers now indicate the location of six concentric oval rings of timber posts. The timber structure is surrounded by a circular bank and ditch and is aligned north-east towards the summer solstice sunrise. A small central flint cairn marks the location of a child burial.

Nearby is Durrington Walls, a massive circular earthwork henge 500 metres (1,640 feet) in diameter, also built in the late Neolithic period, in about 2500 BC. Excavations here have revealed two concentric timber monuments, similar to Woodhenge, and the remains of many small buildings, possibly the houses where the builders or users of Stonehenge lived. At Stonehenge visitor centre you can see replicas based on these, and find out about what prehistoric people at Durrington ate. Recent geophysical surveys suggest that a massive alignment of stones or posts once existed beneath the southern henge bank, making Durrington a still more significant monument; but no traces of these discoveries are visible above ground.

Part of the Stonehenge section of the World Heritage Site.

OPENING TIMES

Any reasonable daylight hours

VISIT US

Direction: 1½ miles N of Amesbury, signposted off A345, just S of Durrington

Train: Salisbury 9 miles

Bus: Salisbury Reds service X5 (not Sun) or X4 (Sun)

ACQ. 1971 Durrington Walls
ACQ. 1932 Woodhenge

♿ 🐕 P Limited car parking.

MAP PAGE 337 (4J)
OS MAP 184, 130: SU151434

Avebury Monuments: Ownership, Guardianship and Management

Avebury Henge and Stone Circles, the Alexander Keiller Museum, West Kennet Avenue and Windmill Hill are in the freehold ownership of the National Trust. The Sanctuary is in Department of Culture, Media and Sport (DCMS) ownership. Silbury Hill and West Kennet Long Barrow are in private ownership.

All the sites are in English Heritage guardianship, in the case of Alexander Keiller Museum on behalf of DCMS. The museum collection is on loan from DCMS.

All the sites are managed by the National Trust on behalf of English Heritage, and the two organisations share the cost of managing and maintaining the properties.

USUAL FACILITIES MAY NOT BE AVAILABLE AROUND THE SUMMER SOLSTICE 20-22 JUNE. PLEASE CALL 01672 539250 BEFORE YOU VISIT.

STONEHENGE

Stonehenge and its surrounding prehistoric monuments are a
World Heritage Site; exploring them is an unforgettable experience.
Follow in the footsteps of Neolithic and Bronze Age ancestors
as you visit the iconic stone circle and investigate a landscape
still packed with secrets. In our visitor centre exhibitions and
reconstructed Neolithic houses, you'll discover more about about
the story of the circle and the people who created and used it.

WILTSHIRE SP4 7DE

Building Stonehenge

The monument was begun in about 3000 BC, in the Neolithic period. First, a circular ditch was dug around a ring of 56 pits, probably holding wooden or stone posts. During this early stage, Stonehenge was used as a cremation cemetery.

Some 500 years later, the central stone settings were raised. The larger 'sarsens', some weighing 30 tons or more, were probably brought from the Marlborough Downs, over 16 miles (25 kilometres) to the north. They were set up in an outer circle of 30 sarsen uprights, probably with a continuous circle of joining lintels. Within this were five trilithons (two upright stones capped by a horizontal lintel) arranged in a horseshoe shape.

Among the sarsens, the smaller bluestones, transported over 150 miles (240 kilometres) from the Preseli Hills in Pembrokeshire, were set in a double arc. Later, about 2300 BC, they were re-arranged to form an outer circle and an inner oval setting. At the centre was the sandstone Altar Stone. The enormous Heel Stone, near the north-east entrance to the circle, may have been among the earliest stones erected.

ASTONISHING PREHISTORIC ENGINEERING

The remains you see today are the remarkable survival of the final phase of this ancient monument, after 4,000 years of decay and destruction.

An extraordinarily well co-ordinated communal effort was needed to build Stonehenge. Transporting the stones over long distances, carefully shaping and working them, and raising them into position, took huge numbers of people. Only simple tools were used to smooth the stones and craft the joints linking the uprights with the horizontal lintels — one of the unique features of Stonehenge. The monument is an astonishing testament to the sophisticated engineering skills of prehistoric people.

There has long been debate about the meaning and function of Stonehenge. Archaeologists still come up with new theories about why people built it. The orientation of the stone settings to the rising and setting of the sun at the solstices is remarkable. Clearly these times were important for the people who built and used Stonehenge.

SPECIAL EXHIBITION

From late May 2019, the special exhibition at the Stonehenge visitor centre will be a solo display of new works by artist Linda Brothwell. Linda's contemporary work aims to promote an understanding of British craft skills and tools by illustrating their value and importance for economic, social and cultural development. This exhibition will feature pieces she has created in response to the Stonehenge landscape, the artefacts found within it and the craftsmanship of its local communities, both past and present. Linda has exhibited nationally and internationally; we are delighted to be working with her on this unique presentation.

Stonehenge was not built in isolation. When it was begun, this area was already the location of an early Neolithic monument complex. This included long barrows and the Stonehenge and Lesser Cursus monuments. The great henge at Durrington Walls (p.131), site of a large Neolithic settlement and several timber monuments, and The Avenue, leading from the stones to the River Avon, were both constructed when Stonehenge was being built. After major construction ended, hundreds of early Bronze Age round barrows were raised nearby.

Visiting the stones and their landscape

The awe-inspiring stone circle will always be the focus of any visit. It now stands in splendid isolation, re-united with its ancient processional approach. You can reach it either on foot or by bus from the visitor centre, which is 1¼ miles (2 kilometres) away and invisible from the circle.

The shuttle takes about 10 minutes. It makes a stop halfway, where you can choose to hop off and walk the rest of the way to the stones, taking in monuments including the Stonehenge Cursus and Cursus Barrows.

If you're keen to explore further, the surrounding landscape (cared for by the National Trust) offers a host of prehistoric monuments, interesting wildlife and different perspectives of the stone circle. Pick up an orientation leaflet and choose a walking route. Information panels explain the historic features you pass by. Sturdy footwear and suitable clothes are recommended if walking.

Visitor Centre: Exhibitions and Facilities

All under one roof, you'll find permanent and temporary exhibitions as well as spacious facilities, so that you can make the most of your day out at Stonehenge.

STEP INSIDE OUR RECONSTRUCTED NEOLITHIC HOUSES

In the exhibition gallery, an immersive 360-degree introductory film gives you the experience of being inside the stone circle and explains what we know of its story, and a widescreen presentation reveals how the Stonehenge landscape changed through prehistory. Large showcases display an intriguing range of archaeological treasures excavated from Stonehenge and nearby sites. You'll discover tools used by the monument's builders, artefacts found at the settlement at Durrington Walls and jewellery unearthed from surrounding burial mounds. Many of the artefacts in the exhibition have kindly been loaned by The Salisbury Museum, and the Wiltshire Museum (see p.301-302 for details).

In our Special Exhibition gallery, you'll find changing displays on Stonehenge-related themes.

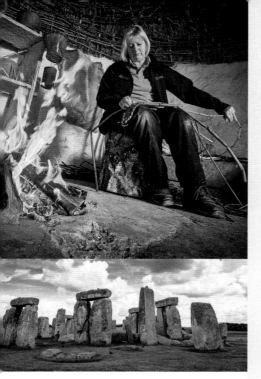

Our light and bright café is a lovely spot for all ages to enjoy refreshments. And the next-door shop has a great range of books and souvenirs, many exclusive to Stonehenge. There's also a multi-functional education room for school and community group visitors.

Just outside the visitor centre, you can discover examples of sarsen and bluestone and try your hand at dragging a replica sarsen. You can also step inside our reconstructed Neolithic houses to experience the lifestyles of the people who built Stonehenge. The houses are based on those excavated at nearby Durrington Walls.

Making the most of your visit

Entrance to Stonehenge is managed through timed tickets. To save time when you visit, booking online in advance is very strongly recommended. During the summer, choose if you can the quieter times of the day, beginning your visit before 10am or after 4pm.

Transformers: The Last Knight.

OPENING TIMES

1 Apr-31 May, daily	9.30am-7pm
1 Jun-31 Aug, daily	9am-8pm
1 Sep-16 Oct, daily	9.30am-7pm
17 Oct-23 Dec, daily	9.30am-5pm
2 Jan-31 Mar, daily	9.30am-5pm
Christmas Opening	
24 Dec – see website for opening times	
25 Dec	Closed
26 Dec & 1 Jan, daily	10am-5pm
27-31 Dec	9.30am-5pm

Last entry 2 hours before closing

Please note: 22 Dec open 10.30am-5pm and from 11.30am for group bookings

In bad weather visitors may not be able to use the walkway round the stone circle

Stone circle access outside normal opening hours by advance booking only. Book during weekday office hours on telephone 0370 333 0605

VISIT US

Address: Stonehenge Visitor Centre, nr Amesbury, Wiltshire SP4 7DE

Direction: satnav – use Stonehenge Visitor Centre. Off A360

Train: Salisbury 9½ miles

Bus: Wilts & Dorset Stonehenge Tour service. See www.thestonehengetour.info

Tel: 0370 333 1181 (Customer Services)

Local Tourist Information: Amesbury Library: 01980 623491 and Salisbury: 01722 342860

NON-MEMBERS

Advanced Pre-booked Prices*
Adult £20.90 | Concession £18.90
Child £12.60 | Family £54.40

Walk Up 'On the Day' Prices
Adult £23.30 | Concession £21.00
Child £14.00 | Family £60.60

***Advanced booking required.** Entrance to Stonehenge is by timed tickets. Although a limited number of tickets will be available on site each day, to guarantee entry book in advance at www.english-heritage.org.uk/stonehenge. Bookings cannot be made by phone

National Trust England members admitted free

Please note: All tourist and education groups must be pre-booked

ACQ 1918 🎧 ♿ ☕ 🖥 🚶 🚻 💂 🅿 🍴 📷 OVP

Audio tours (available in ten languages and hearing loop: subject to availability). The English version is also available to download to your mobile device from the Apple App Store or Google Play Store. Free WiFi is available at the visitor centre.

Guidebooks (available to purchase in English, French, German, Italian, Japanese, Mandarin, Russian and Spanish).

Assistance dogs only. The National Trust has recently created dog free zones in all fields that are grazed by sheep in the Stonehenge landscape where there is permissive access. Further details and map of where dogs are allowed can be found on the NT website.

Parking is free to members and advanced ticket holders.

MAP PAGE 337 (4J)   OS MAP 184, 130: SU122422

THE HERITAGE OF SCILLY

———— ISLES OF SCILLY ————

The stunningly beautiful Isles of Scilly hold vast arrays of archaeological riches both above and below sea level.

This compact archipelago of about 100 islands lies around 28 miles to the south-west of Land's End. None of them is any bigger than three miles across and only five are inhabited. Despite their landmass of only 6.18 square miles, these islands contain a remarkable number of historic sites. These range from traditional farmhouses and dwellings to ritual burial monuments, cist grave cemeteries and Romano-Celtic shrines. Early settlements provide evidence of a distinctively Scillonian prehistoric culture that thrived in the island group from around 4,500 years ago. At that time the sea level was lower, and much of Scilly formed a single landmass.

More recently, defensive monuments constructed during the Civil War and the Second World War stand as testament to the strategic importance of the islands.

The Gulf Stream keeps the climate warm, enabling exotic plants and wildlife to thrive in this designated Area of Outstanding Natural Beauty.

Travel details are available from Island Rover (who operate the round the island tour bus) on 01720 422131. Alternatively St Mary's Community Bus operates a similar route, but to a more frequent timetable. Contact Visit Isles of Scilly on 01720 424031 for details.

BANT'S CARN BURIAL CHAMBER AND HALANGY DOWN ANCIENT VILLAGE

ST MARY'S, ISLES OF SCILLY

The remains of a Romano-British village in a wonderfully scenic location. On the hill above stands a Neolithic or Bronze Age burial mound with entrance passage and inner chamber.

OPENING TIMES
Any reasonable daylight hours

VISIT US
Direction: 1 mile N of Hugh Town

 ACQ.1950

MAP PAGE 336 (5B)
OS MAP 203, 101: SV910123

CROMWELL'S CASTLE

TRESCO, ISLES OF SCILLY

Standing on a rocky promontory guarding the lovely anchorage between Bryher and Tresco, this round tower is one of the few surviving Cromwellian fortifications in Britain, built after the conquest of the Royalist Scillies in 1651.

OPENING TIMES
Any reasonable daylight hours

VISIT US
Direction: On the shoreline, approach with care, ¾ mile NW of New Grimsby

ACQ.1950

MAP PAGE 336 (4A)
OS MAP 203, 101: SV882159

GARRISON WALLS

ST MARY'S, ISLES OF SCILLY

You can enjoy a two-hour walk alongside the ramparts of these defensive walls and earthworks, dating from the 16th to 18th centuries. Other remains include

GARRISON WALLS

the Elizabethan Star Castle and defences from both World Wars.

OPENING TIMES
Any reasonable daylight hours

VISIT US
Direction: Around the headland W of Hugh Town

ACQ.1973

MAP PAGE 336 (5B)
OS MAP 203, 101: SV898104

HARRY'S WALLS

ST MARY'S, ISLES OF SCILLY

An unfinished artillery fort, built above St Mary's Pool harbour in 1552-53.

OPENING TIMES
Any reasonable daylight hours

VISIT US
Direction: ¼ mile NE of Hugh Town

ACQ.1950 P

MAP PAGE 336 (5B)
OS MAP 203, 101: SV909109

INNISIDGEN LOWER AND UPPER BURIAL CHAMBERS

ST MARY'S, ISLES OF SCILLY

Two Neolithic or Bronze Age communal burial cairns of Scillonian type, with fine views. The upper cairn is the best preserved on the islands.

OPENING TIMES
Any reasonable daylight hours

VISIT US
Direction: 1¾ miles NE of Hugh Town

ACQ.1950

MAP PAGE 336 (5B)
OS MAP 203, 101: SV922127

KING CHARLES'S CASTLE

TRESCO, ISLES OF SCILLY

The ruins of a mid-16th-century coastal artillery fort, later garrisoned – hence the name – by Civil War Royalists. Reached from New Grimsby by footpath.

OPENING TIMES
Any reasonable daylight hours

VISIT US
Direction: Located ¾ mile NW of New Grimsby. Coastal location, approach with care

ACQ.1950 ⚠ Sheer drops.
Please do not climb on the walls.

MAP PAGE 336 (4A)
OS MAP 203, 101: SV882161

OLD BLOCKHOUSE

TRESCO, ISLES OF SCILLY

Substantial remains of a small 16th-century gun tower protecting Old Grimsby harbour, vigorously defended during the Civil War.

OPENING TIMES
Any reasonable daylight hours

VISIT US
Direction: On Blockhouse Point, at the S end of Old Grimsby harbour

ACQ.1950 ⚠ Sheer drops within the ruins.

MAP PAGE 336 (4B)
OS MAP 203, 101: SV897155

PORTH HELLICK DOWN BURIAL CHAMBER

ST MARY'S, ISLES OF SCILLY

A large and imposing Scillonian Bronze Age entrance grave, with kerb, inner passage and burial chamber all clearly visible.

OPENING TIMES
Any reasonable daylight hours

VISIT US
Direction: 1¾ miles E of Hugh Town

ACQ.1950

MAP PAGE 336 (5B)
OS MAP 203, 101: SV928108

Wrest Park

TELLING TALES:
THE MYTHS,
LEGENDS AND
FOLKLORE OF
ENGLAND

THE WILD MAN OF ORFORD

According to the chronicler Ralph of Coggeshall, in Henry II's reign the fishermen of Orford caught a 'wild man' in their nets. Naked and covered in hair, he couldn't or wouldn't speak – not even when the constable of **Orford Castle** had him strung up by his feet and tortured. Nor did he show any reverence when taken into church. He ate anything given to him, and squeezed raw fish until it was dry before eating it. Eventually he was allowed to swim in the sea within a triple barrier of nets. He escaped, but rather surprisingly came back of his own free will. He was held captive in the castle for a further two months, after which he quietly slipped away, never to be seen again.

ST EDMUND WAY

22 miles | 2 days
Thetford Priory to Bury St Edmunds Abbey

You begin at Thetford Priory, an important medieval monastery, near the Church of the Holy Sepulchre, whose priests aided medieval pilgrims to Jerusalem. Next is the medieval stone Barnham Cross that marks the boundary between Norfolk and Suffolk, and along the Icknield Way through the King's Forest to West Stow, a reconstructed 5th-7th-century Anglo-Saxon village. A succession of four beautiful Suffolk churches follows before you arrive at Bury St Edmunds, with its ruined Abbey standing side-by-side with the Cathedral, where you can hear its choir sing Evensong.

View more details and a downloadable version of this route at www.english-heritage.org.uk/pilgrimage

START: THETFORD

ICKNIELD WAY TRAIL

THE KING'S FOREST

WEST STOW

ALL SAINTS FORNHAM   ST MARTIN'S FORNHAM

FINISH: BURY ST EDMUNDS

Thetford Priory

Bury St Edmunds Abbey

Discover English Heritage sites along the pilgrimage route

A Thetford Priory *(p.163)*
B Church of the Holy Sepulchre *(p.163)*
C Bury St Edmunds Abbey *(p.164)*

In partnership with

the British Pilgrimage Trust

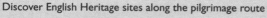

WREST
PARK

There's always something new for you to discover in Wrest Park's vast and infinitely varied gardens. This year, come and admire the restored surroundings of Marchioness Jemima's picturesque Georgian Bath House.

BEDFORDSHIRE MK45 4HR

Enlivened by charming follies and garden buildings, unexpected vistas and a wealth of statues, Wrest's 90-acre gardens reflect England's love affair with landscape. At the heart of the extensive waterside and woodland walks stands the iconic Archer Pavilion. A Baroque showstopper built between 1709 and 1711, it was designed by fashionable architect Thomas Archer. Once the ultimate garden dining room, it still retains its outstanding interior decoration, beneath a dome topped by a gleaming golden orb finial. Its breathtaking setting at the end of the Long Water makes it the most dramatic of the delightful set-pieces for which Wrest's gardens are renowned.

There's a lot more to see in these wonderful gardens. You can wander Capability Brown's pathways to the Chinese Bridge and Chinese Temple, its copper roof bedecked with sparkling golden bells. Nearby you'll find a memorial to 'Capability', one of many leading garden designers employed by the de Grey family to develop Wrest's grounds over three centuries.

This year, it's especially worth seeking out Jemima, Marchioness Grey's enchanting Bath House, disguised in the 'picturesque' style as a thatched Classical ruin. With its setting now fully restored, it's an ideal picnicking spot.

And there's more. Strolling the intricate woodland paths of the Duke of Kent's 18th-century Great Garden, you'll discover a secluded dogs' cemetery for de Grey family pets. Other walks lead you to the splendid 1830s Orangery. Nearer the great mansion, you can view the sculpture gallery in the Dairy, step into the Rose Garden and the vibrantly planted Italian Garden, or visit the formal French Parterre.

All this remarkable garden history is being progressively brought to life in a 20-year-long restoration project. You'll find the gardeners happy to answer questions, and there are free guided tours of the gardens on Tuesdays and Thursdays throughout the summer. Golf buggies are used to provide free of charge hop-on hop-off tours of the 90-acre grounds.

DON'T MISS OUR ST GEORGE'S FESTIVAL HERE ON 27-28 APRIL — THE LARGEST IN THE COUNTRY

NEW FOR 2019

By spring 2019, we'll have revived the area around Marchioness Jemima's delightful 'Classical ruin' Bath House, originally designed by Edward Stevens in 1769-70. The existing paths will be upgraded and new paths added, the cascade water feature will be restored and working again, and the whole area will be freshly planted.

In addition to the gardens, you can visit parts of the ground floor of the French chateau-style mansion, designed and built by Thomas, Earl de Grey in 1834-39. Its unfurnished but opulently decorated state rooms include the Grand Staircase, the Library, the Drawing Room and the Dining Room. Countess Henrietta's Sitting Room, furnished as it appeared in the 1860s, looks through to a lofty conservatory. An interactive exhibition reveals the history of the de Grey family, and you can admire recently returned family portraits.

You can also combine a day out at Wrest Park with a guided journey through 2,000 years of history in the archaeological store, housing treasures from English Heritage sites around the country. This fabulous array of over 153,000 artefacts ranges from prehistoric antlers to Victorian dress-fittings. There are also 6,000 items from London houses and 1,000 historic wallpapers. Guided by experts, you can tour this unrivalled treasure trove on the first Monday of every month.

Within the Walled Garden, the spacious café offers a seasonal menu using locally sourced produce, and has indoor and outdoor seating overlooking a children's play area.

Please note: No flash photography or stiletto heels in the house.

🎬 *Death of Stalin*; TV series, *The Royals*.

🍷 Available for corporate and private hire
🔔 Licensed for civil wedding ceremonies

OPENING TIMES

1 Apr-30 Sep, daily	10am-6pm
1 Oct-3 Nov, daily	10am-5pm
4 Nov-23 Dec, Sat-Sun	10am-4pm
2 Jan-16 Feb, Sat-Sun	10am-4pm
17-23 Feb, daily	10am-4pm
24 Feb-31 Mar, Wed-Sun	10am-4pm
Christmas Opening	
24-26 Dec	Closed
27 Dec-1 Jan, daily	10am-4pm
Last entry one hour before closing	

If the state rooms are closed to visitors due to an event, the exhibition and Countess's Sitting Room will remain open. Last entry to the gardens may sometimes be earlier than the usual '1 hour before closing'. Garden access for those already arrived will continue uninterrupted. Please call to check

VISIT US

Address: Wrest Park, Silsoe, Luton, Bedfordshire

Direction: ¾ mile E of Silsoe off A6, 10 miles S of Bedford

Train: Flitwick 4 miles

Bus: Grant Palmer 41; Stagecoach in Bedford 81; Flittabus

Tel: 01525 860000

NON-MEMBERS

Adult **£12.70** | Concession **£11.50**
Child **£7.60** | Family **£33.00**

Limited number of mobility scooters available. Pre-booking essential.

MAP PAGE 340 (5E)
OS MAP 153, 193: TL091355

BUSHMEAD PRIORY
BEDFORDSHIRE – MK44 2LD

A rare survival of the complete refectory of a small priory of Augustinian 'black canons' – communities of priests living together like monks. Founded in 1195, Bushmead apparently housed only a prior and four canons.

The impressive refectory, where the canons ate together, is its only remaining building. It displays a fine original timber roof and notable early 14th-century wall paintings, including the Creation of Eve.

OPENING TIMES

1 May-30 Sep, entry on the first Sat of the month only. Tel: 01525 860000 (option 2) to book. Pre-booking essential

VISIT US

Direction: Located off B660, 2 miles S of Bolnhurst

Train: St Neots 6 miles

Bus: Grant Palmer 28

NON-MEMBERS

Adult £7.70 | Concession £7.00
Child £4.70 | Family £20.10

ACQ.1974

MAP PAGE 340 (4E)
OS MAP 153, 225: TL115607

DE GREY MAUSOLEUM, FLITTON
BEDFORDSHIRE – MK45 5EJ

Among the largest sepulchral chapels attached to any English church, this mausoleum houses a remarkable sequence of 17 monuments to the de Grey family of Wrest Park. They span nearly 250 years (1614-1859). Download the audio tour from our website before visiting.

OPENING TIMES

Please check the website or call Wrest Park on 01525 860000 (option 2)

VISIT US

Direction: Access is through Flitton church; through Flitton, on an unclassified road, 1½ miles W of A6 at Silsoe

Train: Flitwick 2 miles

Bus: Grant Palmer service 200; also a limited service is provided by Flittabus (of Ampthill)

Tel: 01525 860000 (option 2)

ACQ.1979

MAP PAGE 340 (5E)
OS MAP 153, 193: TL059359

HOUGHTON HOUSE
BEDFORDSHIRE – MK45 2EZ

The shell of a large 17th-century mansion commanding impressive views, reputedly inspiration for the 'Palace Beautiful' in John Bunyan's *Pilgrim's Progress*. It was begun around 1615 for Mary Sidney Herbert, Dowager Countess of Pembroke, an accomplished poet, patron of the arts and pioneer scientist, as a focus for lavish entertaining. The architecture is an unusual mixture of the Jacobean and the new Classical styles: the ground floors of two Italianate loggias survive, possibly the work of Inigo Jones.

Audio tour available to download from our website.

OPENING TIMES

Daily   10am-6pm or dusk if earlier

VISIT US

Direction: 1 mile NE of Ampthill off B530, 8 miles S of Bedford

Train: Flitwick or Stewartby, both 3 miles

Bus: Stagecoach in Northants/Grant Palmer service 42; Flittabus service F5

ACQ.1938

MAP PAGE 340 (5D)
OS MAP 153, 193: TL039395

DENNY ABBEY
AND THE FARMLAND MUSEUM

———— CAMBRIDGESHIRE CB25 9PQ ————

A fascinating building with an immensely varied history, Denny Abbey was founded in 1159 as a Benedictine monastery, became a home for elderly and infirm Knights Templars, and then a convent of 'Poor Clare' nuns.

When Henry VIII dissolved the nunnery in 1539, it became a farm until the 1960s. Among its tenants was Thomas Hobson, the horse-hirer whose refusal to allow customers to select their mounts coined the expression 'Hobson's choice'. Graphic panels help you trace all these changes in the building.

Denny's later farming use can be explored in the nuns' great refectory, whose medieval floor tiles survived its use as a barn, and in Walnut Tree Cottage, which is furnished as a 1940s labourer's home.

THE FARMLAND MUSEUM HOSTS A RANGE OF EVENTS AND ACTIVITY DAYS

Alongside our site is the separate Farmland Museum, housed mainly in farm buildings, including a 17th-century stone threshing barn, where you can discover more about the rural history of Cambridgeshire.

The museum features a collection of farming tools and machinery, displays on local crafts and skills and recreations of a 19th-century fenman's hut, a 1930s village shop and craftsmen's workshops, including those of a wheelwright and a farrier.

The Farmland Museum hosts a range of events, children's activity days and adult art and craft workshops.

Managed by the Farmland Museum.
www.dennyfarmlandmuseum.org.uk

OPENING TIMES

2 Apr-27 Oct, Tue-Sun & Bank Hols	11am-5pm
28 Oct-31 Mar	Closed

VISIT US

Direction: Located 6 miles N of Cambridge on A10

Train: Waterbeach 3 miles

Bus: Stagecoach Cambridge 9

Tel: 01223 860489

NON-MEMBERS

Museum and Abbey
Adult **£5.00** | Concession **£4.00**
Child **£3.00** | Family **£14.00**

There will be a premium payable by all visitors, including members, on special event days – please visit **www.dennyfarmlandmuseum.org.uk** for details

Disabled access (museum and abbey ground floor only).

Dogs on leads (restricted areas only).

Tearoom for museum visitors (11am-4pm at weekends, 11am-4.30pm on Bank Holiday Mondays and 12pm-4.30pm on Wed-Thu during school holidays).

MAP PAGE 341 (4F)
OS MAP 154, 226: TL492685

DUXFORD CHAPEL

CAMBRIDGESHIRE – CB22 4NL

A modest but complete and attractive 14th-century chantry chapel, perhaps originally a hospital.

OPENING TIMES

Any reasonable daylight hours

VISIT US

Direction: Off A505 on Station Road, Whittlesford, between Whittlesford Station car park and the Red Lion Hotel

Train: Whittlesford, adjacent

Bus: Stagecoach Cambridge Citi 7 & A2B 7A. Also Myall service 101 (Tue) & 132 (Sun)

ACQ.1947

MAP PAGE 341 (4F)
OS MAP 154, 209: TL485473

ISLEHAM PRIORY CHURCH

CAMBRIDGESHIRE – CB7 5RX

The best example in England of a small Norman Benedictine priory church. It survives surprisingly unaltered, despite later conversion into a barn.

OPENING TIMES

Any reasonable daylight hours.
Interior: Key available from Mrs R Burton, 18 Festival Road, Isleham CB7 5SY – 5 min walk

VISIT US

Direction: Located in centre of Isleham, 16 miles NE of Cambridge on B1104

Train: Newmarket 8½ miles, Ely 9 miles

Bus: Lords Travel 203 (Tue & Sat); Big Green Bus Company service 204

ACQ.1944

MAP PAGE 341 (3F)
OS MAP 143, 226: TL642743

LONGTHORPE TOWER

CAMBRIDGESHIRE – PE3 6LU

Longthorpe Tower, built in about 1300 as part of a fortified manor house, displays one of the most complete and important sets of 14th-century domestic

---

wall paintings in northern Europe. Rediscovered in 1945, the paintings cover the walls and vault of the tower's Great Chamber. This varied 'spiritual encyclopaedia' of worldly and religious subjects includes the Wheel of the Senses, the Labours of the Months and the Seven Ages of Man, along with scenes of everyday life and depictions of Fenland birds.

Managed by Vivacity Culture and Leisure.
www.vivacity-peterborough.com

OPENING TIMES

6 Apr-27 Oct, Sat-Sun & Bank Hols	10am-5pm
28 Oct-31 Mar	Closed

Last entry 30 mins before closing

Group and education visits outside these times by arrangement

VISIT US

Direction: Located 2 miles W of Peterborough on A47

Train: Peterborough 1½ miles

Bus: Centrebus service 9 & 47; Stagecoach Citi 2, Citi 4

Tel: 01733 864663

NON-MEMBERS

Adult **£3.30** | Concession **£2.20**
Child **£2.20** | Family **£8.80**

There will be a premium payable by all visitors, including members, on special event days – please visit www.vivacity-peterborough.com/vivacity-venues/longthorpe-tower for details

ACQ.1947

Parking in car park at St Botolph's Church, Thorpe Road, approximately 100 metres from site.

No wheelchair access.

MAP PAGE 340 (3E)
OS MAP 142, 227/235: TL162984

AUDLEY END HOUSE AND GARDENS

Whether you're exploring gardens, state rooms or servants' domains, you'll find a warm welcome at Audley End.

ESSEX CB11 4JF

Lived in until 1948, this noble Jacobean mansion in its landscaped setting is simply the best place in England to discover how a great mansion worked, both for servants and their masters. You can experience Victorian servants' lives in the working stables and Service Wing, explore the Nursery Suite and Coal Gallery, and enjoy the re-presented state rooms.

Among the most delightful of English Heritage's treasures, Audley End takes its name from Sir Thomas Audley, Henry VIII's Lord Chancellor. His grandson Thomas Howard, Earl of Suffolk, rebuilt the house on a massive scale between 1603 and 1614. His 'Palace of Audley End' was one of the largest mansions in England. Today, Audley's interior largely represents the taste of the third Lord Braybrooke, who redecorated many of its rooms in the Jacobean style during the 1820s.

The State Rooms

There's no standing on ceremony in the state rooms – feel free to play the piano in the Library, admire the Georgian state bed or step into Lady Braybooke's private apartments, lit for her return from an evening party. Take in the transformational work of the renowned Georgian architect Robert Adam in the Adam Room suite. Visitors unable to access the upper floors can enjoy a virtual tour in the visitor centre.

The Nursery Suite and Coal Gallery

The 1830s Nursery Suite uncovers the hidden world of the privileged Braybrooke children and their nursery maids, governess and tutors. You're invited to try on period costumes, play with hands-on replicas of 1830s toys, and discover the personalities of the eight Braybrooke children.

The sights, sounds and smells within the Coal Gallery showcase the 19th-century innovations which helped servants provide warmth and hot water for the aristocratic family and their guests.

The Stables

Audley End's lovely gabled red-brick stables are set as in the 1880s. The horses are back, and there are riding displays and hands-on demonstrations of horse-care, in which children can take part. Lively interactive displays 'virtually' introduce you to Audley's Victorian outdoor staff.

STAY WITH US

Book a relaxing break in **Cambridge Lodge** here. Enjoy stunning views of the River Cam and the manicured lawns, and stroll through the grounds in private once the gates have closed to the public.

See p.332 for details on staying at **Audley** and our other holiday cottages.

The Service Wing

The Victorian Service Wing provides you with a unique and atmospheric insight into life 'below stairs' during the 1880s. The kitchens, dairy, dry larder and laundries are fully equipped with original and reproduction Victorian fittings, and vividly animated with lifelike sights and sounds. Costumed interpreters demonstrate traditional cooking and washing techniques on selected days. (Every weekend, June-September, plus other days throughout the year.) You can also enjoy volunteer-led guided tours of the Service Wing and Butler's Pantry, to see how the servants kept the household running from early morning to late into the night (call site for details).

AUDLEY END'S GROUNDS OFFER VARIED DELIGHTS

The Gardens

Remodelled by Capability Brown – amid furious disputes with the mansion's owner – Audley End's grounds offer varied delights. Admire the Elysian Garden and Tea House Bridge; walk up to the Classical Temple of Concord to view the house in its setting; visit the memorial to Second World War Polish 'underground' resistance soldiers; or admire the restored 19th-century formal garden. If you're a practical gardener, the renowned Walled Organic Kitchen Garden is a must. Next to it are the children's play area and Cart Yard Café.

Our gardens have won many prizes, including a gold Anglia in Bloom award. These celebrated achievements in conservation, the restoration of historic plantings and the development of a successful composting system.

Please note: Photography in the house is only permitted in the Nursery and Coal Gallery. No stiletto heels allowed in the house.

🖼 *The Crown; Trust.*

You can now pre-order a summer picnic or afternoon tea from our tearoom to enjoy in the grounds of Audley End. Please telephone site 48-hours in advance to book your picnic, presented in an English Heritage jute bag.

OPENING TIMES

House

1 Apr-30 Sep, daily	12pm-5pm
1 Oct-3 Nov, daily	12pm-4pm
4 Nov-31 Mar	Closed

Stables, Service Wing & Gardens

1 Apr-30 Sep, daily	10am-6pm
1 Oct-3 Nov, daily	10am-5pm
4 Nov-23 Dec, Sat-Sun	10am-4pm
2 Jan-16 Feb, Sat-Sun	10am-4pm
17-23 Feb, daily	10am-4pm
24 Feb-31 Mar, Wed-Sun	10am-4pm

Christmas Opening

24-25 Dec	Closed
26 Dec-1 Jan, daily	10am-4pm

Last entry 30 mins before closing.
Gardens only prices available when house closed in winter (Nov-Mar)

VISIT US

Address: Audley End House & Gardens, off London Road, Saffron Walden, Essex

Direction: 1 mile W of Saffron Walden on B1383 (M11 exit 8 or 10)

Train: Audley End 1¼ miles. Note: Footpath is beside busy main road

Bus: Stephensons 6, 59, 60, 301; Viceroy 59, 590; all pass within ¼ mile of entrance

Tel: 01799 522842

Local Tourist Information:
Saffron Walden: 01799 524002
Cambridge: 01223 791500

NON-MEMBERS

House
Adult £20.40 | Concession £18.40
Child £12.30 | Family £53.10

Stables, Service Wing, & Gardens (winter price only)
Adult £14.30 | Concession £12.90
Child £8.60 | Family £37.20

Disabled access (grounds, Great Hall, Stable Yard and Service Wing only. Please call for more information).

MAP PAGE 341 (5F)
OS MAP 154, 195: TL525382

COLCHESTER, BLUEBOTTLE GROVE

ESSEX – CO3 4DU

Ist-century Iron Age earthworks, defending pre-Roman 'Camulodunum', capital of the British Catuvellauni tribe. Conquered by the Romans in AD 43, it later became Colchester. Lexden Earthworks (p.151) are nearby.

Managed by Colchester Borough Council.

OPENING TIMES

Any reasonable daylight hours

VISIT US

Direction: 2 miles W of Colchester off A604. From Lexden Straight Road, turn left into Heath Road, left into Church Lane, right into Beech Hill and follow signs to site

Train: Colchester or Colchester Town, both 2½ miles

Bus: Arriva 4; Hedingham Omnibuses 15 operate closest to the site. Alight in Scott Drive and then a short walk

Tel: 01206 282929

ACQ.1925 ⚑ ⚠

MAP PAGE 341 (5H)
OS MAP 168, 184: TL965246

COLCHESTER, LEXDEN EARTHWORKS

ESSEX – CO3 5EF

Iron Age earthworks defending pre-Roman Colchester. Lexden Tumulus was the burial place of a wealthy British chieftain – perhaps a king. It contained both British and imported Roman treasures. Bluebottle Grove (p.151) is nearby.

Managed by Colchester Borough Council.

OPENING TIMES

Any reasonable daylight hours

VISIT US

Direction: On Lexden Straight Road, 2 miles W of Colchester off A604

Train: Colchester or Colchester Town, both 2½ miles

Bus: Arriva 4; Hedingham Omnibuses 15 operate closest to the site. Alight in Scott Drive and then a short walk

Tel: 01206 282929

ACQ.1925 ⚑ ⚠

MAP PAGE 341 (5H)
OS MAP 168, 184: TL965246

COLCHESTER, ST BOTOLPH'S PRIORY

ESSEX – CO2 7EE

Remains of one of England's first Augustinian priories, founded c. 1100. An impressive example of early Norman architecture, the church has massive pillars and round arches and an elaborate west front.

Managed by Colchester Borough Council.

OPENING TIMES

1-30 Apr, daily	7.30am-7pm
1 May-31 Aug, daily	7.30am-8pm
1-14 Sep, daily	7.30am-7pm
15-30 Sep, daily	7.30am-6.30pm
1-14 Oct, daily	7.30am-6pm
15-31 Oct, daily	7.30am-5pm
1 Nov-28 Feb, daily	7.30am-4pm
1-14 Mar, daily	7.30am-5pm
15-31 Mar, daily	7.30am-6pm

VISIT US

Direction: Nr Colchester Town station

Train: Colchester Town, adjacent

Bus: Bus services to/from Colchester are provided by Beestons (of Hadleigh) Chambers (of Bures), First Essex, Hedingham Omnibuses,

---

Regal Busways, Stephensons of Essex and Arriva Colchester. Priory is 2 minute walk from the bus station

Tel: 01206 282929

ACQ.1912 ⚑

MAP PAGE 341 (5H)
OS MAP 168, 184: TL999249

COLCHESTER, ST JOHN'S ABBEY GATE

ESSEX – CO2 7EZ

This elaborately decorated gatehouse is the sole survivor of the wealthy Benedictine abbey of St John. Built c. 1400 to strengthen the abbey's defences, it was stormed by Parliamentarian troops during the Civil War.

Managed by Colchester Borough Council.

OPENING TIMES

Exterior only: Any reasonable daylight hours

VISIT US

Direction: On St John's Green on southern side of central Colchester

Train: Colchester Town ¼ mile

Bus: Bus services to/from Colchester are provided by Beestons (of Hadleigh) Chambers (of Bures), First Essex, Hedingham Omnibuses, Regal Busways, Stephensons of Essex and Arriva Colchester. Abbey Gate is 2 minute walk from the bus station

Tel: 01206 282929

ACQ.1983 ⚑

MAP PAGE 341 (5H)
OS MAP 168, 184: TL998248

HILL HALL ESSEX – CM16 7QQ

OPENING TIMES

1 Apr-30 Sep	Pre-booked guided tours only

To book please call 0370 333 1181
(Customer Services)

VISIT US

Direction: 3 miles SE of Epping.
Entrance ½ mile N of Theydon
Mount Church

Train: Epping or Theydon Bois
2½ miles

Bus: Closest bus services are
Arriva 375; Go Ahead Blue
Triangle 575 to Passingford Bridge
(2¾ miles)

NON-MEMBERS

Adult **£8.20** | Concession **£7.40**
Child **£4.90** | Family **£21.30**

ACQ.1976

MAP PAGE 341 (6F)
OS MAP 167/177, 174: TQ489995

Built in 1568-77 for the scholar, diplomat and politician Sir Thomas Smith, this splendid Elizabethan mansion is among the earliest Renaissance houses in England.

Its multi-columned Classical-style exterior imitates examples Smith had admired on his ambassadorial travels in France and Flanders. Its interior is adorned with very rare survivals of high-quality figurative wall-paintings, among the finest in English Heritage's collection. Now mainly visible for you to view in two rooms, they seemingly once extended throughout the house. One series depicts the Old Testament story of Hezekiah and the other the Classical legend of Cupid and Psyche. Expertly painted, they may be by Flemish artists, or English imitators: Sir Thomas himself may have overseen their design.

Hill Hall has now been divided into private houses, but parts remain open to the public by prior arrangement.

PRIOR'S HALL BARN, WIDDINGTON ESSEX – CB11 3SB

Among the finest medieval barns in eastern England, probably built for New College, Oxford. Tree-ring dating showed that its timbers were felled in 1417-42. It was originally constructed of around 900 separate timber components, the product of some 400 oaks.

Clad with black weatherboarding in traditional Essex style, it displays a breathtaking aisled interior with a crown post roof, little altered over the centuries. The two huge porches allowed harvest carts to be wheeled in and unloaded under cover.

OPENING TIMES

6 Apr-29 Sep,
Sat-Sun   10am-6pm

VISIT US

Direction: In Widdington, on
unclassified road 2 miles SE of
Newport, off B1383

Train: Newport 2 miles

Bus: Stephensons of Essex 301;
Regal 322

ACQ.1976

MAP PAGE 341 (5F)
OS MAP 167, 195: TL537318

HADLEIGH CASTLE

ESSEX – SS7 2AP

The romantic ruins of a royal castle, on a ridge overlooking the Essex marshes and the Thames Estuary. The first castle was begun in about 1215 by Hubert de Burgh, King John's powerful Justiciar, but it was extensively rebuilt by Edward III during the 1360s, to which date most of the surviving remains belong. Conveniently accessible from London by royal barge, the castle was probably a personal retreat, where Edward could stay in privacy and comfort.

After Edward's death in 1377, Hadleigh's tenancy passed to a series of absentee royal relations, including three of Henry VIII's queens. Eventually it was substantially demolished for building materials. Yet Edward III's two big eastern drum towers still remain, the commanding south-east tower – allegedly used by Georgian revenue men looking out for smugglers – still standing three storeys high.

OPENING TIMES

Any reasonable daylight hours

VISIT US

Direction: ¾ mile S of A13 at Hadleigh

Train: Leigh-on-Sea 1½ miles by direct footpath

Bus: Arriva service 1; Regal Busways 3, 3A, 3B; First 21, 21A, 21B, 26, 27, 27A & 28; all to within ½ mile

ACQ.1948

MAP PAGE 341 (6G)
OS MAP 178, 175: TQ810860

MISTLEY TOWERS

ESSEX – CO11 1HB

Two imposing Classical towers, which stood at each end of a highly unconventional Georgian church. One of only two churches designed by Robert Adam, it was built in about 1776. When the centre of the church was demolished in 1870, the columns from its porticos were added to the towers.

Managed by Mistley Thorn Residents' Association.

OPENING TIMES

Exterior: Any reasonable daylight hours

Interior: Key available from The Mistley Thorn Hotel, High Street, Mistley CO11 1HE, 100m to the right of the site, daily   10am-4pm

VISIT US

Direction: Located on B1352, 1½ miles E of A137 at Lawford, 9 miles E of Colchester

Train: Mistley ¼ mile

Bus: First in Essex service 2, 102, 103, 104

ACQ.1958

Disabled access (exterior only).

Dogs on leads (exterior only).

MAP PAGE 341 (5H)
OS MAP 168/169, 184/197:
TM116320

WALTHAM ABBEY GATEHOUSE AND BRIDGE

ESSEX – EN9 1XQ

Fine 14th-century gatehouse and other remains of the abbey refounded by Earl Godwin, father of Harold, the last Saxon King of England. It later became one of the greatest monasteries in medieval England. According to tradition, King Harold's body was secretly buried here after his death at the Battle of Hastings, and you can see the alleged site of his grave in the abbey grounds.

Managed by Lee Valley Regional Park Authority.

OPENING TIMES

Any reasonable daylight hours

VISIT US

Direction: In Waltham Abbey off A112

Train: Waltham Cross 1¼ miles

Bus: Epping Forest Community Transport 211, 212; Arriva 251; Trustybus 505; EOS 66, 66A, 86

Tel: 0845 677 0600

ACQ.1976

Sensory trail guide.

MAP PAGE 341 (6F)
OS MAP 166, 174
GATEHOUSE: TL381007
HAROLD'S BRIDGE: TL382009

TILBURY FORT

ESSEX RM18 7NR

Tilbury Fort on the Thames Estuary defended London's seaward approach from Tudor times to the Second World War.

Henry VIII built the first permanent fort here, and Queen Elizabeth I famously delivered her Armada Speech at nearby Tilbury in 1588. King Charles II ordered his chief engineer, Sir Bernard de Gomme, to build the great artillery fort you can see today, with work beginning in 1670. It's the best example of a 17th-century bastioned fortress in England, with its complete circuit of moats and outworks still substantially surviving. Highland prisoners were held here after the Jacobite Rising of 1745, and much later the fort's guns helped shoot down a raiding Zeppelin in 1916.

To enter the fort you'll pass through the magnificent Watergate, and you can also see the historic Landport gate. Visit the east gunpowder magazine to take in an exhibition tracing the fort's role in the defence of London and providing information on advances in military engineering. The atmospheric Victorian magazine tunnels in the north east bastion give an insight into the life of a 19th-century gunner. For impressive views of the Thames and the historic riverside town of Gravesend, be sure to step onto the fort ramparts.

🎬 Warner Bros. *Wonder Woman*; *Peterloo*; BBC TV series, *Taboo*; TV series, *SSGB*; *Tulip Fever*; *Sharpe*.

OPENING TIMES

1 Apr-30 Sep, Wed-Sun & Bank Hols	10am-6pm
1 Oct-3 Nov, Wed-Sun	10am-5pm
4 Nov-31 Mar, Sat-Sun	10am-4pm
24-26 Dec & 1 Jan	Closed

Last entry 30 mins before closing

VISIT US

Direction: Located ½ mile E of Tilbury off A126, close to the Port of Tilbury. Beyond the World's End Pub

Train: Tilbury Town 1½ miles

Bus: Ensignbus service 99 connects with trains at Tilbury Town and passes the fort

Ferry: Gravesend – Tilbury Ferry, then ¼ mile walk

Tel: 01375 858489

NON-MEMBERS

Adult £7.20 | Concession £6.50
Child £4.30 | Family £18.70

Disabled access (exterior and Fort Parade Ground).

Dogs on leads (restricted areas).

MAP PAGE 341 (7G)
OS MAP 177/178, 162/163: TQ651753

BERKHAMSTED CASTLE

HERTFORDSHIRE – HP4 1LJ

Substantial remains of a strong motte-and-bailey castle dating from the 11th to 15th centuries. Richard, Earl of Cornwall added a 13th-century palace complex.

OPENING TIMES

Summer, daily	10am-6pm
Winter, daily	10am-4pm
25 Dec & 1 Jan	Closed

VISIT US

Direction: Near 🚉 Berkhamsted

Train: Berkhamsted, adjacent

Bus: Vale Travel service 354/A; Little Jim's service 532 pass the castle. Arriva 500; Red Eagle 30, 31 & 500; Red Rose 501; Little Jim 502 serve the High Street, which is within ¼ mile walk

ACQ.1929 🐾 ⚠

MAP PAGE 340 (6D)
OS MAP 165, 181: SP995082

OLD GORHAMBURY HOUSE

HERTFORDSHIRE – AL3 6AH

Remains of an immense mansion built 1563-68 by Sir Nicholas Bacon, Queen Elizabeth's Lord Keeper, and visited by the queen at least four times. Its elaborate Classical two-storey porch and other elements survive.

OLD GORHAMBURY HOUSE

OPENING TIMES

Any reasonable daylight hours but not earlier than 8am or later than 6pm

Access is via the permissive path Gorhambury Drive. This is closed to the public on 1 June, most Wednesdays and Saturdays from September to January, and occasionally at other times, so it is not possible to visit the site on these days. Please check www.gorhamburyestate.co.uk for current closure details before you visit

The walk or cycle up Gorhambury Drive to the site is about 2 miles from the nearest parking. Closer access by car, followed by a ½ mile walk, is limited to Thu only, May-Sep 2pm-5pm

VISIT US

Direction: Just off A4147 on western outskirts of St Albans by the Roman Theatre of Verulamium (AL3 6AE). Walk or cycle 2 miles up permissive path Gorhambury Drive. Access by car is limited (see opening times)

Train: St Albans Abbey 3 miles, St Albans 3½ miles

Bus: Arriva services 300, 301 pass start of drive

ACQ.1959 🐾 ⚠

MAP PAGE 340 (6E)
OS MAP 166, 182: TL110076

ROMAN WALL, ST ALBANS

HERTFORDSHIRE – AL3 4AJ

Part of the two-mile-long wall built AD 265-70 to defend the Roman city of Verulamium, including the foundations of towers and the London Gate.

OPENING TIMES

Any reasonable daylight hours

VISIT US

Direction: Located in Verulamium Park on the S side of St Albans, ½ mile from the centre, off the A4147

Train: St Albans Abbey ½ mile, St Albans 1¼ miles

Bus: Vale Travel services S8 & S9 operate close to the Roman Wall site

ACQ.1931 🐾

MAP PAGE 340 (6E)
OS MAP 166, 182: TL137066

BACONSTHORPE CASTLE

NORFOLK – NR25 6LE

Atmospherically sited moated ruins of a fortified manor house, chronicling the fortunes of the ambitious Heydon family. Begun during the Wars of the Roses, it was later given its turreted Elizabethan outer gatehouse, before the family went bankrupt.

Download a free audio tour from the English Heritage website before you visit.

OPENING TIMES

Any reasonable daylight hours

VISIT US

Direction: ¾ mile N of village of Baconsthorpe off unclassified road, 3 miles E of Holt

Train: Sheringham 4½ miles

Bus: Sanders service 16 (Tue)

ACQ.1966 🐾 P ⚠

MAP PAGE 341 (1H)
OS MAP 133, 252: TG121382

BERNEY ARMS WINDMILL

NORFOLK – NR30 1SB

One of the tallest marsh mills in the Norfolk Broads, Berney Arms windmill stands over 70 feet (21 metres) high, visible for miles around. Probably built c. 1870 to grind a component of cement, it remained in use until 1948, ending its days powering a still-visible scoop wheel to drain surrounding marshes.

Supported by the RSPB.

OPENING TIMES

Currently closed for essential maintenance work. Please check website for current information

VISIT US

Direction: 3½ miles NE of Reedham on the N bank of River Yare. Accessible by hired boat, or by footpath from Halvergate (3½ miles)

Train: Berney Arms ¼ mile

Tel: 01493 857900

ACQ.1950 🎯 ⚠

MAP PAGE 341 (2J)
OS MAP 134, OL40: TG465049

BINHAM MARKET CROSS

NORFOLK – NR21 0DW

Tall shaft of a 15th-century cross, on the site of an annual fair held from the 1100s until the 1950s.

OPENING TIMES

Any reasonable daylight hours

VISIT US

Direction: Located on the Binham village green

Train: Wighton on the Wells & Walsingham Light Railway 3½ miles

Bus: Sanders service 13 (Thu) & 46

ACQ.1949

MAP PAGE 341 (1H)
OS MAP 132, 251: TF984396

BINHAM PRIORY

NORFOLK – NR21 0DQ

Among the most impressive monastic ruins in Norfolk. The virtually complete nave adjoining the ruins is now the parish church, with a striking 13th-century west front, tiers of Norman arches and painted screens.

Site-finds display and children's activity area within the church.

Managed by Binham Parochial Church Council.

OPENING TIMES

Binham Priory (monastic ruins):
Any reasonable daylight hours

Priory Church:
Summer, daily   9am-6pm
Winter, daily   9am-4pm

VISIT US

Direction: ¼ mile NW of village of Binham on road off B1388

Train: Wighton on the Wells & Walsingham Light Railway 3½ miles

Bus: Sanders service 46

Tel: 01328 830362

ACQ.1933 ♿ 🅴 ⚡ ⚡ 🅿 ⚠

Toilets available in Church.

MAP PAGE 341 (1H)
OS MAP 132, 251: TF982399

BLAKENEY GUILDHALL

NORFOLK – NR25 7NA

Remains of a 15th-century merchant's house with brick-vaulted undercroft, recalling Blakeney's medieval prosperity. Later the Guildhall of local fish merchants.

Managed by Blakeney Parish Council.

OPENING TIMES

1 Apr-31 Oct, daily
Any reasonable daylight hours

1 Nov-31 Mar, Sat-Sun
Any reasonable daylight hours

Access may be possible on winter weekdays by contacting the key keeper in advance on 07518 149312

VISIT US

Direction: In Blakeney off A149

Train: Sheringham 9 miles

Bus: Stagecoach Norfolk Coasthopper service; Sanders service 46

Tel: 01263 741106

ACQ.1956 🎯 ⚠

MAP PAGE 341 (1H)
OS MAP 133, 251: TG028441

BURGH CASTLE

NORFOLK – NR31 9QB

The imposing towered walls of a Roman 'Saxon Shore' fort, with panoramic views over Breydon Water.

Owned and managed by Norfolk Archaeological Trust.

OPENING TIMES

Any reasonable daylight hours

Free 45-minute guided walks Jun-Sep, Sun, weather permitting from 2.30pm

VISIT US

Direction: At far W end of Breydon Water on unclassified road, 3 miles W of Great Yarmouth

Train: Great Yarmouth 5 miles

Bus: First 5 from Great Yarmouth then a short walk

ACQ.1929 [icons]

Car park locked at 6pm.

MAP PAGE 341 (2J)
OS MAP 134, OL40: TG475047

CAISTER ROMAN FORT NORFOLK – NR30 5JS

Excavated remains of a Roman 'Saxon Shore' fort, built around AD 200 and occupied until the late 4th century.

Managed by Great Yarmouth Borough Council.

OPENING TIMES

Any reasonable daylight hours

VISIT US

Direction: From Great Yarmouth, follow the A149 northbound and then the A149 Caister Bypass. Follow brown tourist signs for Caister Roman Fort. From other directions follow signs for Great Yarmouth and then brown tourist signs from the Caister Bypass roundabout. Parking and the entrance to the Fort are situated off a lay-by on Norwich Road ¼ mile from the roundabout

Train: Great Yarmouth 3 miles

Bus: First services 1, 1A, 4 & 8 pass the site; Sanders 6 within ½ mile

Tel: 01493 846534

ACQ.1954 [icon]

MAP PAGE 341 (2J)
OS MAP 134, OL40: TG517123

CASTLE RISING CASTLE NORFOLK – PE31 6AH

One of the most complete and lavishly decorated Norman keeps in England, surrounded by stupendous earthworks. Begun in 1138, in the 14th century it became the luxurious prison of Queen Isabella, widow (and alleged murderess) of Edward II.

Owned and managed by Lord Howard of Rising.

www.castlerising.co.uk

OPENING TIMES

1 Apr-1 Nov, daily (or dusk if earlier in Oct)	10am-6pm
2 Nov-31 Mar, Wed-Sun	10am-4pm
24-26 Dec	Closed

VISIT US

Direction: Located 4 miles NE of King's Lynn off A149

Train: King's Lynn 4½ miles

Bus: Stagecoach Norfolk Coastal Hopper service 10 & 11; Lynx 35 to Castle Rising

Tel: 01553 631330

NON-MEMBERS

Adult £4.50 | Concession £3.80
Child £3.00 | Family (2+2) £14.00

There will be a premium payable by all visitors, including members, on special event days – please check www.castlerising.co.uk for details

ACQ.1958 [icons]

Disabled access (exterior only, toilets).

Dogs allowed on leads in the grounds only.

MAP PAGE 341 (2G)
OS MAP 132, 250: TF666246

CASTLE ACRE CASTLE AND BAILEY GATE

NORFOLK PE32 2XB

The delightful village of Castle Acre boasts an extraordinary wealth of history.

Situated on the Peddar's Way, a major trade and pilgrim route to Thetford, Bromholm Priory and Walsingham, it's a very rare and complete survival of a Norman planned settlement. It includes a castle, town, fine parish church and associated monastery. All this is the work of a powerful Norman baronial family, the Warennes, mainly during the 11th and 12th centuries.

The first William de Warenne founded the castle soon after the Conquest, probably as a stone 'country house'. But during the early 12th century more disturbed conditions prompted its conversion into a strong keep, further defended by stone walls and an immense system of colossal banks and ditches. It offers perhaps the finest medieval castle earthworks anywhere in England.

Meanwhile, the 'planned town' established outside the castle was also protected by earthwork defences with stone gates. The Bailey Gate of c. 1200 survives, with the road into the village running between its towers.

You can trace the ancient street layout of this attractive village, lined with flint or brick houses, before exploring both the great castle earthworks and the extensive priory remains.

Pick up a family trail available from Castle Acre Priory.

OPENING TIMES

Any reasonable daylight hours

VISIT US

Direction: Castle (PE32 2XB) located at SE edge of Castle Acre, 5 miles N of Swaffham. Parking in Pye's Lane. Bailey Gate (PE32 2AG) located in the centre of Castle Acre at the top of Bailey St

Bus: Peelings service 1 (Tue & Fri)

ACQ.1970 Castle   ACQ.1938 Bailey Gate

🎫 P ⚠ (Castle only)

MAP PAGE 341 (2G)
OS MAP 132, 236/238
BAILEY GATE: TF819152
CASTLE: TF819152

CASTLE ACRE PRIORY

—————— NORFOLK PE32 2XD ——————

A family trail and fresh displays offer plenty for you to enjoy at the priory.

Among the best preserved monastic sites in England, the immense size and variety of Castle Acre Priory can't fail to impress. Founded in about 1090 by William de Warenne II, it reflected his family's devotion to the famous French monastery of Cluny. You can see Cluny-style architectural decoration displayed in the beautiful west front of the great 12th-century priory church. Explore beyond and discover the impressive remains of the cloister and monks' living quarters, including a gigantic, two-storey, 24-seater toilet block.

The west range is virtually complete and fully roofed. Its flint-chequered porch and oriel-windowed prior's lodging make a striking group with the church's west front. A mansion in itself, the lodging includes a chamber sumptuously revamped in early Tudor times, with a ceiling painted with Tudor roses. The adjacent prior's chapel displays intriguing traces of medieval wall-paintings.

Be sure to leave time to explore the display of archaeological site-finds and take an audio tour featuring a 15th-century chant from a Castle Acre song book.

OPENING TIMES

1 Apr-30 Sep, daily	10am-6pm
1 Oct-3 Nov, daily	10am-5pm
4 Nov-31 Mar, Sat-Sun	10am-4pm
24-26 Dec & 1 Jan	Closed

Last entry 30 mins before closing

VISIT US

Direction: ¼ mile W of village of Castle Acre, 5 miles N of Swaffham

Bus: Peelings service 1 (Tue & Fri)

Tel: 01760 755394

NON-MEMBERS

Adult £8.60 | Concession £7.70
Child £5.20 | Family £22.40

ACQ.1929

Disabled access (ground floor and grounds only). Virtual audio tour for those unable to climb the spiral staircase.

Toilets (a short walk. Not accessible for wheelchairs; 50 metres from entrance, with single step for access).

MAP PAGE 341 (2G)
OS MAP 132, 236/238: TF814148

COW TOWER, NORWICH

NORFOLK – NR1 4AA

Among the earliest purpose-built English artillery blockhouses, this brick tower of c. 1398-9 commands a strategic point in Norwich's defences.

External viewing only.

Managed by Norwich City Council.

OPENING TIMES

Exterior only: Any reasonable daylight hours

VISIT US

Direction: In Norwich, near cathedral (approx. 1 mile walk)

Train: Norwich ½ mile

Bus: From surrounding areas

Tel: 01603 706229

ACQ.1950 🐾

MAP PAGE 341 (2J)
OS MAP 134, OL40/237: TG240092

CREAKE ABBEY

NORFOLK – NR21 9LF

CREAKE ABBEY

Set in tranquil countryside, the flint-walled ruins of this Augustinian abbey church tell a sad story of monastic disaster. After a devastating 15th-century fire, it was drastically reduced in size, with arches and windows blocked. Then plague struck, the last abbot died alone, and in 1506 the abbey closed.

Managed by Mr and Mrs A C Scott.

www.creakeabbey.co.uk

OPENING TIMES

Any reasonable daylight hours

VISIT US

Direction: N of North Creake off B1355

Bus: Sanders service 27

ACQ.1950 🐾

MAP PAGE 341 (1G)
OS MAP 132, 251: TF856395

NORTH ELMHAM CHAPEL

NORFOLK – NR20 5JU

A small Norman chapel, probably on the site of the Saxon cathedral of East Anglia. Later converted into a 14th-century fortified mansion by Henry Despenser, warrior-Bishop of Norwich.

Managed by North Elmham Parish Council.

OPENING TIMES

Any reasonable daylight hours

NORTH ELMHAM CHAPEL

VISIT US

Direction: Located 6 miles N of East Dereham on B1110

Train: Wymondham 17 miles

Bus: Konectbus service 18 & 21

ACQ.1948 🐾 ⚠

MAP PAGE 341 (2H)
OS MAP 132, 238: TF988216

ST OLAVE'S PRIORY

NORFOLK – NR31 9HE

The wonderfully complete, 14th-century, brick-vaulted refectory undercroft – later a cottage occupied until 1902 – of a small Augustinian priory.

OPENING TIMES

Any reasonable daylight hours

VISIT US

Direction: Located 5½ miles SW of the town of Great Yarmouth on A143

Train: Haddiscoe 1¼ miles

Bus: Borderbus service 580

ACQ.1921 🐾

Disabled access (exterior only).

Dogs allowed on leads in the grounds only.

MAP PAGE 341 (3J)
OS MAP 134, OL40: TM459996

GREAT YARMOUTH ROW HOUSES
AND GREYFRIARS' CLOISTERS

NORFOLK NR30 2RG

These unique and vividly presented houses are rare survivors of Yarmouth's once-crowded 'Rows', narrow alleyways linking the town's main thoroughfares.

Most 'Row houses' were destroyed by Second World War bombing or post-war clearances. These surviving examples are now presented at various stages in their history, leading you into centuries of fishing-port life. There are toys in the children's upstairs bedrooms.

CENTURIES OF FISHING-PORT LIFE

Both Row 111 House and the Old Merchant's House were built in the early 17th century as wealthy merchants' residences, but later sub-divided into tenements. You'll find the Old Merchant's House, which has spectacular Jacobean plaster ceilings, appearing as it was in the 1850s, when fish merchant Simon Fleet occupied half the property, and in the 1890s when the other half housed Martha King's family – represented here by models. Adjacent Row 111 House is shown as in 1942 (just before it suffered a direct hit by an incendiary bomb), with figures of the family which then occupied it.

Nearby stands Greyfriars' Cloisters, the remains of a medieval friary later converted into a number of Row dwellings. You can still see traces of their interior features on the walls of the cloister and church, which also display early 14th-century wall-paintings. Access to Greyfriars' Cloisters is by guided tour only.

OPENING TIMES

1 Apr-27 Sep, Mon-Fri	11am-4pm
28 Sep-31 Mar	Closed
Last entry 30 mins before closing	

Access to Greyfriars' Cloisters is by guided tour only (no booking necessary) on Mondays & Wednesdays at 11.30am, 12.45pm and 2pm, leaving from Great Yarmouth Row Houses, Row 111 House. Private tours can be booked in advance for groups of 11 or more. For more information contact Great Yarmouth Row Houses on 01493 857900

VISIT US

Direction: Great Yarmouth, follow signs for Historic Quay. The houses are directly behind the Norfolk Nelson Museum on the Historic South Quay

Train: Great Yarmouth ½ mile

Bus: Bus services to Great Yarmouth are operated by Anglian (of Beccles), Ambassador Travel and First in Suffolk & Norfolk and Sanders of Holt

Tel: 01493 857900

NON-MEMBERS

Adult £6.30 | Concession £5.70
Child £3.80 | Family £16.40

Guided tours of Greyfriars' Cloisters are included in the Row Houses admission price

ACQ.1950 ♨ ⌂ ▼ ✉ ✗ ⌂ ⚠ OVP

MAP PAGE 341 (2J)
OS MAP 134, OL40
HOUSES: TG525072 CLOISTERS: TG524073

GRIME'S GRAVES
PREHISTORIC FLINT MINE

—— NORFOLK IP26 5DE ——

Grime's Graves is the only Neolithic flint mine in Britain open to visitors.

A lunar landscape of over 400 shafts, quarries and spoil dumps, they were first named Grim's Graves by the Anglo-Saxons – meaning the pagan god Grim's quarries, or 'the Devil's holes'. Not until one was excavated in 1868-70 were they identified as flint mines dug over 5,000 years ago, during the later Neolithic and early Bronze Ages.

Prehistoric miners sought the fine quality, jet-black flint floorstone, which occurs some 9 to 12 metres (approximately 33 feet) below surface level. Digging with red-deer antler picks, they sank shafts and dug radiating galleries following the seams of flint. Today, you can have the unforgettable experience of descending 9 metres (30 feet) by ladder into one excavated shaft.

Grime's Graves flint was prized for its distinctive colour and easily 'knapped' qualities. Rough-outs of axes and other tools were made here, but then traded on and finished elsewhere. Set amid the unique Breckland heath landscape, Grime's Graves is also a Site of Special Scientific Interest, the habitat of a variety of rare and distinctive plants and animals.

DON'T MISS OUR FLINT FESTIVAL IN JULY, A HANDS-ON CELEBRATION OF THINGS FLINTY FOR ALL THE FAMILY. SEE OUR WEBSITE FOR DETAILS.

Our family explorer kit helps interpret clues about this fascinating site. Discover more about Neolithic mining in the introductory exhibition, including a virtual tour of the mines and landscape and touchable reproduction Neolithic tools.

OPENING TIMES

1 Apr-29 Sep, daily	10am-6pm
30 Sep-3 Nov, Wed-Sun	10am-5pm
4 Nov-31 Mar	Closed

Last entry 30 mins before closing

VISIT US

Direction: Located 7 miles NW of Thetford off A134

Train: Brandon 3½ miles

Tel: 01842 810656

NON-MEMBERS

Adult **£5.40** | Concession **£4.90**
Child **£3.20** | Family **£14.00**

No entry to the excavated mine shafts for under-10s

[ACQ.1931] [♿] [⚑] [E] [♨] [▢] [↟] [⚑] [P] [📷] [⚠] [OVP]

Disabled access (exhibition area only; access track rough).

Dogs on leads (restricted areas).

Visitors intending to descend the shaft should wear flat shoes.

MAP PAGE 341 (3G)
OS MAP 144, 229: TL817899

THETFORD, CHURCH OF THE HOLY SEPULCHRE

NORFOLK – IP24 3PW

The only remains in England of a priory church of Canons of the Holy Sepulchre, later used as a barn.

Managed by Thetford Town Council.

OPENING TIMES

All year, daily (or dusk, whichever is earlier)	10am-5pm
25 Dec	Closed

VISIT US

Direction: Located on the W side of Thetford on A134

Train: Thetford ¾ mile

Bus: Coach Services of Thetford 40, 81, 84, 86, 200, 201, 332

Tel: 01842 754038

ACQ.1977

MAP PAGE 341 (3G)
OS MAP 144, 229: TL865831

THETFORD PRIORY

NORFOLK – IP24 1AD

Extensive remains of one of the most important East Anglian monasteries, the Cluniac Priory of Our Lady of Thetford. Founded in the early 12th century, it owed much of its prosperity to a miraculous appearance of the Virgin Mary. Her statue here was discovered to conceal relics

of saints and became a magnet for pilgrims. Survivals include church and cloister walls, the impressive shell of the priors' lodging and an almost complete 14th-century gatehouse. Burial place of the earls and dukes of Norfolk for 400 years, it enjoyed their powerful protection. It was almost the last English monastery to be suppressed, in 1540.

Managed by Thetford Town Council.

OPENING TIMES

1 Apr-30 Sep, daily	8am-6pm
1 Oct-31 Mar, daily	8am-4pm
25 Dec	Closed

VISIT US

Direction: Near Thetford station

Train: Thetford ¾ mile

Bus: Coach Services of Thetford 40, 81, 84, 86, 200, 201, 332

Tel: 01842 754038

ACQ.1932

MAP PAGE 341 (3G)
OS MAP 144, 229: TL865831

THETFORD WARREN LODGE

NORFOLK

Probably built c. 1400 by the Prior of Thetford as a refuge from armed poachers. Much later used by local 'warreners', who harvested rabbits here.

THETFORD WARREN LODGE

OPENING TIMES

Exterior only: Any reasonable daylight hours

VISIT US

Direction: Located 2 miles W of Thetford off B1107

Train: Thetford 2½ miles

Bus: Coach Services of Thetford 40, 86, 200

ACQ.1948

MAP PAGE 341 (3G)
OS MAP 144, 229: TL839984

WEETING CASTLE

NORFOLK – IP27 0RQ

The ruins of a substantial early medieval moated manor house, built in local flint.

OPENING TIMES

Any reasonable daylight hours. Access via steps

VISIT US

Direction: Located 2 miles N of Brandon off B1106

Train: Brandon 1½ miles

Bus: Coach Services of Thetford 40

ACQ.1926

MAP PAGE 341 (3G)
OS MAP 144, 229: TL778891

BURY ST EDMUNDS ABBEY

SUFFOLK – IP33 IUZ

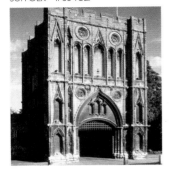

Extensive remains of the wealthiest and most powerful English Benedictine monastery, shrine of St Edmund. They include the Great Gate and Norman Tower and ruins of the immense church.

Managed by St Edmundsbury Borough Council.

OPENING TIMES

Apr-Oct, Mon-Sat Sun	7.30am-8pm 9am-8pm
Nov-Feb, Mon-Sat Sun	7.30am-4.30pm 9am-4.30pm
Mar, Mon-Sat Sun	7.30am-6pm 9am-4.30pm

VISIT US

Direction: E end of town centre

Train: Bury St Edmunds 1 mile

Bus: Services to the town are operated by H.C. Chambers, Coach Services of Thetford, Galloway European, High Suffolk Community Transport, Mulley's Motorways, Simonds of Diss, Stagecoach Cambridgeshire, Stephensons of Essex and Suffolk Norse

Tel: 01284 764667

ACQ.1955 🦮 🚶 🚻

MAP PAGE 341 (4G)
OS MAP 155, 211: TL857642

LEISTON ABBEY

SUFFOLK – IP16 4TD

Among Suffolk's most impressive monastic ruins, the mainly 14th-century remains of an abbey of Premonstratensian canons.

Managed by Pro Corda Trust.

OPENING TIMES

Any reasonable daylight hours

VISIT US

Direction: N of Leiston off B1069

Train: Saxmundham 5 miles

Bus: First services 64 & 65; Borderbus service 521 serve Leiston (1½ miles walk)

Tel: 01728 831354

ACQ.1964 🦮 🐾 P ⚠

MAP PAGE 341 (4J)
OS MAP 156, 212: TM445642

LINDSEY ST JAMES'S CHAPEL

SUFFOLK – IP7 6QA

A pretty, thatched, 13th-century chapel with lancet windows.

OPENING TIMES

All year, daily   10am-4pm

VISIT US

Direction: Located on an unclassified road ½ mile E of Rose Green and 8 miles E of Sudbury

Train: Sudbury 8 miles

Bus: Hadleigh Community Transport 'Suffolk Links Cosford' demand responsive bus service. Telephone 01473 826242 to book

ACQ.1930 🦮 🐾

Disabled access (single step).

MAP PAGE 341 (4H)
OS MAP 155, 196: TL9784444

MOULTON PACKHORSE BRIDGE

SUFFOLK – CB8 8SR

A pretty, four-arched, late medieval bridge spanning the River Kennet on the old route from Cambridge to Bury St Edmunds.

OPENING TIMES

Any reasonable daylight hours

VISIT US

Direction: In Moulton off B1085, 4 miles E of Newmarket

Train: Kennett 2 miles

Bus: Stephensons 16, 16A; Suffolk Norse service 310, 311A; Mulleys service 312

ACQ.1977 🦮 🐾 P

MAP PAGE 341 (4G)
OS MAP 154, 210/226: TL698645

STAY WITH US

Each one of our luxurious self-catering holiday cottages is in a unique historic setting.

See p.332 for details.

LANDGUARD FORT

SUFFOLK IP11 3TW

Landguard Fort defends the approach to Harwich Harbour, an important haven for shipping. The Fort stands near a nature reserve and a busy container port.

An earlier fort here was the site of the last opposed seaborne invasion of England, when the Royal Marines (in their first land battle) repulsed a Dutch attack in 1667. The current polygonal fort was begun in the 18th century and updated in Victorian times, with emplacements for heavy guns and a fortified barrack block. Outside batteries were added in 1901, and in 1951 part of the fort became a 'Cold War' control room.

Guided tours and audio tours of the fort are supplemented by an audio-visual presentation and guided tours of the outside batteries.

Managed by Landguard Fort Trust. www.landguard.com

The Felixstowe Museum – an award-winning visitor atttraction – is next to the fort in a building originally used for harbour defence and submarine mining. (For museum opening times and prices see www.felixstowemuseum.org or call 01394 674355.)

OPENING TIMES

1 Apr–27 Oct, daily	10am–5pm
28 Oct–31 Mar	Closed

Last entry one hour before closing. Pre-booked group and education visits are welcome

VISIT US

Direction: 1 mile S of Felixstowe town centre – follow signs to Landguard Point

Train: Felixstowe 2½ miles

Bus: First in Suffolk services 77 & 77A

Bicycle: The Fort lies on National Cycle Route 51 between Ipswich and Harwich

Tel: 01394 675900

NON-MEMBERS

Adult £5.50 | Concession £4.50 | Child £2.50

Free entry for children under 5 and wheelchair users

There may be a premium payable by all visitors, including members, on event days – please check www.landguard.com for details

ACQ 1975 🎧 🐾 🛡 📖 ✉ 🅿 📷 ⚠

MAP PAGE 341 (5J)
OS MAP 169, 197: TM284319

FRAMLINGHAM CASTLE

One of medieval England's finest baronial fortresses, impressive
Framlingham Castle offers you re-invigorated interpretation,
plenty of hands-on children's activities and a spacious café
in a historic setting.

SUFFOLK IP13 9BP

Framlingham Castle's spectacular walls are more than 10 metres (32 feet) high and 2 metres (6.5 feet) thick, and studded with 13 strong towers. Raised in the 1190s, they were among the first of their kind ever built in England. They proclaim the power and status of the earls and dukes of Norfolk, who owned the fortress for over four centuries.

You can follow the wall-top walk round them to view eight centuries of history from above, guided by a lively audio tour and panels which tell you about the castle's surroundings – the pretty market town, the parkland, the castle's outer earthworks and the Mere, the lake which mirrored the fortress walls. Don't forget to look up at the tall Tudor chimneys, which crown every tower, each one decorated in a different pattern. There's a lift for easier access to our exhibition.

The exhibition, 'Power and Poverty', traces how Framlingham housed both the very richest and the very poorest over the centuries. You'll discover how successive noble dynasties – the defiant Bigods, the mighty Mowbrays and the scheming Howards of Tudor times – wielded influence in East Anglia which rivalled kingly power. Mary Tudor famously mustered her supporters here in 1553 before being crowned queen. Later, in complete contrast, the castle walls sheltered a workhouse for the local poor, which operated until 1839.

The presentation includes Tudor and workhouse display costumes and interactive games, and you can try on hats from a Norman helmet to a pauper's cap. The 'Who Ate What' game helps you create plates of imitation foods and match them to the people – aristocrats, the very poor or 'everyone else' – who would have eaten them.

If this gives you an appetite, our revamped café serves a range of Tudor-inspired dishes, locally-sourced food and Suffolk specialities, in a baronial setting with stone walls, round-arched windows and a huge fireplace.

There's plenty more to see and do at Framlingham. The Lanman Museum within the castle displays an intriguing variety of local artefacts, from kitchenware to a parish coffin. Outside the walls, you can explore the castle's outer defences, including the deep ditch and the grassy outer court between fortress and Mere. Leave time, too, to wander the picture-book market town and admire the impressive tombs of the Howard castle-owners, and that of Henry Fitzroy, Henry VIII's illegitimate son, in the parish church.

OPENING TIMES

1 Apr-30 Sep, daily	10am-6pm
1 Oct-3 Nov, daily	10am-5pm
4 Nov-23 Dec, Sat-Sun	10am-4pm
2 Jan-16 Feb, Sat-Sun	10am-4pm
17-23 Feb, daily	10am-4pm
24 Feb-31 Mar, Sat-Sun	10am-4pm
Christmas Opening 24-25 Dec	Closed
26 Dec-1 Jan, daily	10am-4pm
Last entry 30 mins before closing	

VISIT US

Address: Framlingham Castle, Church Street, Framlingham, Suffolk

Direction: In Framlingham on B1116

Train: Wickham Market 6½ miles; Saxmundham 7 miles

Bus: Galloway European 118, 119; Simonds 482; PF Travel 62

Tel: 01728 724922

Local Tourist Information: Woodbridge: 01394 382240

NON-MEMBERS

Adult £11.00 | Concession £9.90
Child £6.60 | Family £28.60

Disabled access (grounds and ground floor only).

Parking charges apply to non-members.
Parking free for Members.

MAP PAGE 341 (4J)
OS MAP 156, 212: TM287637

ORFORD CASTLE

SUFFOLK IP12 2ND

New features help you discover the unique polygonal tower-keep of Orford Castle, set in a pretty Suffolk coastal town.

Built by Henry II between 1165 and 1173, the castle was intended to curtail the power of turbulent East Anglian barons such as Hugh Bigod of Framlingham Castle. An 18-sided drum with three square turrets and a forebuilding reinforcing its entrance, its keep was built to a revolutionary new design.

Today, both exterior and interior survive almost intact, allowing you to explore the basement, with its vital well, and the lower and upper halls. Around these polygonal rooms, a maze of passages lead you to the chapel, kitchen and other chambers in the turrets. From the roof you can enjoy magnificent views seaward to Orford Ness.

In the upper hall, take in the Orford Museum Trust's exhibition, featuring changing displays of local finds.

NEW FOR 2019

There'll be more for you to enjoy at Orford Castle this year. We will have new multimedia guides, including one for families, and a large model of the castle will show you how it appeared in the 12th century. Fresh displays, reconstructions and hands-on features will guide you round the rooms, and reveal how they might originally have been used.

OPENING TIMES

1 Apr-30 Sep, daily	10am-6pm
1 Oct-3 Nov, daily	10am-5pm
4 Nov-23 Dec, Sat-Sun	10am-4pm
2 Jan-16 Feb, Sat-Sun	10am-4pm
17-23 Feb, daily	10am-4pm
24 Feb-31 Mar, Sat-Sun	10am-4pm
Christmas Opening 24-25 Dec	Closed
26 Dec-1 Jan, daily	10am-4pm
Last entry 30 mins before closing	

VISIT US

Direction: In Orford on B1084, 20 miles NE of Ipswich

Train: Wickham Market 8 miles

Bus: PF Travel service 71

Tel: 01394 450472

Local Tourist Information: Woodbridge: 01394 382240

NON-MEMBERS

Adult **£8.60** | Concession **£7.70**
Child **£5.20** | Family **£22.40**

ACQ.1962 | OVP

Toilets (close-by in Orford town).

Parking charges apply to non-members. Parking free for Members.

MAP PAGE 341 (4J)
OS MAP 169, 212: TM419499

SAXTEAD GREEN POST MILL

SUFFOLK IP13 3QQ

Before the arrival of steam and electricity, mills powered by wind or water played a vital role in English history, grinding corn into flour for daily bread.

This striking four-sailed corn-grinding windmill stands in an idyllic village-green setting, not far from Framlingham Castle. A 'post mill' whose whole body – turned by a secondary windmill or 'fantail' – revolves on its three-storey roundhouse base, it's of a type characteristic of Suffolk since around the 13th century. It originates from about 1796, but has been rebuilt and raised three times: in 1854 it was given a full set of new cast-iron machinery, only the brake wheel being of oak. Though commercial milling ceased when the last miller died in 1947, the mill is still in full working order. Climb the stairs to the various floors, which are full of fascinating mill machinery.

OPENING TIMES

The Mill is currently undergoing a major conservation project and will remain closed until late in the 2019/20 season. Please check the website for updated information

VISIT US

Direction: 2½ miles NW of Framlingham on A1120

Train: Wickham Market 9 miles

Bus: Galloway European 119; High Suffolk Community Transport (Tue)

Tel: 01728 685789

ACQ.1951 〔M〕〔✕〕〔◻〕〔⚠〕〔OVP〕

MAP PAGE 341 (4J)
OS MAP 156, 212: TM253644

Bolsover Castle

DRA

MATIC

West Yorkshire

North Lincolnshire

North East Lincolnshire

South Yorkshire

Glossop

.7

23　|4
Gainsborough

Market Rasen

Worksop

Lincolnshire

Buxton
Bakewell
.1　Chesterfield
.5　.8　3
.2
.6　4　.9
Mansfield
.24

|5
Lincoln

.13　Skegness

.17

.16

Nottinghamshire

Derbyshire

Nottingham

Derby

Grantham

Boston

Staffordshire

Spalding

West Midlands

.10　Loughborough

Leicestershire

12　||
Leicester

Oakham

Rutland

.25
.21　.18
Corby
22　20
Kettering

Norfolk

Cambridgeshire

Market Harborough

Northamptonshire

19

Daventry
Northampton

Bedfordshire

Essex

Warwickshire

Brackley

Buckinghamshire

Gloucestershire

TELLING TALES: THE MYTHS, LEGENDS AND FOLKLORE OF ENGLAND

HOB HURST'S HOUSE

Hob Hurst's House is one of our most remote sites – it's high up on hard-to-reach Peak District moorland. The 'house' is an unusually shaped prehistoric burial mound, possibly dating from the Bronze or Iron Age. But legend says it's also the home of a 'hob' or 'hobthrush'. These were goblins, and they often figure in the folklore of northern England, where several natural caves are also called 'hob holes'. Hobs could be helpful, invisibly doing jobs around houses and farms in the dead of night, often in return for just a bowl of cream. But they were very easily offended, and if a farmer got on the wrong side of a hob his cows would fall sick, their milk would go sour, and everything on the farm would go wrong.

PEAK DISTRICT OLD STONES WAY

32 miles | 3 days | Carl Wark to Arbor Low

High on the Pennine moorlands south west of Sheffield, the rock fortress of Carl Wark stands proud, overlooking the destination of Minninglow hill, 25 miles south, resting place of prehistoric chieftains in their chambered cairns. This route takes in the old stones of the Nine Ladies and Stanton Moor's sacred groves, Robin Hood's Stride and Arbor Low, the Neolithic 'clock' whose massive recumbent stones are aligned to midwinter sunrise and midsummer sunset.

View more details and a downloadable version of this route at www.english-heritage.org.uk/pilgrimage

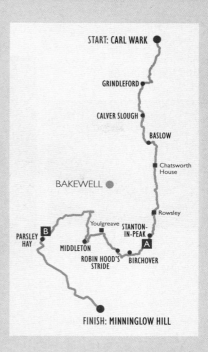

Nine Ladies Stone Circle

Arbor Low Stone Circle and Gib Hill Barrow

Discover English Heritage sites along the pilgrimage route

A Nine Ladies Stone Circle *(p.174)*

B Arbor Low Stone Circle and Gib Hill Barrow *(p.174)*

In partnership with

the British Pilgrimage Trust

ARBOR LOW STONE CIRCLE AND GIB HILL BARROW
DERBYSHIRE – DE45 IJS

An important Neolithic henge atmospherically set amid moorland. Within an earthen bank, some 50 recumbent slabs surround a central stone 'cove'. Gib Hill is a burial mound.

Please note: Access charge of £1 per person to use path across private land to the stone circle.

Managed by Peak District National Park Authority.

OPENING TIMES
Any reasonable daylight hours

Access through private land, for which the landowner levies a charge of £1 per person

VISIT US
Direction: ½ mile E of A515, 2 miles S of Monyash

Train: Buxton 10 miles

Bus: One weekday journey on High Peak bus 441 and alternate Mondays Warringtons service 449 serve Parsley Hay, which is within a 1 mile walk to the two locations. Otherwise closest bus service is Hulley's 171 and one journey on 172 to Middleton-by-Youlgreave (2 mile walk) every 2 hours

Tel: 01629 816200

ACQ.1884 🎫 **P** ⚠

Beware – cattle may be grazing.

MAP PAGE 342 (2E)
OS MAP 119, OL24: SK160636

BOLSOVER CUNDY HOUSE
DERBYSHIRE – S44 6BQ

This charming cottage-like 17th-century conduit house, with vaulted stone-slab roof, once supplied water to Bolsover Castle.

Managed by Bolsover Civic Society.

OPENING TIMES
Exterior only: Any reasonable daylight hours

VISIT US
Direction: Off M1 at junction 29A, follow signs for Bolsover Castle. Between junctions of Craggs Rd and Houfton Rd with Bolsover Hill, Bolsover, 6 miles E of Chesterfield on A362

Train: Chesterfield 6 miles or Langwith – Whaley Thorns 4½ miles

Bus: Stagecoach service 82 & TM Travel Bolsover town services B2 & B3 actually pass the property. Stagecoach services 53, 53A and TM Travel 81 serve Hilltop Avenue, a short walk from the Cundy House

Tel: 01246 822844 (Bolsover Castle)

ACQ.1945 🎫

MAP PAGE 343 (2F)
OS MAP 120, 269: SK471709

HOB HURST'S HOUSE
DERBYSHIRE – DE4 2NT

A square prehistoric burial mound with earthwork ditch and bank, amid remote moorland. Named after a local goblin.

Managed by Peak District National Park Authority.

OPENING TIMES
Any reasonable daylight hours

Access is across moorland with gates and stiles

VISIT US
Direction: On open moorland from unclassified road off B5057, 9 miles W of Chesterfield

Train: Chesterfield 9 miles

Bus: Little's Travel (Weekdays); TM Travel (Sun) service 217 to Beeley then walk 2 mile

Tel: 01629 816200

ACQ.1884 🎫 ⚠

MAP PAGE 342 (2E)
OS MAP 119, OL24: SK287692

NINE LADIES STONE CIRCLE
DERBYSHIRE – DE4 2LS

A small Bronze Age stone circle, traditionally believed to represent nine ladies turned to stone.

Managed by Peak District National Park Authority.

OPENING TIMES
Any reasonable daylight hours

Access is through fields and woodland with gates and stiles

VISIT US
Direction: From an unclassified road off A6, 5 miles SE of Bakewell

Train: Matlock 4½ miles

Bus: Hulleys service 172 to Stanton in Peak (within 1 mile)

Tel: 01629 816200

ACQ.1883 🎫 ⚠

MAP PAGE 342 (2E)
OS MAP 119, OL24: SK249635

HARDWICK OLD HALL
DERBYSHIRE – S44 5QJ

A rare opportunity to explore the 'bare bones' of a towering Elizabethan mansion, built by the formidable Bess of Hardwick. Daughter of an impoverished local squire, Bess rose via four increasingly advantageous marriages to become Countess of Shrewsbury, and perhaps the richest woman in England. Built on the site of her birthplace, the Old Hall proclaimed her success. Before it was finished, she began the even grander Hardwick Hall nearby.

Though the Old Hall is now roofless, you can still ascend through four storeys to admire lavishly decorated plasterwork and overmantels in the former state rooms, and explore the basement kitchen and service rooms. There are fine views of Hardwick Hall and the surrounding countryside, an audio tour and a revealing ground floor exhibition.

Managed by English Heritage and owned by the National Trust.

OPENING TIMES
Due to essential conservation works, entry to the site is limited. Please check the website before planning your visit

VISIT US
Direction: 8 miles SE of Chesterfield, off A6175 (J29 of M1)

Train: Chesterfield 8 miles

Bus: Trent Barton/Stagecoach 'Pronto' service or G&J Holmes 'Hallmark' service 49 (alight Glapwell 'Young Vanish', then 2 mile walk) or Stagecoach/TM Travel services 56/X56 to Hardstoft and 2 mile walk

Tel: 01246 850431

NON-MEMBERS
Adult **£7.70** | Concession **£7.00**
Child **£4.70** | Family **£20.10**

ACQ.1959 ⬡ 🍴 E 🏛 🚶 👤 P 📷 ⚠ OVP

MAP PAGE 343 (2F)
OS MAP 120, 269: SK462637

STAY WITH US
Holiday cottage available to let – see p.332.

SUTTON SCARSDALE HALL
DERBYSHIRE – S44 5UR

The spectacular hilltop shell of Sutton Scarsdale Hall tells the story of the rise and fall of a great mansion. It was built in 1724-9 for the fourth Earl of Scarsdale, employing the very finest craftsmen; but its immense cost almost bankrupted his heirs. Eventually, in 1919, its lavish interiors were stripped out and sold; several rooms still survive in American museums. Having narrowly escaped demolition, the impressive roofless shell is still being conserved. The 'virtual' backdrop to the 2016 film *Batman vs Superman*.

OPENING TIMES
Exterior only:	
Summer, daily	10am-6pm
Winter, daily	10am-4pm
24-26 Dec & 1 Jan	Closed

Due to a major conservation project, the interior will be inaccessible for most of the year. Please check the website for further details

VISIT US
Direction: Between Chesterfield and Bolsover, 1½ miles S of Arkwright Town

Train: Chesterfield 5 miles

Bus: G&J Holmes 'Hallmark' service 48

Tel: 01604 735464

ACQ.1971 ♿ P 🏠 ⚠

MAP PAGE 343 (2F)
OS MAP 120, 269: SK442689

BOLSOVER CASTLE

Exquisitely restored to recreate its past glories, this unique Stuart showpiece was the hilltop pleasure-palace of a horse-mad Cavalier playboy.

DERBYSHIRE S44 6PR

Our imaginative yet carefully researched re-presentation brings to life the golden days of the fairy-tale Stuart mansion and its larger-than-life creator, William Cavendish. Visit today and you'll find there's plenty to see and do.

Bolsover Castle was always something special. Neither a fortress nor a conventional country house, it was designed purely to impress, entertain and intrigue visitors, particularly King Charles I and his court in 1634. Replacing a now-vanished medieval hilltop fortress, its site was carefully chosen both to dominate the landscape for many miles around and to astonish visitors with unrivalled panoramas.

Bolsover is again dazzling visitors with its entertainments. Explore the playfully pinnacled and battlemented 'Little Castle', the core of the mansion and focus of its magic. Begun by Sir Charles Cavendish in 1612, this Stuart millionaire's fantasy was completed, decorated and furnished regardless of expense by his son William — playboy, poet, courtier and later Royalist general and Duke of Newcastle. There's a wealth of details to enjoy; its original exquisitely carved fireplaces, painted panelling and above all its array of dramatic murals — a miraculous survival. You can absorb the atmosphere of its Star Chamber and Marble Closet with their striking replica tapestries, satin wall-hangings and red velvet upholstery. Interactive 'cabinets of curiosity' reveal how the rooms, including the extraordinary 'Elysium Closet' with its painted ceiling and frieze of naked Classical gods, were used to intrigue and impress noble visitors. It's well worth wandering the whole building, from its top-floor bedchambers to its cavernous basement kitchen complex.

EXPLORE THE PLAYFULLY PINNACLED AND BATTLEMENTED 'LITTLE CASTLE'

Outside you can stroll the wall walk round the Venus Garden, where Stuart courtiers promenaded to see and be seen. Look into the attentively recreated garden, with its naked-Venus Fountain and borders planted with flowers fashionable in Bolsover's heyday. Enjoy truly astonishing vistas over the surrounding countryside beyond.

The easy-to-use handheld multimedia guide helps you experience Bolsover Castle at whatever level of detail you choose.

Narrated by actor Rupert Penry-Jones, the touchscreen guide lets you select playlets or videos, reconstructions of room interiors or interviews with experts explaining how this captivating pleasure-house operated.

There's plenty more to discover at Bolsover. William Cavendish's passion for training horses is reflected in the mighty indoor Riding House and in his great Stables, where you'll find a stylish interactive exhibition (including a replica 17th-century saddle for children to try). Children have their own entertainment too. A custom-built play area, inspired by the castle's battlements and towers, is ideally sited next to the tearoom's outdoor seating. In the Little Castle both children and adults can dress up in theatrical costumes and take the stage, echoing 'Love's Welcome at Bolsover', the masque performed here for Charles I at the zenith of the castle's now-revived glory.

Stop off at the tearoom, with indoor and outdoor seating and fantastic views towards the Riding House, for a refreshing break while exploring the site.

Every weekend from April to September (excluding some event weekends, see website for details and costs) you can watch riders in 17th-century attire give three spectacular performances of 'classical dressage', which takes horse and rider years to learn. Booking is highly recommended (call customer services on 0370 333 1181).

OPENING TIMES

1 Apr-30 Sep, daily	10am-6pm
1 Oct-3 Nov, daily	10am-5pm
4 Nov-23 Dec, Sat-Sun	10am-4pm
2 Jan-16 Feb, Sat-Sun	10am-4pm
17-23 Feb, daily	10am-4pm
24 Feb-31 Mar, Sat-Sun	10am-4pm
Christmas Opening 24-25 Dec	Closed
26 Dec-1 Jan, daily	10am-4pm
Last entry 30 mins before closing	

VISIT US

Address: Bolsover Castle, Castle Street, Bolsover, Derbyshire S44 6PR

Direction: In Bolsover, 6 miles E of Chesterfield on A632. Off M1 at junction 29A (signposted)

Train: Chesterfield 6 miles

Bus: G&J Holmes service 49; TM Travel 81, B2 & B3; Stagecoach services 53, 53A, 82 & 83 all pass close to the castle entrance

Tel: 01246 822844

Local Tourist Information:
Chesterfield: 01246 345777

NON-MEMBERS

Adult £13.00 | Concession £11.70
Child £7.90 | Family £33.90

The coach drop-off point is in the council car park opposite.

There is good access to the grounds, but please note that the Little Castle is not accessible to wheelchairs.

MAP PAGE 343 (2F)
OS MAP 120, 269: SK470707

PEVERIL CASTLE DERBYSHIRE – S33 8WQ

WINGFIELD MANOR
DERBYSHIRE – DE55 7NH

Towering high above the pretty Peak District market town of Castleton, Peveril is among the most spectacularly sited castles in England.

Climbing the steep path from the visitor centre (there are benches along the way) you might be surprised that this is the easiest access to the castle. Reaching the top, you'll discover that it's defended on the other sides by sheer drops into Cave Dale and Peak Cavern Gorge. These natural defences encouraged William the Conqueror's trusted knight William Peverell to raise one of the first stone castles in England here, very soon after 1066. Look out for the characteristic early Norman zig-zag herringbone masonry in the curtain walls.

A century later, in the 1170s, the great royal fortress-builder Henry II further strengthened the castle, adding the hallmark keep on the hill summit. Still rising almost to its original height, it's entered for security at first floor level; its main chamber is equipped with a garderobe toilet draining into the chasm below; a real 'loo with a view'.

Breathtaking views over the Peak District's hills and valleys are the great reward for venturing up to this wonderfully positioned castle. In the visitor centre at the foot of the hill you'll find a model of the original fortress, and displays revealing how Peveril was for centuries the hub of the Forest of the Peak, a jealously-guarded royal hunting preserve.

OPENING TIMES

1 Apr-30 Sep, daily	10am-6pm
1 Oct-3 Nov, daily	10am-5pm
4 Nov-16 Feb, Sat-Sun	10am-4pm
17-23 Feb, daily	10am-4pm
24 Feb-31 Mar, Sat-Sun	10am-4pm
24-26 Dec & 1 Jan	Closed
Last entry 30 mins before closing	

VISIT US

Direction: Via the marketplace in Castleton; 15 miles W of Sheffield on A6187

Train: Hope 2½ miles

Bus: Hulley's 68, 173, 174, 273 (Sun), 274, 276; First/Hulleys 271, 272; TM Travel 273/274 (Sun) to Castleton then short walk

Tel: 01433 620613

Local Tourist Information: 01433 620679

NON-MEMBERS

Adult **£6.90** | Concession **£6.20**
Child **£4.10** | Family **£17.90**

ACQ 1932 🐕 🦅 🛝 🖥 🧗 🚹 📷

⚠️ OVP

Wheelchair access to visitor centre only.

Parking (in town).

Warning: moderately challenging 10-15 mins uphill walk to castle from visitor centre.

MAP PAGE 342 (2E)
OS MAP 110, OL1: SK149826

The vast ruins of a palatial medieval manor house, built in the 1440s for Ralph, Lord Cromwell, Treasurer of England.

Please note: Wingfield Manor is part of a working farm. Please respect the owner's privacy at all times. No public access except by pre-booked guided tours.

OPENING TIMES

Entry by pre-booked guided tours only, on the first Sat of the month from Apr-Sep. To book please call 0370 333 1181

Call for full details of opening times and other site facilities

VISIT US

Direction: 17 miles N of Derby; 11 miles S of Chesterfield on B5035; ½ mile S of South Wingfield. From M1 junction 28, W on A38, A615 (Matlock Road) at Alfreton, 1½ miles and turn onto B5035

Train: Alfreton 4 miles

Bus: Littles 140 (TM Travel Sun) 142 & 150. Alight South Wingfield and then ½ mile walk

Tel: 0370 333 1181 to book (Customer Services)

NON-MEMBERS

Adult **£8.00** | Concession **£7.20**
Child **£4.80** | Family **£20.80**

ACQ 1960 🦅 ⚠️

Parking (none on site or in gateway).

MAP PAGE 343 (3F)
OS MAP 119, 269: SK374548

ASHBY DE LA ZOUCH CASTLE

LEICESTERSHIRE LE65 1BR

Ashby de la Zouch Castle forms the backdrop to the famous jousting scenes in Sir Walter Scott's classic novel, *Ivanhoe*.

The castle began as a manor house in the 12th century, and achieved castle status in the 15th century. Between 1474 and his execution by Richard III in 1483, Edward IV's friend Lord Hastings added the chapel and the impressive keep-like Hastings Tower – a castle within a castle. For fine views, climb 24 metres (78 feet) to the top of the tower.

Later, the castle hosted many royal visitors, including Henry VII, Mary Queen of Scots, James I and Charles I. A Royalist stronghold during the Civil War, Ashby finally fell to Parliament in 1646, and was then made unusable. You can still explore an underground passage from the kitchen to the tower, probably created during the Civil War.

OPENING TIMES

1 Apr-30 Sep, Wed-Sun & Bank Hols	10am-6pm
1 Oct-3 Nov, Wed-Sun	10am-5pm
4 Nov-16 Feb, Sat-Sun	10am-4pm
17-23 Feb, Wed-Sun	10am-4pm
24 Feb-31 Mar, Sat-Sun	10am-4pm
24-26 Dec & 1 Jan	Closed

Last entry 30 mins before closing

VISIT US

Direction: In Ashby de la Zouch, 12 miles S of Derby on A511. Restricted parking on site, please park in town car park

Train: Burton on Trent 9 miles

Bus: Macpherson Coaches 1, 2 & 3; Arriva 29, 29A; Paul S. Winson Travel 129; Midland Classic 9, 19

Tel: 01530 413343

Local Tourist Information: 01530 411767

NON-MEMBERS

Adult **£6.90** | Concession **£6.20**
Child **£4.10** | Family **£17.90**

ACQ.1932

Disabled access (grounds only).

Parking (restricted on site, please park in town car park – charge applies).

MAP PAGE 343 (4F)
OS MAP 128, 245: SK361166

JEWRY WALL

LEICESTERSHIRE – LEI 4LB

Among the most massive survivals of Roman masonry in Britain, this wall of a town-centre Roman bath-house complex still stands over 9 metres (30 feet) high. The baths were completed by about AD 160.

Managed by Leicester City Council.

OPENING TIMES

Access to the site is currently closed during refurbishment of the Jewry Wall Museum

VISIT US

Direction: In St Nicholas Street, W of Church of St Nicholas

Train: Leicester ¾ mile

Bus: First 12, 16, 18 & 19; Stagecoach 48; Arriva 50, 51, 52, 104, 153 & 158; Centrebus UHL service 162 and Roberts Coaches 103 & 203. Alight at St Nicholas Circle

Tel: 01604 735464

 ⓘ P

Parking (by museum, within St Nicholas Circle).

MAP PAGE 343 (4F)
OS MAP 140, 233: SK582045

KIRBY MUXLOE CASTLE   LEICESTERSHIRE – LE9 2DH

The picturesque moated remains, including the fine gatehouse and a complete corner tower, of a largely brick-built fortified mansion recently conserved by English Heritage. Begun in 1480 by Lord Hastings, a leading supporter and close friend of Edward IV, the 'castle' was constructed in the most up-to-date style in the fashionable new brick building material, and cosmetically equipped for artillery defence with gunports, some of them 'dummies'. But at a council meeting in 1483 the new king Richard III suddenly denounced his former ally Hastings as a traitor. He had Hastings immediately beheaded and the showpiece mansion was never finished.

OPENING TIMES

1-30 Apr	Closed
1 May-1 Sep, Sat-Sun & Bank Hols	10am-5pm
2 Sep-31 Mar	Closed

Last entry 30 mins before closing

VISIT US

Direction: 4 miles W of Leicester off B5380; close to M1 junction 21A, northbound exit only

Train: Leicester 5 miles

Bus: Arriva 153 to Kirby Muxloe then a ½ mile walk

Tel: 0116 238 6886

NON-MEMBERS

Adult **£5.30** | Concession **£4.80**
Child **£3.20** | Family **£13.80**

ACQ.1912 **ⓘ ⌂ P ⚠ OVP**

MAP PAGE 343 (4F)
OS MAP 140, 233: SK524046

GAINSBOROUGH OLD HALL

LINCOLNSHIRE DN21 2NB

Well worth seeking out, Gainsborough Old Hall is one of the biggest, grandest and best-preserved medieval manor houses in England. Lavishly built in timber-framing and brick, it dates mainly from the later 15th century, with Elizabethan additions.

You'll discover the magnificent great hall with its soaring roof and big bay window, served by a complete set of original rooms for preparing food and drink. The huge medieval kitchen is among the most impressive in the country, with everything you could want for cooking feasts. Like many of the Old Hall's rooms, it's been furnished and equipped as it might have appeared when Richard III visited in 1483.

You'll also find recreated medieval bedchambers and rooms furnished as in the 17th century, when the wealthy Hickman family owned the Old Hall. There's a tower to climb for views, an audio tour, and children's games and dressing-up boxes to help families explore the mansion's amazingly varied history. This included a visit in 1541 by Henry VIII and his ill-fated Queen Catherine Howard – look out for graffiti left by a courtier.

Don't miss a wander round the Old Hall's impressive exterior, enhanced by period-style plantings. With so much to see and do, you'll deserve a break in the open-to-all tearoom, which offers indoor and outdoor seating.

Managed by Lincolnshire County Council.
www.gainsborougholdhall.com

NEW FOR 2019

Discover more about the Old Hall's links with the Mayflower Pilgrims in our new exhibition, opening May 2019.

OPENING TIMES

1 Apr-31 Oct, Mon-Fri	10am-5pm
Sat-Sun	11am-5pm
1 Nov-28 Feb, Mon-Fri	10am-4pm
Sat-Sun	11am-4pm
1-31 Mar, Mon-Fri	10am-5pm
Sat-Sun	11am-5pm
24 Dec-1 Jan	Closed

Last entry 45 mins before closing

The site may close on Fri and Sat between May and Oct for weddings – phone site to check for latest details

VISIT US

Direction: In Parnell Road, Gainsborough, opposite the library

Train: Gainsborough Central ½ mile, Gainsborough Lea Road 1 mile

Bus: Stagecoach operate services to Gainsborough bus station from surrounding areas. It is a short walk from there to the Old Hall

Tel: 01427 677348

NON-MEMBERS

Adult **£9.80** | Concession **£8.50**
Child **£5.35** | Family **£27.00**
Free entry for children under 5

Admission price payable by all visitors, including members, on occasional special event days

10% discount on rates for groups of 15 or more paying a lump sum (includes guided tour)

ACQ.1969

Disabled access (most of ground floor).

No dedicated parking at site. Free parking (max 1 hour) in surrounding streets, and longer-term paid parking at Riverside car park, 100m away.

MAP PAGE 343 (1G)
OS MAP 112/121, 280: SK813900

BOLINGBROKE CASTLE

LINCOLNSHIRE – PE23 4HH

Remains of a once-impressive, multi-towered 13th-century castle, begun in the 1220s by Ranulf, Earl of Chester and Lincoln. Famous as the birthplace in 1367 of Henry of Bolingbroke, the future King Henry IV. A Civil War Royalist base, it was besieged and taken in 1643 by Oliver Cromwell, and reduced to ruin.

Managed by Heritage Lincolnshire.

OPENING TIMES

Any reasonable daylight hours

VISIT US

Direction: In Old Bolingbroke, 16 miles N of Boston off A16

Train: Thorpe Culvert 9 miles

Bus: Translinc Spilsby Call Connect (TC Minicoaches) service 6S will operate to Old Bolingbroke on request. To book telephone 0345 234 3344

Tel: 01529 461499

ACQ.1949 🐾 ⚠

MAP PAGE 343 (2J)
OS MAP 122, 273: TF349650

LINCOLN MEDIEVAL BISHOPS' PALACE

LINCOLNSHIRE – LN2 1PU

These intriguing remains of a medieval bishops' palace stand in the shadow of Lincoln Cathedral, in the heart of the ancient city.

They're currently benefiting from a major conservation project. Using a mix of modern technology and traditional methods, we're conserving and consolidating the delicate and important stonework throughout the site. This will ensure that the palace is accessible for many generations to come.

OPENING TIMES

A major conservation maintenance project will get under way in 2019, so access to the palace will be limited

VISIT US

Direction: On the south side of Lincoln Cathedral. From Exchequer Gate, follow the wall to your right to the doorway directly opposite cathedral south porch, then take Chesney Gate tunnelled walkway. Entrance to the left down the pathway

Train: Lincoln 1 mile

Bus: From surrounding areas

NON-MEMBERS

Please check the website for prices before planning your visit

ACQ.1954 ⚠

MAP PAGE 343 (2H)
OS MAP 121, 272: SK978717

SIBSEY TRADER WINDMILL

LINCOLNSHIRE – PE22 0SY

This six-storey Victorian mill is undergoing major conservation and isn't currently working. But you can still go up the mill tower to see the machinery and displays. Enjoy produce made from local stoneground flour in the award-winning tearoom.

Managed by Ian Ansell.

www.sibseytraderwindmill.co.uk

OPENING TIMES

1-30 Apr, Sat-Sun & Bank Hols	11am-6pm
1 May-30 Sep, Tue, Sat-Sun & Bank Hols	11am-6pm
1-31 Oct, Sat-Sun	11am-6pm
1-30 Nov, Sat-Sun	11am-5pm
1 Dec-28 Feb, Sat	11am-5pm

SIBSEY TRADER WINDMILL

1-31 Mar, Sat-Sun	11am-6pm
22 Dec-3 Jan	Closed

Last entry 30 mins before closing

Group and education visits outside these hours by arrangement

VISIT US

Direction: ½ mile W of Sibsey off A16, 5 miles N of Boston

Train: Boston 5 miles

Bus: Brylaine B11 to Sibsey, then ½ mile walk. Boston Call Connect service also serves Sibsey – call 0345 234 3344 to book

Tel: 01205 460647/07718 320449

NON-MEMBERS

Adult £2.50 | Concession £2.00
Child £1.00

ACQ.1975 ♿ 👤 👤 🚫 P ☕ ⚠ OVP

Disabled access (exterior only).

MAP PAGE 343 (3J)
OS MAP 122, 261: TF345510

TATTERSHALL COLLEGE

LINCOLNSHIRE – LN4 4LG

Remains of a grammar school for church choristers, founded in the mid-15th century by Ralph, Lord Cromwell, builder of Wingfield Manor (p.179) and nearby Tattershall Castle (National Trust).

Managed by Heritage Lincolnshire.

OPENING TIMES

Any reasonable daylight hours

VISIT US

Direction: In Tattershall, 14 miles NE of Sleaford on A153

Train: Ruskington 10 miles

Bus: Brylaine service Inter Connect service 5 and service A8 and Hornsby & Woodhall Spa Call Connect service

Tel: 01529 461499

ACQ.1972 🐾

MAP PAGE 343 (2H)
OS MAP 122, 261: TF213578

APETHORPE PALACE   NORTHAMPTONSHIRE – PE8 5DJ

Visitors now have a unique opportunity to discover stately Apethope Palace, owned by Elizabeth I and favourite royal residence of James I and Charles I.

Among England's greatest stately homes, Apethorpe Palace holds a particularly important place in history because of its ownership by, and role in entertaining, Tudor and Stuart monarchs.

Elizabeth I once owned the building, which she had inherited from Henry VIII. For a period, Apethorpe was a royal palace lived in regularly by James I and Charles I.

James I so loved Apethorpe that he personally contributed to its extension, to make it more suitable for his 'princely recreation' and 'commodious entertainment', particularly for hunting in the nearby royal forest of Rockingham. The resulting series of state rooms, including the King's Bedchamber and the impressive long gallery, is one of the most complete to survive from the Jacobean period.

Apethorpe Palace now has a private owner, who is committed to opening the gardens and the state rooms to the public.

Please note: There are lots of stairs, and no resting/seating points available. Children under 16 must be accompanied by an adult. We are unable to admit children under 5.

OPENING TIMES

Entrance by pre-booked guide tour only (charge applies). Guided tours from 4 Jul-26 Aug, Wednesday to Monday. Please call 0370 333 1183 for details

VISIT US

Direction: Located off the A43 towards King's Cliffe. If entering Apethorpe via King's Cliffe Road, advance to Laundry Lane, not the High Street. If entering via Bridge St, pass the stone cross and turn left into Laundry Lane

Train: 14 miles from Peterborough 🚉. Trains via Kings Cross to Peterborough (approx. 45 mins)

Bus: Call Connect services (Mon-Sat) 0345 263 8153. Bus services must be booked in advance

Tel: 0370 333 1181

NON-MEMBERS

Please call for details

ACQ.2004 P

Access via narrow residential lane – please observe 10mph speed limit at all times.

MAP PAGE 343 (5H)
OS MAP 141, 224/234: TL023954

CHICHELE COLLEGE

NORTHAMPTONSHIRE – NN10 8DX

The remains of a residence for priests serving the parish church, founded by locally born Henry Chichele, Archbishop of Canterbury 1414-43. Often exhibits local artists' work.

Managed by Higham Ferrers Tourism, Business and Community Partnership.

OPENING TIMES

Garden:
Any reasonable daylight hours

Interior: Open during events and exhibitions – please check our website for details

VISIT US

Direction: College Street, Higham Ferrers

Train: Wellingborough 5 miles

Bus: Stagecoach 49, 50, X46, X47; Expresslines of Fenlake HI

Tel: 01933 314006

ACQ.1949 🐕 ⚠

Dogs on leads (restricted areas only).

MAP PAGE 343 (5H)
OS MAP 153, 224: SP960687

ELEANOR CROSS, GEDDINGTON

NORTHAMPTONSHIRE – NN14 1AD

This stately triangular cross is the finest survivor of the 'Eleanor Crosses', which marked the places where the body of Eleanor of Castile, wife of Edward I, rested on its way to Westminster Abbey.

OPENING TIMES

Viewing from adjacent highway. Any reasonable daylight hours

VISIT US

Direction: In Geddington, off A43 between Kettering and Corby

Train: Kettering 4 miles

Bus: Centrebus 8 to Geddington

ACQ.1915 🐕

MAP PAGE 343 (5G)
OS MAP 141, 224: SP894830

KIRBY HALL

NORTHAMPTONSHIRE NN17 3EN

Kirby Hall is one of England's greatest Elizabethan and 17th-century houses. Begun by Sir Humphrey Stafford, it was purchased by Sir Christopher Hatton, one of Queen Elizabeth I's 'comely young men' and later her Lord Chancellor.

Hatton hoped in vain to receive the queen here during one of her 'progresses'. Although this vast mansion is partly roofless, most of its walls survive to their full impressive height. So too does the prodigious three-tier inner porch, begun following French pattern books and later embellished in the Classical style by the sculptor Nicholas Stone.

Visiting today, you can view the rich decoration which set the successive owners of Kirby Hall at the forefront of new ideas about architecture and design. The Great Hall and state apartments remain roofed, with interiors redecorated to authentic 17th and 18th-century specifications.

Sir Christopher Hatton the Fourth added the great gardens in the late 17th century. They have been recreated as they may have appeared then, and you can examine elaborate period style 'cutwork', statues, urns, seating, topiary and other features.

The gardens and ground floor of the mansion are wheelchair accessible. Peacocks roam freely round the site. An audio tour guides you through the house and gardens, accompanied by commentaries from experts in garden history, conservation and country houses.

Owned by the Earl of Winchilsea and managed by English Heritage.

STAY WITH US

Peacock Cottage is named after the birds that freely wander the grounds and ruins of the 17th-century hall. Once the public have left at the end of the day, guests have exclusive use of the grounds and gardens.

See p.332 for details on staying at **Kirby** and our other holiday cottages.

OPENING TIMES

1 Apr-30 Sep, Wed-Sun & Bank Hols	10am-6pm
1-29 Oct, Wed-Sun	10am-5pm
30 Oct-31 Mar, Sat-Sun	10am-4pm
24-26 Dec & 1 Jan	Closed

Last entry 30 mins before closing

VISIT US

Direction: On an unclassified road off A43, 4 miles NE of Corby

Train: Corby 4 miles; Kettering 11 miles

Bus: Closest bus is Carters 67. Alight at Kirby Lodge from which it is a 1 mile walk

Tel: 01536 203230

NON-MEMBERS

Adult £8.70 | Concession £7.90
Child £5.20 | Family £22.60

ACQ 1930

Disabled access (grounds, gardens and ground floor only).

Dogs on leads (restricted areas).

MAP PAGE 343 (5G)
OS MAP 141, 224: SP926927

RUSHTON TRIANGULAR LODGE

NORTHAMPTONSHIRE NN14 1RP

An intriguing survival from Elizabethan England, this delightful triangular building was designed in 1593 by Sir Thomas Tresham, father of one of the Gunpowder Plotters.

Tresham was a passionate Roman Catholic, frequently imprisoned for his faith. The lodge is a testament both to his devotion and his obsession with symbols. The number three, symbolising the Holy Trinity, is apparent everywhere. There are three floors, trefoil windows and each side is 33⅓-feet-long, with three triangular gables. Inside is a 33-letter inscription and mysterious numbers, some still unexplained. The entrance front bears the proclamation 'Tres Testimonium Dant' ('there are three that bear witness'), a Biblical quotation from St John's Letters referring to the Trinity. It's also a pun on Tresham's name: his wife called him 'Good Tres', and 'tres' is Latin for 'three'.

OPENING TIMES

1 Apr-3 Nov, Wed-Sun & Bank Hols	11am-5pm
4 Nov-31 Mar	Closed

Last entry 30 mins before closing

VISIT US

Direction: 1 mile W of Rushton, on unclassified road; 1 mile from Desborough on A6

Train: Kettering 5 miles

Bus: Stagecoach service 19 from Kettering to Corby via Desborough stops outside the site

Tel: 01536 710761

NON-MEMBERS

Adult £4.80 | Concession £4.30
Child £2.90 | Family £12.50

Dogs on leads (restricted areas only).
Parking in lay-by on opposite side of road to entrance.

MAP PAGE 343 (5G)
OS MAP 141, 224: SP830831

MATTERSEY PRIORY

NOTTINGHAMSHIRE – DN10 5HN

Remote remains (mainly the refectory) of a tiny priory housing just six Gilbertine canons – the only wholly English monastic order. Sculpted panels from here are now in the village church.

OPENING TIMES

Daily   9am-5pm or dusk if earlier

VISIT US

Direction: Approx. 1 mile from Mattersey village. No vehicular access. Park in village, then walk from church along Abbey Road (bridleway). Access is by landowner's permission

Train: Retford 7 miles

Bus: Stagecoach East Midlands service 27 to village centre then ¾ mile walk

Tel: 01604 735464

ACQ.1913 ⚠

Access to the site is over a stile and there may be animals grazing.

MAP PAGE 343 (1G)
OS MAP 112/120, 280: SK703896

RUFFORD ABBEY

NOTTINGHAMSHIRE – NG22 9DF

England's best-preserved remains of a Cistercian abbey west cloister range, dating from c. 1170. Incorporated into part of a 17th-century and later mansion, in Rufford Country Park.

Owned by Nottinghamshire County Council and managed by Parkwood Outdoors.

OPENING TIMES

1 Apr-31 Oct, daily	10am-5.00pm
1 Nov-31 Mar, daily	10am-4.30pm
25 Dec	Closed

See www.parkwoodoutdoors.co.uk/centre/rufford-abbey for full details

VISIT US

Direction: 2 miles S of Ollerton off A614

Train: Mansfield 8 miles

Bus: 'The Sherwood Arrow' (Stagecoach) service Nottingham – Worksop; also Travelwright 227 (Wed & Fri)

Tel: 01623 821338

ACQ.1959 🅿 ♿ 🐕 🍴 🎫 👁 ✽ 🔔
🚹 ♿ ♣ P 🅿 🍴 📷 💷 ⚠

Parking (charge applies – not managed by English Heritage).

Shops in Stable Block.

MAP PAGE 343 (2G)
OS MAP 120, 270: SK646648W

LYDDINGTON BEDE HOUSE   RUTLAND – LE15 9LZ

Set beside the church in a picturesque village, Lyddington Bede House originated as a medieval palace of the Bishops of Lincoln. By 1600 it had passed to Sir Thomas Cecil, who converted it into an almshouse for twelve poor 'bedesmen' and two women, all free of lunacy, leprosy or the French pox. It continued as an almshouse until the 1930s. You can explore the bedesmen's rooms, and view the Bishops' Great Chamber with its beautiful Tudor ceiling cornice. Interpretation includes audio boxes where you can hear letters read by the 'bedesmen'. A bedesman's and a bedeswoman's room have been recreated as they appeared in Victorian times.

OPENING TIMES

1 Apr-30 Sep, Wed-Sun & Bank Hols	10am-6pm
1 Oct-3 Nov, Wed-Sun	10am-5pm
4 Nov-31 Mar	Closed

Last entry 30 mins before closing

VISIT US

Direction: In Lyddington, 6 miles N of Corby; 1 mile E of A6003, next to the church

Train: Oakham 7 miles

Bus: Centrebus 'Rutland Flyer' service 1 Corby – Oakham (passes close to ⊠ Oakham)

Tel: 01572 822438

NON-MEMBERS

Adult **£6.50** | Concession **£5.90**
Child **£3.90** | Family **£16.90**

ACQ.1952 🍴 🏠 🎫 📷 ⚠ OVP

Dogs on leads in restricted areas only.

MAP PAGE 343 (4G)
OS MAP 141, 234: SP876970

ROM

Kenilworth Castle and Elizabethan Garden

ANTIC

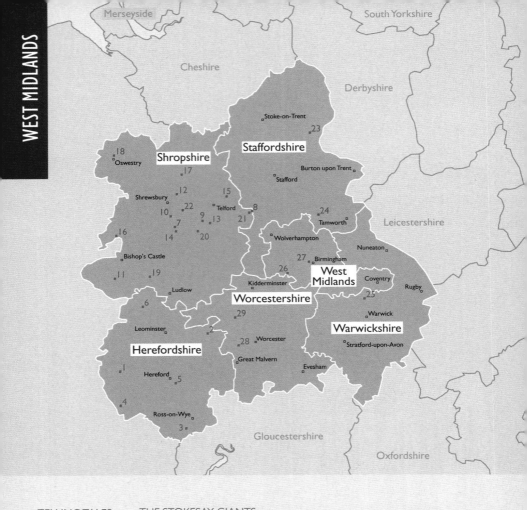

Merseyside
South Yorkshire
Cheshire
Derbyshire
18
Oswestry
Shropshire
Stoke-on-Trent
23
Staffordshire
17
Burton upon Trent
Stafford
12
15
Shrewsbury
22
Telford
8
24
10
9
13
21
Tamworth
Leicestershire
7
Wolverhampton
16
14
20
Nuneaton
Bishop's Castle
27
Birmingham
West
26
Midlands
Coventry
11
19
Kidderminster
Rugby
Ludlow
Worcestershire
25
6
29
Warwick
Leominster
Warwickshire
2
Stratford-upon-Avon
28
Worcester
1
Great Malvern
Evesham
Hereford
5
4
Ross-on-Wye
3
Gloucestershire
Oxfordshire

TELLING TALES:
THE MYTHS, LEGENDS AND FOLKLORE OF ENGLAND

THE STOKESAY GIANTS

Legend has it that the wooded hills overlooking **Stokesay Castle** were once home to two giants. One lived on View Edge to the west, the other on Norton Camp hillfort to the east. They were brothers, and they kept their money in a strongly locked chest in the castle vaults. They had one key between them, and threw it to one another across the valley when they needed to use it. One day it fell short, and it dropped into the castle moat. The giants searched long and hard, but never found it.

The story goes that their treasure chest still lies beneath the castle. It is, however, guarded by a fierce raven, ready to attack anyone who tries to get into it without the key. Perhaps you'll find it on your next visit to Stokesay Castle.

THE ABBESSES' WAY

20 miles | 2 days
Wenlock Priory to Shrewsbury Abbey

Begin at magnificent Wenlock Priory, once a great pilgrimage site of 8th-century abbess St Milburga's relics. Visit Much Wenlock's holy wells of St Milburga and St Owen before ascending the poetry-inspiring ridge of Wenlock Edge. Revel in the rolling Shropshire landscape, especially at the well-positioned Kenley Church, before descending to Langley Chapel and Acton Burnell, with its church right next to a castle built by a bishop. Then follow field and road to St Eata's Church, Atcham, before the final approach via the River Severn and Rea Brook to Shrewsbury Abbey, where a small part of the shrine to the 7th-century abbess St Winefride still survives.

View more details and a downloadable version of this route at www.english-heritage.org.uk/pilgrimage

FINISH: SHREWSBURY

ST EATA CHURCH, ATCHAM

ALL SAINTS CHURCH, BERRINGTON

START: MUCH WENLOCK

C

B

A

Discover English Heritage sites along the pilgrimage route

A Wenlock Priory *(p.201)*
B Langley Chapel *(p.198)*
C Acton Burnell Castle *(p.195)*

Wenlock Priory   Acton Burnell Castle

In partnership with

the
**British
Pilgrimage
Trust**

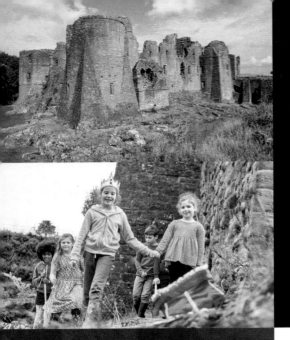

GOODRICH CASTLE

A fun new family game and newly refreshed interpretation offer even more reasons to visit Goodrich – the perfect medieval castle.

HEREFORDSHIRE HR9 6HY

Set in beautiful wooded country, Goodrich Castle guarded a strategic crossing of the River Wye. The earliest fortress here – 'Godric's Castle' – was begun in the late 11th century by an English landowner called Godric. A generation later, the de Clare family added the well-preserved little Norman keep which still stands at the core of the castle. Then, after ownership by William the Marshal (renowned as 'the Greatest Knight'), the castle was rebuilt in the most up-to-date style by King Edward I's uncle William de Valence, Earl of Pembroke.

This late 13th-century castle is revealed as you walk up the gentle slope from the ticket office. Still almost completely walled, it has massive round towers reinforced by distinctive 'spur buttresses', the latest fashion in castle building. It's surrounded by a rock-cut ditch, which you'll cross by a once-fortified bridge modelled on one at the Tower of London – another symbol of William's almost-royal status. Passing through the heavily defended gatehouse, you'll find the courtyard crowded with buildings.

Goodrich, in fact, boasts one of the most complete sets of medieval living quarters surviving in any English castle. From rare surviving records, we know a lot about how these were used by William's widow Countess Joan. She often stayed here, packing nearly 200 servants, staff and guests into the castle.

Pick up the new game from the ticket office, and you can join her household. Leading you on a tour of the castle, it features nine cartoon characters ranging from Countess Joan herself to the baker's assistant. You can choose how they might have answered questions – or make up your own cheeky replies. Adventurous (and relatively fit) visitors can venture into the pitch-dark dungeon, or climb the steep narrow stairway to the keep-top, for breathtaking all-round views over the castle and its surroundings. Don't miss the chapel, with its two striking modern stained-glass windows.

ENJOY A FINE SELECTION OF LIGHT REFRESHMENTS MADE FROM LOCALLY SOURCED HEREFORDSHIRE INGREDIENTS IN THE DELIGHTFUL TEAROOM

In the courtyard you'll also meet 'Roaring Meg', the only surviving Civil War mortar. During Goodrich's greatest crisis, the two-month siege of 1646, it lobbed deadly exploding 'bombs' into the Royalist-held castle, eventually forcing its surrender. One struck and buried the well, which has produced a fascinating array of finds, from Civil War weapons to everyday household objects. You'll find some displayed in the ticket office exhibition.

Before returning for a break in the tearoom (which has indoor and outdoor seating), it's worth walking right round the castle's dry moat. It's a great place to picnic, and the frowning walls above you are a reminder of how strong Goodrich was. Look out for the garderobe tower, which housed multiple medieval loos, with an aperture at its base to allow the 'gong-farmer' to clear the cesspit.

OPENING TIMES

1 Apr-30 Sep, daily	10am-6pm
1 Oct-3 Nov, daily	10am-5pm
4 Nov-16 Feb, Sat-Sun	10am-4pm
17-23 Feb, daily	10am-4pm
24 Feb-31 Mar, Wed-Sun	10am-4pm
Christmas Opening 24-26 Dec & 1 Jan	Closed
Last entry 30 mins before closing	

VISIT US

Address: Goodrich Castle, Castle Lane, Goodrich, Ross-on-Wye, Herefordshire

Direction: 5 miles S of Ross-on-Wye off A40

Bus: Stagecoach service 34; H&H Coaches service 411 (Wed) to within ½ mile

Tel: 01600 890538

NON-MEMBERS

Adult £9.30 | Concession £8.40
Child £5.60 | Family £24.20

Disabled access (limited, please call for details or ask the Visitor Centre on arrival.

Warning: The stairs to the keep top are steep, dark and narrow.

The tearoom will close 30 minutes before the site closes.

Parking charges apply to non-members. Parking free for Members.

MAP PAGE 342 (7C)
OS MAP 162, OL14: SO577200

ARTHUR'S STONE

HEREFORDSHIRE – HR3 6AX

Ridge-top Neolithic chambered tomb made of great stone slabs, with spectacular views over the Golden Valley.

According to legend, King Arthur killed a giant here; certainly Charles I picnicked here in 1645.

OPENING TIMES

Any reasonable daylight hours

VISIT US

Direction: 7 miles E of Hay-on-Wye via B4348, signposted from Dorstone off steep minor road to Bredwardine

Train: Hereford 16 miles

Bus: Stagecoach in South Wales service 39; Yeomans Canyon service 39A (Sun) ⊞ Hereford – Brecon to within ¾ mile

 ACQ 1909

> MAP PAGE 342 (6B)
> OS MAP 148/161, OL13/201:
> SO319431

EDVIN LOACH OLD CHURCH

HEREFORDSHIRE – HR7 4PW

The ruins of an 11th-century and later church built within the earthworks of a Norman motte-and-bailey castle, with a Victorian church nearby.

OPENING TIMES

Any reasonable daylight hours

VISIT US

Direction: Located 4 miles N of Bromyard on an unclassified road off B4203

Bus: The closest town is Bromyard (3½ miles). Bus services operated by DRM/First 420; DRM 469, 476; First 404, 405, 482, 672 & 674

 ACQ 1980

> MAP PAGE 342 (6C)
> OS MAP 149, 202: SO663584

LONGTOWN CASTLE

HEREFORDSHIRE – HR2 0LE

A powerful round keep of c. 1200, characteristic of the Welsh Borders, on a large mound within a stone-walled bailey. In the beautiful Olchon Valley, with magnificent views of the Black Mountains.

Managed in association with Longtown Village Pride.

OPENING TIMES

Any reasonable daylight hours

VISIT US

Direction: Located in the centre of Longtown

Bus: Yeomans services 441 (Wed) & 442 (Tue)

ACQ 1973

Parking in lay-by.

> MAP PAGE 342 (7B)
> OS MAP 161, OL13: SO321291

ROTHERWAS CHAPEL

HEREFORDSHIRE – HR2 6NR

The family chapel of the Roman Catholic Bodenham family. The originally simple medieval building has a fine Elizabethan timber roof, a rebuilt 18th-century tower, and striking Victorian interior decoration and furnishings by the Pugins.

Managed in association with the Friends of Rotherwas Chapel.

OPENING TIMES

Key available Mon-Fri and second Sat of every month	10am-4pm

Key available from Herefordshire Archive and Records Centre, Fir Tree Lane, Rotherwas, Hereford HR2 6LA. Tel: 01432 260750. Visit www.herefordshire.gov.uk/archives

VISIT US

Direction: 1½ miles SE of Hereford on B4399, left into Chapel Road

Train: Hereford 3½ miles

Bus: Yeomans services 78, 78A, 78X, 454 then ½ mile walk

ACQ 1928

Disabled access, ground floor only – one step.

> MAP PAGE 342 (6C)
> OS MAP 149, 189: SO536383

WIGMORE CASTLE

HEREFORDSHIRE – HR6 9UB

Among the most unusual ruins in England, this stronghold of the turbulent medieval Mortimer family is now maintained as a romantic ruin and conserved for its wildlife habitats. Many of its part-buried fortifications survive, including its towering keep-mound.

OPENING TIMES

Any reasonable daylight hours

VISIT US

Direction: Located 8 miles W of Ludlow on A4110. Accessible via footpath ¾ mile from the village on Mortimer Way

Train: Bucknell 6 miles, Ludlow 10 miles

Bus: Lugg Valley 489 (Tue & Fri); Roy Brown Coaches XI1 (Mon)

ACQ 1995

Toilets in the village hall are open from Easter to October half term, inclusive. There is a disabled toilet with ramp access.

There are steep steps to the summit, which are hazardous in icy and wet conditions. Children must stay under close control. Do not climb on the walls or banks. Strong footwear is recommended.

> MAP PAGE 342 (5B)
> OS MAP 137/148, 203: SO408693

ACTON BURNELL CASTLE

SHROPSHIRE – SY5 7PE

The dramatic battlemented red sandstone shell of one of the earliest medieval English fortified mansions, in an atmospheric wooded setting by an attractive Shropshire village. Begun after 1284 by Bishop Robert Burnell, a local man who rose to prominence as King Edward I's Lord Chancellor, its large windows demonstrate that it was designed for show rather than defence. It once contained the lavish private apartments at the core of a much larger house, where King Edward stayed in 1283, holding a famous Parliament nearby. Bishop Burnell's impressive church stands beside it.

OPENING TIMES

Any reasonable daylight hours

VISIT US

Direction: Located in Acton Burnell, signposted from A49, 8 miles S of Shrewsbury

Train: Shrewsbury or Church Stretton, both 8 miles

Bus: Boultons (of Cardington) service 540

ACQ.1930 ♿ ⛩ P ⚠

Please do not climb on the walls.

> MAP PAGE 342 (4C)
> OS MAP 126, 241: SJ534019

BUILDWAS ABBEY

SHROPSHIRE – TF8 7BW

Impressive ruins of a Cistercian abbey, including its unusually unaltered 12th-century church, beautiful vaulted chapter house and crypt chapel.

In a wooded Severn-side setting, near the Iron Bridge (p.199) and Wenlock Priory (p.201).

OPENING TIMES

Apr-Oct, daily	10am-6pm
Nov-Mar, daily	10am-4pm

VISIT US

Direction: On S bank of River Severn on A4169, 2 miles W of Ironbridge

Train: Telford Central 6 miles

Bus: Arriva Midlands service 96

Tel: 01952 433274

ACQ.1925 ♿ ⛩ ⬛ P ⚠

Disabled access is limited.

> MAP PAGE 342 (4C)
> OS MAP 127, 242: SJ643043

Many of our properties are available to hire as unique and memorable settings for all types of events from drinks parties to private dinners and hospitality events, and even for a magical wedding.

Visit www.english-heritage. org.uk/venuehire

CANTLOP BRIDGE

SHROPSHIRE – SY5 7DD

A single-span, cast-iron road bridge over the Cound Brook. Possibly designed and certainly approved by the great engineer Thomas Telford, who was instrumental in shaping industrial Shropshire and the West Midlands.

OPENING TIMES

Any reasonable daylight hours

VISIT US

Direction: ¾ mile SW of Berrington on an unclassified road off A458

Train: Shrewsbury 5 miles

Bus: Boultons (of Cardington) service 540

ACQ.1977 ♿ ⛩ P

Parking in lay-by.

> MAP PAGE 342 (4C)
> OS MAP 126, 241: SJ517062

BOSCOBEL HOUSE
AND THE ROYAL OAK

Boscobel House and its famous Royal Oak tree draw you into
one of the most dramatic adventure stories in English history.
There's now also a tearoom to enjoy.

SHROPSHIRE ST19 9AR

A picturesque timber-framed house with a many-layered history, Boscobel was converted into a hunting lodge in the 1620s by the Roman Catholic Giffard family. Originally set amid dense woodland, it probably doubled as a hiding place for persecuted Catholics. So it was an ideal refuge for the young Charles II, forced to flee for his life after defeat at the Battle of Worcester in 1651.

The exhausted and heavily disguised king snatched a hurried dawn snack and foot-wash in Boscobel's parlour. Then he hid all day in a tree later called the Royal Oak, while Cromwell's patrols searched below. After a cramped night in a 'priest's hole' which you can still see in the house, he relaxed in the garden before travelling on to more adventures and eventual exile in France. The 17th-century style Knot Garden and its 'pretty arbour' have now been recreated as in Charles's time.

After Charles II's Restoration in 1660, Boscobel became famous. A 19th-century owner revamped its interiors to help tell its story: they are now set as in late Victorian times. He also established a thriving dairy farm, whose Victorian farmyard – including fully-equipped dairy and smithy – is a joy to explore. There's also a 1940s-themed tearoom in the stables (not managed by English Heritage) and a second-hand bookshop in the dairy.

Children can dress up as Roundheads or Cavaliers in the family room, and play Victorian games in the garden. Guided tours are available, and for less mobile visitors there's a virtual tour of the whole site in the shop.

A descendant of the Royal Oak stands a short stroll away, and a pleasant 20-minute walk takes you to White Ladies Priory (p.200), another of Charles II's hiding places.

OPENING TIMES

1 Apr–3 Nov, Wed–Sun & Bank Hols	10am–5pm
4 Nov–31 Dec, Sat–Sun	10am–4pm
1 Jan–31 Mar	Please check website for details

House will be closed for one hour at 11am and 2pm for guided tours. Guided tours are subject to availability and booking is advisable

Last entry 1 hour before closing

VISIT US

Direction: On minor road from A41 to A5, 8 miles NW of Wolverhampton, 5 mins drive from M54 J3

Train: Cosford 3 miles

Bus: Select Bus 877 & 878 to Bishopswood then 1 mile walk

Tel: 01902 850244

NON-MEMBERS

Adult £9.00 | Concession £8.10
Child £5.40 | Family £23.40

ACQ.1954 ▧ E f ✳ ⬜ ⬧ ✦ ❈ P ⬚ ⬜ 🖐
♿ ⚠ OVP

Dogs on leads (grounds only).

Parking (coaches welcome).

Disabled access limited: please call site for details. Visually impaired can listen to the virtual tour and a short account of Charles II's story on headphones in the shop.

MAP PAGE 342 (4D)
OS MAP 127, 242: SJ838082

CLUN CASTLE

SHROPSHIRE – SY7 8JT

Dramatic riverside ruins and earthworks of a Welsh Border castle, its tall 13th-century keep unusually set on the side of its mound. Panels tell the story of the castle and adjacent town.

OPENING TIMES

Any reasonable daylight hours

VISIT US

Direction: In Clun, off A488, 18 miles W of Ludlow

Train: Hopton Heath 6½ miles; Knighton 6½ miles

Bus: Minsterley 745 (Mon-Fri); M&J service 860 (Tue)

ACQ.1991 ⚑ P 🅿 ⚠ Deep water.

Toilets available in car park (not managed by English Heritage).

MAP PAGE 342 (5B)
OS MAP 137, 201: SO299809

LANGLEY CHAPEL

SHROPSHIRE – SY5 7HU

Experience what churches looked like before the Victorians. This uniquely unaltered chapel, amid remote countryside, has a perfect set of rustic Jacobean furnishings, including gentry box pews, canopied pulpit and musicians' pew.

OPENING TIMES

1 Apr-31 Oct, daily	10am-6pm
1 Nov-31 Mar, daily	10am-4pm
24-26 Dec & 1 Jan	Closed

VISIT US

Direction: 9½ miles S of Shrewsbury and 1½ miles S of Acton Burnell, on an unclassified narrow road. Signposted from Acton Burnell

Train: Shrewsbury 7½ miles

Bus: Boultons (of Cardington) service 540 (then 1¼ mile walk)

ACQ.1914 ⚑ P

Very limited parking (2 cars).

MAP PAGE 342 (4C)
OS MAP 126/127/138, 217/241: SJ538001

LILLESHALL ABBEY

SHROPSHIRE – TF10 9HW

Extensive Augustinian abbey ruins, in a deeply rural setting. Much of the church survives, unusually viewable from gallery level, along with an elaborate processional doorway.

OPENING TIMES

1 Apr-31 Oct, daily	10am-6pm
1 Nov-31 Mar, daily	10am-4pm
24-26 Dec & 1 Jan	Closed

VISIT US

Direction: On an unclassified road off A518, 4 miles N of Oakengates

Train: Oakengates 4½ miles

Bus: Arriva service 5 Telford – Stafford (passes close to ⧉ Telford Central & Stafford) to Lilleshall Church Road then ½ mile walk or Arriva 115/116 (Sat) pass close to ⧉ Shinall) to within 1 mile – alight between Sheriffhales and Heath Hill

ACQ.1950 ⚑ P

Disabled access via kissing gate only.

1 Nov-29 Mar, parking on roadside only with access via kissing gate.

Please do not climb on the walls.

MAP PAGE 342 (4C)
OS MAP 127, 242: SJ738142

HAUGHMOND ABBEY SHROPSHIRE – SY4 4RW

Extensive remains of an Augustinian abbey, including its abbots' quarters and cloister. The chapter house displays rich 12th and 14th-century carving and a fine timber roof.

OPENING TIMES

1 Apr-31 Oct, daily	10am-6pm
1 Nov-31 Mar, daily	10am-4pm
24-26 Dec & 1 Jan	Closed

VISIT US

Direction: Located 3 miles NE of Shrewsbury off B5062

Train: Shrewsbury 3½ miles

Bus: Arriva 519 Shrewsbury – Newport

Tel: 01743 709661

ACQ.1931 ⚑ P ⚠

Disabled access is limited.

MAP PAGE 342 (4C)
OS MAP 126, 241: SJ542152

IRON BRIDGE

SHROPSHIRE TF8 7JP

This famous structure is the world's very first iron bridge, an iconic symbol of the Industrial Revolution. Come and see how our newly completed £3.6m conservation project, the biggest since we became a charity, has safeguarded the bridge for future generations.

Britain's best-known industrial monument was erected over the River Severn in 1779. It gave its name to spectacular wooded Ironbridge Gorge, once an industrial powerhouse and the cradle of the Industrial Revolution. Ironbridge Gorge is now a World Heritage Site.

In the early 18th century, Abraham Darby I pioneered the process of using coke made from local coal to smelt iron ore. Local expansion was hampered by the lack of a bridge over the Severn here, and any bridge had to be a single span to allow barge traffic. Abraham Darby III cast the bridge in his Coalbrookdale foundry, using 378 tons of iron, at a cost of over £6,000. A crucial turning point in design and engineering, this testament to the achievements of Shropshire ironmasters remained in use by traffic until 1934.

Over the 240 years since it was built, the bridge suffered many stresses, some dating from its original construction. Ground movement in the surrounding gorge, countless floods and even an earthquake in 1896 had left the historic structure under threat, placing stresses on the ironwork and leading to cracking. Following years of research, analysis and planning, our major conservation work has repaired and protected the bridge for the future. Among changes you'll notice is the colour of the bridge, now restored to its original dark red-brown after samples of the earliest historic paintwork were discovered as part of the project.

Find out much more about the conservation programme at our Iron Bridge webpage.

Get 20% discount off Annual Passport tickets to **Ironbridge Gorge Museums** with your membership card. See p.308 for details.

OPENING TIMES

Any reasonable daylight hours

Members can also get a Passport discount at Ironbridge Gorge Museums. Discount only available at time of booking. See p.308 for details

VISIT US

Direction: Adjacent to A4169

Train: Telford Central 5 miles

Bus: Arriva 9, 18 & 96. Also the Ironbridge Park & Ride and Gorge Connect services operated by Telford & Wrekin Council (Summer Public Holidays and weekends)

 🚻 ♿ P

Parking (charge applies). Car park not managed by English Heritage.

MAP PAGE 342 (4C)
OS MAP 127, 242: SJ672034

MITCHELL'S FOLD STONE CIRCLE

SHROPSHIRE – SY15 6OE

Neolithic stone circle, the focus of many legends, set amid dramatic moorland. It once consisted of some 30 stones, 15 are still visible.

OPENING TIMES

Any reasonable daylight hours

VISIT US

Direction: 16 miles SW of Shrewsbury, on unclassified road off A488

Train: Welshpool 10 miles

Bus: Minsterley Motors service 553 Shrewsbury – Bishop's Castle (passes close Shrewsbury ▣). Also Minsterley Motors 745 (Mon & Fri) & 775 (Wed) – all to White Grit A488 junction within 1 mile

Tel: 0845 678 9068

 ACQ.1915 🐴 P

Parking in lay-by at end of track – no vehicular access onto the moor.

MAP PAGE 342 (4B)
OS MAP 137, 216: SO304984

While in the area, why not visit Shrewsbury Flaxmill Maltings Visitor Centre. **See p.307 for details.**

MORETON CORBET CASTLE

SHROPSHIRE – SY4 4DW

Ruins of the castle and Tudor mansion of the Corbets, dominated by the theatrical shell of an Elizabethan wing, devastated during the Civil War.

OPENING TIMES

Any reasonable daylight hours

VISIT US

Direction: In Moreton Corbet off B5063 (a turning off A49), 7 miles NE of Shrewsbury

Train: Yorton 4 miles

Bus: Arriva service 64 to Shawbury then ¾ mile walk

ACQ.1939 ♿ 🐴 P

Disabled access is limited.

MAP PAGE 342 (4C)
OS MAP 126, 241: SJ561231

OLD OSWESTRY HILLFORT

SHROPSHIRE – SY11 1HT

Among the most hugely impressive Iron Age hillforts on the Welsh Borders, covering 40 acres, with formidable multiple ramparts.

OPENING TIMES

Any reasonable daylight hours

VISIT US

Direction: 1 mile N of Oswestry, off an unclassified road off A483

Train: Gobowen 2 miles

Bus: Arriva service 2 & 53 or Tanat Valley 449 to Gobowen Road or Arriva Oswestry town service 404 to Old Fort Way then short walk

 ACQ.1946 🐴 P

Sheep grazing on site.

MAP PAGE 342 (3B)
OS MAP 126, 240/258: SJ295310

WHITE LADIES PRIORY

SHROPSHIRE – WV8 1QZ

Ruined church of a nunnery of 'white ladies', later part of a vanished mansion. Charles II rested here in 1651 before seeking refuge at nearby Boscobel House (p.196).

Reachable via a footpath from Boscobel House (approximately 20 minutes' walk).

OPENING TIMES

Any reasonable daylight hours

VISIT US

Direction: Located 1 mile SW of Boscobel House off an unclassified road between A41 and A5; 8 miles NW of Wolverhampton

Train: Cosford 2½ miles

Bus: Select Bus 877 & 878 to Bishopswood then 1½ mile walk. Alternatively Banga Travel service 891 to Cosford and then 2 mile walk

 ACQ.1938 🐴

MAP PAGE 342 (4D)
OS MAP 217, 242: SJ826076

WENLOCK PRIORY

SHROPSHIRE TF13 6HS

The tranquil ruins of Wenlock Priory are picturesquely sited on the fringe of Much Wenlock.

An Anglo-Saxon monastery was founded here by King Merewalh of Mercia, whose abbess daughter Milburga became a saint. Her relics were miraculously rediscovered here in 1101, attracting both pilgrims and prosperity.

By then Wenlock had been re-founded as a Norman Cluniac priory. Its impressive remains reflect everywhere the Cluniac love of elaborate decoration. Parts of the great 13th-century church still stand high; and there is a replica of an unusual monks' washing fountain with 12th-century carvings. The priory's greatest glory is the extravagantly decorated chapter house, its walls bedecked with interlocking round arches on multiple carved columns.

Set in a topiary-filled garden, against the backdrop of the monastic infirmary wing, later converted into a mansion and still a private residence.

OPENING TIMES

1 Apr-30 Sep, daily	10am-6pm
1 Oct-3 Nov, daily	10am-5pm
4 Nov-16 Feb, Sat-Sun	10am-4pm
17-23 Feb, daily	10am-4pm
24 Feb-31 Mar, Sat-Sun	10am-4pm
24-26 Dec & 1 Jan	Closed

Last entry 30 mins before closing

VISIT US

Direction: In Much Wenlock

Train: Telford Central 9 miles

Bus: Arriva Midlands service 18 & Easy Coach service 436

Tel: 01952 727466

NON-MEMBERS

Adult £6.60 | Concession £6.00
Child £4.00 | Family £17.20

ACQ.1964 🎧 ♿ 🐕 f ❄ 🏠 🚹 👥 P 📷 OVP

New guidebook.

Parking charges apply to non-members.
Parking free for Members.

MAP PAGE 342 (4C)
OS MAP 127/138, 217/242: SJ625001

STOKESAY CASTLE

Imaginative new interpretation and an exciting children's riddle quest help you to explore Stokesay Castle, the finest and best-preserved fortified medieval manor house in England.

SHROPSHIRE SY7 9AH

A treasure by-passed by time, the moated manor, timber-framed gatehouse and parish church make an unforgettably picturesque group. Though 'builded like a castle', Stokesay was really a lightly defended mansion, designed for comfort and show. Lawrence of Ludlow, a wealthy local wool-merchant who wanted to become a country gentleman, began rebuilding it in about 1285. Tree-ring dating proves that he'd completed work by 1291, using the same team of carpenters throughout. Amazingly, the dating also revealed that Stokesay has altered very little since; there are very few places in England where you can see so much medieval timberwork.

So that you can discover Stokesay's story while still enjoying its unspoiled atmosphere, we've just installed new information panels into period-style features, showing how the rooms were used. There's also an absorbing audio tour. Families can set out on the intriguing puzzle quest, inspired by the legend of two giants who lived on wooded hills flanking the castle, throwing the key to their treasure-chest from one to the other until they lost it. Solving riddles and searching for clues (in buckets, fireplaces, barrels and even a chamber-pot) will lead you into every nook and cranny of the castle, from cellar to tower roof.

There's plenty to see. In the magnificent open-hearthed great hall you can admire a fine timber roof, shuttered gable windows and a steep medieval staircase with treads cut from whole tree trunks. The north tower stands to one side, with an original medieval tiled floor. On the other side is a 'solar', or private apartment, block and the tall south tower – the most castle-like part of the house – offering wonderful views from its battlements.

The solar block includes one of the few later additions to Stokesay, a magnificent panelled chamber. It's dominated by a fireplace with a richly carved overmantel, where you can trace original painting in five colours. This was added in about 1641, at the same time as the delightful gatehouse, an outstanding example of the Welsh Marches style of lavishly showy timber-framing. Look out for the 'Stokesay dragons' and charming carvings of Adam and Eve.

You can explore the gardens in the moat surrounding the castle, and enjoy our new Edwardian-style cottage garden in the courtyard. And don't miss the parish church with its unchanged 17th-century interior (not managed by English Heritage). Just outside the castle, our attractive recently opened cottage tearoom is open to passers-by as well as castle visitors. Serving locally sourced food, it has an outdoor play space, and additional outdoor seating with all-round views to the surrounding Welsh Border hills.

OPENING TIMES

1 Apr-30 Sep, daily	10am-6pm
1 Oct-3 Nov, daily	10am-5pm
4 Nov-23 Dec, Sat-Sun	10am-4pm
2 Jan-16 Feb, Sat-Sun	10am-4pm
17-23 Feb, daily	10am-4pm
24 Feb-31 Mar, Wed-Sun	10am-4pm
Christmas Opening 24-25 Dec	Closed
26 Dec-1 Jan, daily	10am-4pm

Last entry 30 mins before closing

VISIT US

Address: Stokesay Castle, Nr Craven Arms, Shropshire

Direction: 7 miles NW of Ludlow off A49

Train: Craven Arms 1 mile

Bus: Minsterley Motors (of Stiperstones) 435 to Stokesay. Request stop on the turning on the A49 then 250 yard walk

Tel: 01588 672544

Local Tourist Information:
Ludlow: 01584 875053

NON-MEMBERS

Adult £9.50 | Concession £8.60
Child £5.80 | Family £24.80

ACQ.1986

Disabled access (call site for details).

Dogs allowed within the grounds on a lead but not allowed within the castle.

Entrance to the courtyard is through a historic gate. Unsuitable for motorised scooters and unassisted wheelchair users. Cottage tearoom fully accessible.

Cottage tearoom is outside the castle and open to all. It closes 30 minutes before castle.

Parking charges apply to non-members. Parking free for Members.

MAP PAGE 342 (5B)
OS MAP 137/148, 203: SO436815

WROXETER ROMAN CITY

SHROPSHIRE SY5 6PJ

Discover how the Romans lived 2,000 years ago at Wroxeter (or Viriconium) – once the fourth largest city in Roman Britain, with up to 5,000 citizens. Eventually covering some 180 acres, it was equal in size to Pompeii in Italy.

Wroxeter began as a legionary fortress and developed into a thriving civilian city, populated by traders and retired soldiers. Today its ruins stand in open fields. The most impressive features are the remains of the 2nd-century municipal baths and the huge wall dividing them from the exercise hall, once in the heart of the city.

The audio tour describes how Wroxeter worked in its heyday, and you can explore a wealth of site-finds in the fascinating museum. The military weapons and equipment, fashion accessories and medical instruments reveal details of the citizens' everyday life. Trace the rise, flourishing, post-Roman survival and eventual abandonment of the city through the vivid interpretation.

Be sure to see the on-site re-creation of a Roman townhouse, complete with painted rooms including dining room, bedroom and bath-suite and replicas of Roman furniture. Inspired by houses excavated here, it was built using traditional methods as interpreted by six modern building-trade workers, for the Channel 4 series 'Rome Wasn't Built in a Day'.

OPENING TIMES

1 Apr-30 Sep, daily	10am-6pm
1 Oct-3 Nov, daily	10am-5pm
4 Nov-31 Mar, Sat-Sun	10am-4pm
24-26 Dec & 1 Jan	Closed

Last entry 30 mins before closing

VISIT US

Direction: 5 miles SE of Shrewsbury, on a minor road signposted from the B4380

Train: Shrewsbury 5½ miles; Wellington Telford West 6 miles

Bus: Arriva service 96; also Arriva service 81 serves Norton, about ½ mile walk

Tel: 01743 761330

NON-MEMBERS

Adult **£8.00** | Concession **£7.20**
Child **£4.80** | Family **£20.80**

An education room is available for schools.

Light refreshments are available.

MAP PAGE 342 (4C)
OS MAP 126, 241: SJ565087

CROXDEN ABBEY   STAFFORDSHIRE – ST14 5JG

The impressive ruins of an abbey of Cistercian 'white monks', once prosperous from sheep farming. They include the towering west walls and tall lancet windows of its 13th-century church, its infirmary and 14th-century abbot's lodging. Information panels and a decorative stonework display tell the story of Croxden's spectacular architecture.

OPENING TIMES

1 Apr-31 Oct, daily	10am-5pm
1 Nov-31 Mar, daily	10am-4pm
24-26, 31 Dec & 1 Jan	Closed

VISIT US

Direction: 5 miles NW of Uttoxeter off A522

Train: Uttoxeter 6 miles

Bus: Closest service is Staffordshire Mobility Link 411 to Hollington (Wed). Otherwise First 32 to Fole or First 32A to Alton then 2½ miles walk

ACQ.1936 ♿ 🍴 P

Do not climb on the walls.

Limited parking.

MAP PAGE 342 (3E)
OS MAP 128, 259: SK066397

WALL ROMAN SITE (LETOCETUM)   STAFFORDSHIRE – WS14 0AW

An important staging post on Watling Street, the Roman military road to North Wales, Wall provided overnight accommodation for travelling Roman officials and imperial messengers. It displays foundations of an inn and bath-house, with excavated finds in the on-site museum.

Managed by English Heritage for the National Trust, with thanks to the Friends of Letocetum.

OPENING TIMES

Open Air Site

1 Apr-31 Oct, daily	10am-5pm
1 Nov-31 Mar, daily	10am-4pm
24-26 Dec & 1 Jan	Closed

Museum
30-31 Mar, 20-22, 27-28 Apr, 4-6, 25-27 May, 29-30 Jun, 27-28 Jul, 3-4, 10-11, 17-18, 24-26 Aug, 28-29 Sep, 26-27 Oct   11am-4pm or dusk, whichever comes sooner

VISIT US

Direction: Off Eastbound A5 at Wall, near Lichfield

Train: Shenstone 1½ miles

Bus: Central Buses service 35B

ACQ.1949 🍴 P

MAP PAGE 342 (4E)
OS MAP 139, 244: SK098066

KENILWORTH CASTLE AND ELIZABETHAN GARDEN

Spend a right royal day out enjoying the many delights of spectacular Kenilworth Castle. In the remains of the miniature palace where Queen Elizabeth I stayed, you can stand on lofty viewing platforms to experience a 'queen's-eye view' of the castle and its surroundings. Be sure to take in the meticulously recreated Elizabethan garden, and don't miss the 'Speed and Power' exhibition.

WARWICKSHIRE CV8 1NG

A vast medieval fortress, which experienced a famous siege and later became an Elizabethan palace, Kenilworth Castle is among Britain's biggest historic sites. Extensive developments highlight Kenilworth's famous associations with Queen Elizabeth I and her favourite, Robert Dudley.

Spanning more than five centuries, Kenilworth's varied buildings reflect its long connection with English monarchs. Henry I's treasurer began the massive Norman keep in the 1120s, Henry II made Kenilworth a royal castle and King John greatly strengthened it. Thus it could withstand the longest siege in medieval English history in 1266, when rebellious barons held out here for six months. In the impressively timbered Tudor stables, which also house the tearoom, you can see trebuchet balls from the siege in the interactive display of the castle's history.

John of Gaunt, Duke of Lancaster, rebuilt Kenilworth's inner court, beginning the castle's transition into a favourite residence of the Lancastrian and early Tudor kings. By Henry VIII's time it was already renowned for its 'many fair chambers'. The scene was set for Kenilworth's greatest period of fame.

NEW FOR 2019

Summer 2019 sees the 10th anniversary of the opening of our Elizabethan Garden. We're celebrating with a new children's trail, fresh plants and garden tours. Please see the website for more details.

ADMIRE FANTASTIC VIEWS OVER THE CASTLE AND SURROUNDING COUNTRYSIDE

This began when Queen Elizabeth I's favourite, Robert Dudley, Earl of Leicester, took possession of the castle in 1563. He then lavished fortunes on converting it into a great showpiece mansion, designed to receive the queen and her court on their ceremonial 'progresses' around England. You can see striking evidence of his transformation everywhere at Kenilworth, including the tall, mansion-sized 'Leicester's Building' designed specifically for the queen's use.

Viewing platforms within 'Leicester's Building' allow you to climb 18 metres (59 feet) to the level of the queen's apartments. Here you can admire fantastic views over the castle and surrounding countryside, once enjoyed only by Elizabeth and her favoured courtiers. Interpretation helps you imagine this miniature palace in its heyday.

'Leicester's Gatehouse' is the imposing entrance to his transformed 'wonder-house'. Discover its lower floor chambers re-created as they might have appeared in the 1930s. On its top floor, take in an exhibition telling the story of Elizabeth I's relationship with Dudley and her four visits to his castle.

On the most famous of these visits, in July 1575, Elizabeth stayed for 19 days. Dudley not only entertained her royally throughout; he also created a fabulous garden especially for her visit. Lost for centuries, we've brought the garden back to life. It presents the most complete evocation of an Elizabethan garden anywhere in the world.

Among the glories of the garden you'll discover a Renaissance aviary; plantings abundant in colour, perfume and fruit and an imposing fountain carved from Carrara marble. Its re-creation was made possible by advances in garden archaeology and the miraculous survival of a contemporary eye-witness description of the Kenilworth garden. It opens a window on the period's most enduring love story – that of Elizabeth I and her favourite, Robert Dudley.

The 'Speed and Power' exhibition in the gatehouse highlights a personality from the castle's more recent history – Coventry-based motoring and aviation pioneer John Siddeley, who became first Baron Kenilworth and gave the castle to the nation in 1938. In the interwar years his glamorous Armstrong Siddeley luxury cars were loved by the rich and famous, including the honeymooning Queen Mother. His drawing office took refuge here from Second World War bombing. Exhibits celebrate his cars and planes, and families can design their own car and game-play an epic 1933 'Siddeley Special' car journey.

OPENING TIMES

1 Apr-30 Sep, daily	10am-6pm
1 Oct-3 Nov, daily	10am-5pm
4 Nov-23 Dec, Sat-Sun	10am-4pm
2 Jan-16 Feb, Sat-Sun	10am-4pm
17-23 Feb, daily	10am-4pm
24 Feb-31 Mar, Wed-Sun	10am-4pm
Christmas Opening	
24-25 Dec	Closed
26 Dec-1 Jan, daily	10am-4pm

Last entry 30 mins before closing

Access to Leicester's Gatehouse and/or the Stables Tearoom may be limited if there is a private event booked, please call or check the website before you visit

VISIT US

Address: Kenilworth Castle, Castle Green, off Castle Road, Kenilworth, Warwickshire

Direction: In Kenilworth off A46. Clearly signposted from the town centre, off B4103

Train: Kenilworth 1 mile

Bus: IGO service 539 passes the castle site; Travel Coventry 11; Stagecoach U17 all serve Kenilworth from surrounding areas

Tel: 01926 852078

Local Tourist Information:
Kenilworth: 0300 555 8171

NON-MEMBERS

Adult £13.00 | Concession £11.70
Child £7.90 | Family £33.90

Audio tours available (English, French, German and a children's version). Audio tours not available on Bank Holiday weekends or special event days.

Tearoom open as per site, closing 30 minutes before the site closes.

Parking charges apply to non-members.
Parking free for Members.

MAP PAGE 342 (5E)
OS MAP 140, 221: SP278723

J.W. EVANS SILVER FACTORY BIRMINGHAM – B1 3EA

One of the most complete surviving historic factories in Birmingham's Jewellery Quarter, established in 1881. Behind the frontage of terraced houses, the workshops retain their dies for silverware manufacture, working equipment, stock and business records. English Heritage rescued the factory in 2008. Pre-booked guided tours only.

OPENING TIMES

Pre-booked tours only (charge applies). Max 10 persons per tour. See website for details

VISIT US

Direction: 54-57 Albion Street, ½ mile from City Centre

Train: New Street ½ mile

Bus: From surrounding areas

Tel: 0370 333 1181

ACQ 2008

MAP PAGE 342 (5E)
OS MAP 139, 220: SP062870

HALESOWEN ABBEY

WEST MIDLANDS – B62 8RJ

Remains of an abbey founded by King John in the 13th century.

OPENING TIMES

Open to view from the public footpath only

VISIT US

Directions: Off A456, ½ mile W of J3, M5

Train: Old Hill 2½ miles

Bus: Diamond services 002; National Express West Midlands services 9 & 241 then ½ mile walk

ACQ 1976

MAP PAGE 342 (5D)
OS MAP 139, 219: SO975828

WORCESTERSHIRE

LEIGH COURT BARN

WORCESTERSHIRE – WR6 5LB

An outstanding display of medieval carpentry, this huge 14th-century timber-framed barn is the largest cruck-framed structure in Britain, 46 metres (150 feet) long.

OPENING TIMES

1 Apr-31 Oct, daily	10am-6pm
1 Nov-31 Mar, daily	10am-4pm
24-26 Dec & 1 Jan	Closed

VISIT US

Direction: 5 miles W of Worcester on an unclassified road off A4103

Train: Worcester Foregate Street 5 miles

Bus: LMS Travel 423 to Leigh village; Astons service 417 to Bransford within 1 mile

ACQ 1990

Parking in lay-by.

Access via kissing gate.

MAP PAGE 342 (6D)
OS MAP 150, 204: SO783535

WITLEY COURT AND GARDENS

Inspire the whole family with a day out at Witley Court. Explore the spectacular shell of a colossal Victorian country house mansion amid vast and beautiful grounds, with an imaginative wilderness play area.

WORCESTERSHIRE WR6 6JT

In its late-Victorian heyday Witley Court was staffed by over 100 servants, and hosted lavish house parties attended by the Prince of Wales – later Edward VII – and his opulent friends. Falling into decline after the First World War, it was accidentally burnt to a roofless shell in 1937. Wandering through its dramatic Italianate ruins conjures up its glamorous past, when the huge ballroom's Christmas tree was hung with jewellery for female guests.

We've colourfully recreated the mansion's formal gardens, originally laid out from the 1850s by the leading landscape designer William Andrews Nesfield. The East Parterre, with its Flora Fountain, imitates embroidery, while the elegant South Parterre focusses on the astonishing Perseus and Andromeda fountain.

One of Europe's greatest fountains, this dramatically depicts the legendary Greek hero Perseus swooping down on his winged horse Pegasus to rescue the beautiful Andromeda, who's been chained to a rock as a sacrifice to a sea monster. Its central jet reaches a height

STAY WITH US

The substantial **Pool House** holiday cottage can sleep up to eight people, and has its own well-screened garden with sheltered dining terrace.

See p.332 for details on staying at **Witley** and our other holiday cottages.

of up to 30 metres, complemented by nearly 30 more jets hidden among shells, sea nymphs and dolphins. Fully restored to working order, between April and October it fires on the hour from 11am until an hour before closing – a sight and sound not to be missed.

DON'T MISS THE 'FIRING' OF THE STUPENDOUS FOUNTAIN, AN EXPERIENCE YOU WON'T FORGET

Wend your way up to the mansion through Witley's paradise of wild gardens, with their winding paths, rustic bridges, surprise lake vistas, trees and flowering shrubs from all over the world. Enchanted woodland walks are signposted for you, including a lakeside path to the Victorian boathouse: they offer glimpses of the park's abundant wildlife. Near the visitor centre is an 'organic' wilderness play area for children. With lots of exciting activities for different age groups, it's sure to fire their imaginations. The centrepiece is a tree house, reached by a wobbly bridge. A section for younger children includes a nest-like basket swing and wooden animal rides. There's also an adventure area with a scramble net and rope walks. However many visits they make, children will have a different experience every time they come.

Leave time to visit Great Witley Church, attached to the mansion, with its golden dome and gleaming gilded Baroque interior. There's a tearoom near the church. (Please note: church and tearoom not managed by English Heritage.)

OPENING TIMES

1 Apr-30 Sep, daily	10am-6pm
1 Oct-3 Nov, daily	10am-5pm
4 Nov-16 Feb, Sat-Sun	10am-4pm
17-23 Feb, daily	10am-4pm
24 Feb-31 Mar, Wed-Sun	10am-4pm
Christmas Opening 24-26 Dec & 1 Jan	Closed

Last entry one hour before closing

VISIT US

Address: Witley Court, Worcester Road, Great Witley, Worcestershire

Direction: 10 miles NW of Worcester on A443

Train: Droitwich Spa 8½ miles

Bus: Yarranton Bros service 758 Worcester – Tenbury Wells (passes close Worcester Foregate Street ≥); to Great Witley village hall then ½ mile walk

Tel: 01299 896636

Local Tourist Information: Worcester: 01905 726311

NON-MEMBERS

Adult **£9.90** | Concession **£9.00**
Child **£6.00** | Family **£25.80**

Disabled access (exterior and grounds only). A terrain guide is available on the website.

Tearoom (seasonal): Easter-31 October (not managed by EH).

Parking charges apply to non-members. Parking free for Members.

MAP PAGE 342 (6D)
OS MAP 138/150, 204: SO769649

HAUN

TING

Whitby Abbey

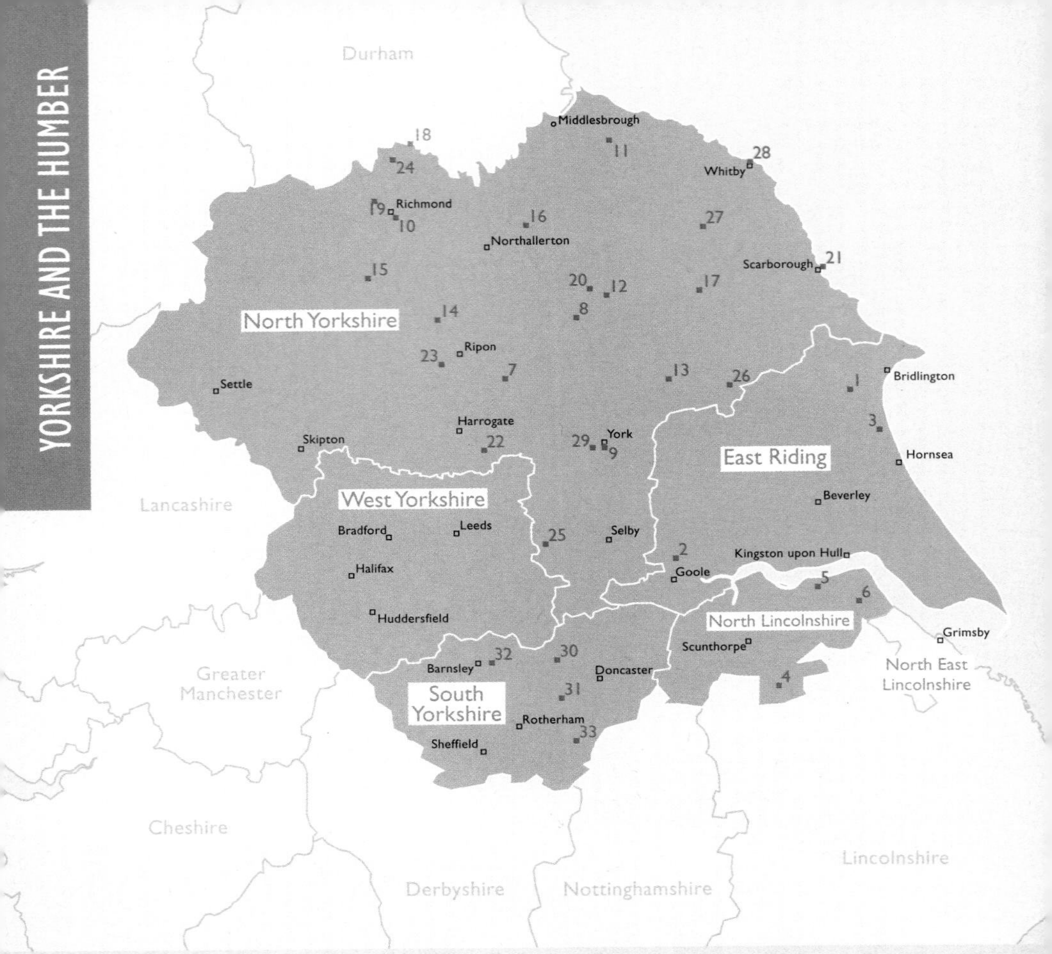

Durham
Middlesbrough
18
24
11
28
Whitby
19 Richmond
10
16
27
Northallerton
15
20 12
Scarborough 21
8 17
North Yorkshire
14
23 Ripon
7 13 26
Settle
1 Bridlington
Harrogate
3
Skipton
22
29 York
Hornsea
9
East Riding
West Yorkshire
Lancashire
Bradford Leeds
25 Selby
Beverley
Halifax
2 Kingston upon Hull
Goole
Huddersfield
5
Greater
Manchester
North Lincolnshire
6
Grimsby
Scunthorpe
32
30 Doncaster
North East
Barnsley
Lincolnshire
31
South
4
Yorkshire
Rotherham
33
Sheffield
Cheshire
Derbyshire Nottinghamshire
Lincolnshire

TELLING TALES: THE MYTHS, LEGENDS AND FOLKLORE OF ENGLAND

HILD AND THE SNAKES

Hild was an Anglo-Saxon royal princess who became the first abbess of **Whitby Abbey** in AD 657. She was a formidable woman, honoured and respected for her wisdom by kings, churchmen and ordinary folk alike. Later legend told how she dealt with a plague of snakes in the abbey with the help of a 'holy or magical wand'. She drove them over the cliff, and they smashed their heads in the fall. Her prayers then miraculously turned them to stone. You can still sometimes find these 'petrified' snakes on Whitby's beaches – they're actually ammonite fossils, and millions of years old, but they look rather like coiled headless snakes. They were used on the abbey's coat of arms, and they can still be spotted on the coat of arms of Whitby town. You can find out more about Hild in the new exhibition at Whitby Abbey.

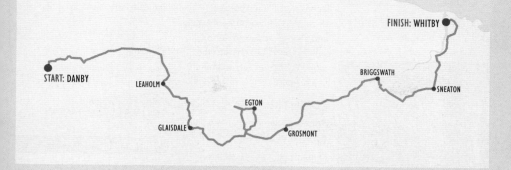

ST HILDA'S WAY

22 miles | 2 days | Danby to Whitby

St Hilda's Way celebrates the life of St Hild, Anglo-Saxon princess, spiritual leader, arts enthusiast and peacemaker, by visiting places dedicated to her in the beautiful North Yorkshire countryside. In 664 she hosted the famous Synod of Whitby as the first abbess of the double monastery of Streonshalh, now known as Whitby Abbey. You follow the River Esk, Yorkshire's only salmon river, to finish at Whitby Abbey. Make your way to the start at Danby by the railway, which follows the pilgrimage route along the Esk Valley back to Whitby, allowing easy transport back to the start of each day's pilgrimage.

View more details and a downloadable version of this route at www.english-heritage.org.uk/pilgrimage

Discover English Heritage sites along the pilgrimage route

Whitby Abbey *(p.234)*

In partnership with

the **British Pilgrimage Trust**

BURTON AGNES MANOR HOUSE

EAST RIDING OF YORKSHIRE
– YO25 4NB

A medieval manor house interior, with an atmospheric vaulted Norman undercroft and a 15th-century roof. Encased in brick walls in the 18th century, when it became a laundry.

OPENING TIMES

| 1 Apr-31 Oct, daily | 11am-5pm |
| 1 Nov-31 Mar | Closed |

The nearby Burton Agnes Hall and Gardens are privately owned and are not managed by English Heritage

VISIT US

Direction: In Burton Agnes village, 5 miles SW of Bridlington on A166

Train: Nafferton 5 miles

Bus: East Yorkshire service 45, 46 & 121

ACQ.1948

Parking (in Hall and Gardens car park).

MAP PAGE 345 (3J)
OS MAP 101, 295: TA102632

HOWDEN MINSTER

EAST RIDING OF YORKSHIRE
– DN14 7BS

HOWDEN MINSTER

The ruins of an elaborately decorated 14th-century chancel and chapter house (exterior viewing only), attached to the working 'minster' parish church of Howden.

OPENING TIMES

Any reasonable daylight hours

| 24-26, 31 Dec & 1 Jan | Closed |

VISIT US

Direction: In Howden, 23 miles W of Kingston Upon Hull, 25 miles SE of York, near the junction of A63 and A614

Train: Howden 1½ miles

Bus: Arriva Yorkshire service 4; East Yorkshire services X55, 155

ACQ.1971

Parking (on-street parking nearby – pay and display).

MAP PAGE 345 (4H)
OS MAP 105/106, 291: SE748283

SKIPSEA CASTLE

EAST RIDING OF YORKSHIRE

Impressive earthworks of a huge Norman motte-and-bailey castle and settlement, perhaps dating from the 1070s and among the first built in Yorkshire. Recent research, however, claims that the immense motte – 85 metres in diameter and 13 metres tall – is actually a re-used Iron Age burial mound. If so, it would be unique in Britain.

OPENING TIMES

Any reasonable daylight hours

VISIT US

Direction: Located 8 miles S of Bridlington, W of Skipsea village

Train: Bridlington 9 miles

SKIPSEA CASTLE

Bus: BusKing service 136 passes within ⅓ mile; East Yorkshire service 130 serves Skipsea village

ACQ.1911

Dogs on leads (restricted areas only).

Waterproof footwear recommended.

MAP PAGE 345 (3J)
OS MAP 107, 295: TA162551

GAINSTHORPE MEDIEVAL VILLAGE

NORTH LINCOLNSHIRE

One of the best-preserved deserted medieval villages in England, clearly visible as a complex of grassy humps. According to legend, the village was inhabited by thieves and was demolished by locals who could tolerate them no more.

OPENING TIMES

Any reasonable daylight hours

VISIT US

Direction: Located on minor road W of A15 – towards Cleatham; S of Hibaldstow; 5 miles SW of Brigg

Train: Kirton Lindsey 3 miles

Bus: Hornsby Travel service 94

ACQ.1974

Access via grazing field.

Beware – livestock may be grazing on site.

MAP PAGE 345 (5H)
OS MAP 112, 281: SE954011

THORNTON ABBEY & GATEHOUSE

NORTH LINCOLNSHIRE DN39 6TU

Among the most extraordinary medieval buildings in England, Thornton Abbey's ornate gatehouse is worth travelling a long way to see.

This largest and most magnificent of all English monastic gatehouses was raised around the 1380s. An early example of large-scale English building in brick, it's bedecked with an extravaganza of turrets, sculpture and carved figures. Within the entrance arch, look out for the original 14th-century doors and medieval graffiti of sailing ships.

Though it's also lavishly equipped with arrow-loops and other castle-like features, the gatehouse was built principally for show rather than defence. It proclaimed the wool-trade-based wealth and power of one of the richest Augustinian monasteries in England.

You can explore the gatehouse's intriguing interior, with its two floors of passageways and stairways, 'garderobe' toilets, tiny chambers and two big rooms, one probably housing the abbot's law courts. Now this 'great chamber' displays a wealth of carvings from the ruins, along with an exhibition tracing Thornton Abbey's history, including Henry VIII's visit, the abbey's brief rebirth as a Tudor 'college', and its role in huge Victorian Temperance rallies. There's a further display of site-finds and tactile features in the small ground-level visitor centre.

Don't miss the tranquil remains of the abbey itself, notably two beautifully decorated walls of the octagonal chapter house of 1282-1308. Full of fascinating features to discover, they're also an ideal place to picnic and relax.

St Peter's Church, Barton-upon-Humber (see p.218) is nearby.

OPENING TIMES

1 Apr-30 Jun, Wed-Sun & Bank Hols	10am-5pm
1 Jul-31 Aug, daily	10am-6pm
1 Sep-3 Nov, Sat-Sun	10am-5pm
4 Nov-31 Mar, Sat-Sun	10am-4pm
24-26 Dec & 1 Jan	Closed

Last entry 30 mins before closing

VISIT US

Direction: 18 miles NE of Scunthorpe, on a road N of A160; 7 miles SE of the Humber Bridge, on a road E of A1077

Train: Thornton Abbey ¼ mile

Tel: 01469 541445

NON-MEMBERS

Adult **£6.60** | Concession **£6.00**
Child **£4.00** | Family **£17.20**

ACQ.1938 | ♿ | ■ | E | ♨ | P | ⚕ | ⚤ | ⛱ | 🔒 | OVP

Disabled access (except gatehouse interior and part of abbey ruins).

No dogs allowed.

MAP PAGE 345 (4J)
OS MAP 113, 284: TA118189

ST PETER'S CHURCH,
BARTON-UPON-HUMBER

NORTH LINCOLNSHIRE DN18 5EX

OPENING TIMES

1 Apr-30 Sep, Sun & Bank Hols	10am-3pm
1 Oct-31 Mar	Closed

Last entry 30 mins before closing

VISIT US

Direction: In Barton-upon-Humber

Train: Barton-upon-Humber ½ mile

Bus: Stagecoach in Lincolnshire services 260, 450 and Humber Flyer; Stagecoach/East Yorkshire Humber Fast Cat service 350 also passes close by

Tel: 01652 632516
Thornton Abbey: 01469 541445

NON-MEMBERS

Adult £5.30 | Concession £4.80
Child £3.20 | Family £13.80

ACQ.1923 | 🚻 E ♿ 🏠 🚹 🚾 🏛 OVP

MAP PAGE 345 (4J)
OS MAP 107, 112, 281: TA035219

This famous Anglo-Saxon and medieval church is an archaeological as well as an architectural treasure, and among Britain's most important sources for historic bone analysis. The study of over 2,800 burials excavated here, ranging from Anglo-Saxon to Victorian times, has revealed remarkable insights into historic disease, diet and burial practices.

Begun in about 970 and partly made of recycled Roman masonry, the Anglo-Saxon church consisted of the tower and small adjacent baptistery. Look out for the tower's characteristically Saxon triangular-headed windows and decoration with thin stone strips – a feature echoing Saxon timber-framed buildings. The old church was progressively enlarged in medieval times, eventually reaching six times its original size. It displays a variety of medieval styles, and the upper tier of big 15th-century windows fill it with light. Declared redundant in 1972, it has become one of the most comprehensively studied churches in Britain.

The 'Buried Lives' exhibition tracks the story of this renowned church, following its fortunes and those of its people through 1,000 years. Thornton Abbey and Gatehouse (see p.217) is nearby.

ALDBOROUGH ROMAN SITE
NORTH YORKSHIRE – YO51 9ES

Aldborough was the 'capital' of the Romanised Brigantes, the largest tribe in Britain. Sections of the early Roman walls are visible amid a Victorian arboretum, with two mosaic pavements in their original positions. Outstanding collection of Roman artefacts.

OPENING TIMES

1 Apr-30 Sep, Sat-Sun & Bank Hols	10am-6pm
1 Oct-31 Mar	Closed
Last entry 30 mins before closing	
Friends of Roman Aldborough tour Every first Sun	11am & 2pm

VISIT US

Direction: Located in Aldborough, ¾ mile SE of Boroughbridge on a minor road off B6265; within 1 mile of junction of A1 and A6055

Train: Cattal 7½ miles

Bus: Harrogate Connect 1A and Transdev York Little Explorers 22 and 23

Tel: 01423 322768

NON-MEMBERS

Adult **£5.30** | Concession **£4.80**
Child **£3.20** | Family **£13.80**

ACQ.1952 🐎 🅿️ ♿ 📷 🚶 🚻 📹 🛍️ 📷 OVP

Dogs on leads (restricted areas only).

MAP PAGE 345 (3F)
OS MAP 299, 99: SE405662

BYLAND ABBEY   NORTH YORKSHIRE – YO61 4BD

At Byland Abbey you can admire one of Yorkshire's greatest Cistercian monasteries – and enjoy the Abbey Inn's hospitality.

Set against a backdrop of wooded hills, Byland was planned to the grandest of designs. The immense church, which today dominates the ruins, was the most ambitious Cistercian church in 12th-century Europe, and helped to pioneer the new Gothic style of architecture in northern England. You can trace the transition today in the combination of round Norman and pointed Gothic arches, and the towering west front. Decorative tiled floors still adorn many parts of the church.

You can also explore the remains of the monastic buildings, which originally housed some 300 monks and lay brothers, later reduced to just 14 by plague and Scots raiders.

Take a rest from exploring and enjoy a grand Yorkshire tea in the adjacent Abbey Inn tearoom (see opposite).

OPENING TIMES

1 Apr-30 Jun, Wed-Sun & Bank Hols	10am-5pm
1 Jul-31 Aug, daily	10am-5pm
1 Sep-3 Nov, Wed-Sun	10am-4pm
4 Nov-31 Mar, Sat-Sun	10am-3pm
24-26 Dec & 1 Jan	Closed
Last entry 30 mins before closing	
Access to parts of site limited during conservation work	

VISIT US

Direction: 2 miles S of A170, between Thirsk and Helmsley; near Coxwold village

Train: Thirsk 10 miles

Bus: Stephensons service 31, 31X

ACQ.1921 ♿ 🐎 🅿️ 🎭 f 🤚 📷
📷 🛍️ ⚠️ OVP

Parking (adjacent to Abbey Inn).

Toilets at Abbey Inn.

MAP PAGE 345 (2G)
OS MAP 100, OL26/299: SE549789

CLIFFORD'S TOWER, YORK

Clifford's Tower crowns the mighty earthwork mound raised by William the Conqueror in 1068. For centuries it was the keep and chief strongpoint of York Castle, the greatest royal fortress in medieval northern England.

NORTH YORKSHIRE YO1 9SA

The medieval castle was much altered in later centuries, and Clifford's Tower is now its principal surviving remnant. Like the city it once overawed, it has a rich history. The first Norman castle here – along with its sister fortress across the river, Baile Hill – was raised to protect newly conquered York from northern English rebels and their Viking allies. In 1190, a timber predecessor of the Tower was burnt when York's Jewish community of around 150 people committed mass suicide there to avoid massacre by a mob.

The Tower you see today was built in the 1250s for Henry III. Its four-lobed shape – hence its old local nickname 'the Minced Pie' – is unique in England. Throughout the long Scottish wars of Edward I and Edward II, York Castle was the Crown's principal northern base. The Tower housed the royal treasury and exchequer, lodgings for royal and noble visitors, and a richly decorated first-floor chapel above the entrance. You can still find traces of all these within its walls. The Tower's commanding position also made it an ideal backdrop for high-profile public executions. In 1322, Roger de Clifford, a baronial rebel against Edward II, was hanged from its walls, allegedly giving the Tower its name, and in 1537 Robert Aske, leader of the Pilgrimage of Grace rebellion against Henry VIII, was hanged in chains here.

Plots by a crooked Elizabethan custodian to sell off the Tower's stonework were foiled when outraged York citizens protested, and during the Civil War it was strengthened to serve as a Royalist gun platform. Its guns fought duels with the besieging Parliamentarian artillery. At first they scattered enemy gunners, but the Tower was then damaged by return fire. Years later, in 1684, a peacetime St George's Day gun-salute shot from its ramparts caused an accidental blaze which destroyed its internal buildings.

The impressive shell of the Tower continued to dominate the castle and its prison – which once housed the highwayman Dick Turpin and, later, German prisoners of war. After the prison finally closed in 1929, its exterior walls were demolished to open up views of the Tower – whose mound was restored to its original form – and the fine Georgian buildings in the old castle bailey.

Today Clifford's Tower offers you amazing 360-degree panoramas from its lofty rampart walk. Enjoy unrivalled views of the Minster and the city of York, with its medieval and later churches and civic buildings. In the distance you can see the Yorkshire Wolds and even the North York Moors.

OPENING TIMES

1 Apr-30 Sep, daily	10am-6pm
1 Oct-3 Nov, daily	10am-5pm
4 Nov-31 Mar, daily	10am-4pm
24-25 Dec	Closed

Last entry 30 mins before closing

VISIT US

Direction: Tower St, York

Train: York 1 mile

Bus: From surrounding areas

Tel: 01904 646940

Local Tourist Information:
York: 01904 550099

NON-MEMBERS

Adult £6.30 | Concession £5.70
Child £3.80 | Family £16.40

ACQ 1915 [f] [♨] [▢] [✈] [P] [📷] [⚠] [OVP]

Parking (local charge).

Access (via steep steps).

MAP PAGE 345 (3G)
OS MAP 105, 290: SE605515

EASBY ABBEY
NORTH YORKSHIRE – DL10 7EU

Impressive ruins of a Premonstratensian abbey, set by the River Swale. It includes a lavishly appointed refectory of c. 1300 and extensive monastic buildings. The neighbouring parish church displays outstanding 13th-century wall-paintings.

Easby can also be reached via a pleasant walk from Richmond Castle (p.228).

OPENING TIMES

1 Apr-30 Sep, daily	10am-6pm
1-31 Oct, daily	10am-5pm
1 Nov-31 Mar, daily	10am-4pm
24-26, 31 Dec & 1 Jan	Closed

VISIT US

Direction: 1 mile SE of Richmond, off B6271

Bus: Dales & District 29, 55 & X34 to St Trinian's Hall then c. ¾ mile walk via footpath

Guidebook (from Richmond Castle).

MAP PAGE 345 (2F)
OS MAP 92, 304: NZ185003

GISBOROUGH PRIORY
NORTH YORKSHIRE – TS14 6HG

The ruins of an Augustinian priory founded by the Bruce family, afterwards kings of Scotland. They are dominated by the dramatic skeleton of the 14th-century church's east end.

Managed by Gisborough Priory Project.

OPENING TIMES

1 Apr-31 Oct, Wed-Sun & Bank Hols	10am-4pm
1 Nov-29 Feb	Closed
1-31 Mar, Wed-Sun	10am-4pm

Managed alongside historic woodland gardens by the Gisborough Priory Project. Please check the Gisborough Priory Project website for additional open days and more information

VISIT US

Direction: In Guisborough town, next to the parish church

Train: Marske 4½ miles

Bus: Arriva services 5, 5A, 28, 81, X93 (Arriva services 5, 5A & 81 actually pass by)

Tel: 07391 351757
The number is manned by volunteers but any messages left will be responded to as soon as possible

Toilets and parking (in town).

MAP PAGE 345 (1G)
OS MAP 94, OL26/306: NZ617160

KIRKHAM PRIORY
NORTH YORKSHIRE – YO60 7JS

Extensive ruins of a priory founded by Walter Espec of Helmsley Castle, in an idyllic setting by the River Derwent. Highlights include the magnificent heraldry-bedecked gatehouse, and fine stone-carving on the refectory doorway and the 'laver' where canons washed.

OPENING TIMES

1 Apr-31 Jul, Wed-Sun & Bank Hols	10am-6pm
1-31 Aug, daily	10am-6pm
1-30 Sep, Wed-Sun	10am-6pm
1 Oct-3 Nov, Wed-Sun	10am-5pm
4 Nov-31 Mar	Closed

Last entry 30 mins before closing

VISIT US

Direction: 5 miles SW of Malton, on a minor road off A64

Train: Malton 6 miles

Bus: Ryecat service 184 (Tue). Otherwise Yorkshire Coastliner services 840, 843 & 845 to Whitwell Hill and then ¾ mile walk

Tel: 01653 618768

NON-MEMBERS

Adult £5.30 | Concession £4.80
Child £3.20 | Family £13.80

MAP PAGE 345 (3H)
OS MAP 100, 300: SE736658

HELMSLEY CASTLE

NORTH YORKSHIRE YO62 5AB

Explore the impressive ruins of a great medieval castle, set beside the attractive market town of Helmsley. Discover how life was lived here over the centuries.

The spectacular ditches surrounding the fortress were created after 1120 for Walter Espec, the Norman baron 'of gigantic stature' who also founded nearby Rievaulx Abbey. Within them Robert de Roos – crusader, Knight Templar and Magna Carta baron – and his descendants raised the stonework defences you see today, including the lofty east tower which still dominates the ruins and the town.

Following the castle's only military trial, when its Civil War Royalist defenders were starved into submission after a three-month siege, its ruins became a romantic 'eye-catcher' for Duncombe Park. Enjoy sweeping views over Duncombe's parkland and recreated walled garden.

But Helmsley wasn't only a fortress. In Elizabethan times its chamber block became a luxurious country house. You can still see some of its fine panelling and plasterwork alongside displays tracing the castle's history as home as well as stronghold. There's a wealth of site finds, and plenty of interactive and hands-on features.

Book a free monthly expert-guided tour of Helmsley Archaeology Store, housing fascinating artefacts from English Heritage's sites in northern England. Call 01439 770442 for details.

Rievaulx (p.230) and Byland (p.219) Abbeys are both nearby. Rievaulx can be reached on foot via the Cleveland Way National Trail. Approx. 1½ hours (2½ miles) each way. Strong footwear is required.

OPENING TIMES

1 Apr-30 Sep, daily	10am-6pm
1 Oct-3 Nov, daily	10am-5pm
4 Nov-16 Feb, Fri-Sun	10am-4pm
17-23 Feb, daily	10am-4pm
24 Feb-31 Mar, Fri-Sun	10am-4pm
24-26 Dec & 1 Jan	Closed

Last entry 30 mins before closing

Helmsley Archaeology Store Tours
For tour times and dates, please check our Helmsley Archaeology Store webpage. Booking essential, call Customer Services on 0370 333 1181

Tours are free to members and non-members and are led by the Collections Curators

VISIT US

Address: Helmsley Castle, Castlegate, Helmsley, North Yorkshire YO62 5AB

Direction: Near the town centre, adjacent to the long-stay car park off the B1257

Bus: Stephenson's 31, 31X; Scarborough & District 128

Tel: 01439 770442

NON-MEMBERS

Adult £8.00 | Concession £7.20
Child £4.80 | Family £20.80

Audio tours.

Parking (large car park adjacent to castle; charge payable).

Toilets (in car park and town centre).

MAP PAGE 345 (2G)
OS MAP 100, OL26: SE611836

MARMION TOWER

NORTH YORKSHIRE – HG4 5JQ

Fine 15th-century gatehouse of a vanished riverside manor house, with a beautiful oriel window. Monuments of the Marmion family owners grace the adjacent church.

OPENING TIMES

1 Apr-30 Sep, daily	10am-6pm
1-31 Oct, daily	10am-5pm
1 Nov-31 Mar, daily	10am-4pm
24-26, 31 Dec & 1 Jan	Closed

VISIT US

Direction: On A6108 in West Tanfield

Train: Thirsk 10 miles

Bus: Dales & District service 159

ACQ.1976 🦮 ⚠

MAP PAGE 345 (2F)
OS MAP 99, 298: SE268787

PIERCEBRIDGE ROMAN BRIDGE

NORTH YORKSHIRE

Stonework foundations of a bridge, now marooned in a field, which once led to Piercebridge Roman Fort.

OPENING TIMES

Any reasonable daylight hours

VISIT US

Direction: At Piercebridge; 4 miles W of Darlington, on B6275

Train: Darlington 5 miles

Bus: Arriva X75 & X76

ACQ.1975 🦮 ⚠

Parking available at nearby George Hotel. May infrequently be restricted when hosting large functions. Not managed by English Heritage.

MAP PAGE 345 (1F)
OS MAP 93, 304: NZ214155

PICKERING CASTLE

NORTH YORKSHIRE – YO18 7AX

Impressive ruins of a medieval royal castle, set in an attractive moors-edge market town. Towered 13th- and 14th-century curtain walls surround a high Norman 'motte' mound, which you can climb for spectacular views.

OPENING TIMES

1 Apr-30 Sep, daily	10am-6pm
1 Oct-3 Nov, daily	10am-5pm
4 Nov-31 Mar	Closed

Last entry 30 mins before closing

VISIT US

Direction: In Pickering; 15 miles SW of Scarborough

Train: Malton (9 miles) or Pickering (North Yorkshire Moors Railway) ¼ mile

Bus: Scarborough & District 128, Ryecat 173, 174 & 175; Yorkshire Coastliner 840; Hayesway Travel 170 & 171

Tel: 01751 474989

NON-MEMBERS

Adult £6.30 | Concession £5.70
Child £3.80 | Family £16.40

Disabled access (except motte).

MAP PAGE 345 (2H)
OS MAP 100, OL27: SE799845

ST MARY'S CHURCH, STUDLEY ROYAL

NORTH YORKSHIRE – HG4 3DY

Magnificent High Victorian Anglican church, designed in the 1870s by the flamboyant architect William Burges. Its extravagantly decorated interior survives unaltered.

Owned by English Heritage and managed by the National Trust as part of the Fountains Abbey and Studley Royal Estate (see p.309).

OPENING TIMES

1 Apr-30 Sep, daily	12pm-4pm
1 Oct-31 Mar	Closed

Some additional opening may be available in March and October. Please see website for details

VISIT US

Direction: Located 2½ miles W of Ripon, off B6265; in the grounds of the Studley Royal Estate

Bus: Dales & District 139 (Mon, Thu & Sat)

Tel: 01765 608888

ACQ.1975 ♿ 🦮 P

Parking (at visitor centre or Studley Royal).

MAP PAGE 345 (3F)
OS MAP 99, 298/299: SE275693

MIDDLEHAM CASTLE

NORTH YORKSHIRE DL8 4QG

One of Yorkshire's most impressive medieval fortresses, Middleham Castle became the northern power-base of King Richard III. It stands in an attractive Wensleydale market town.

The castle's core is the mighty Norman keep, among the biggest in England. Three storeys high, it was probably built during the 1170s. Around this keep the powerful Neville family, Earls of Westmorland and of Warwick, progressively constructed three ranges of luxurious lodgings. By the mid-15th century the castle had turned into a fortified palace – 'the Windsor of the North'. Though roofless, most of the castle's buildings survive, including a multi-storey latrine tower and remains of a unique 16th-century horse-powered mill, making Middleham a rewarding place to explore.

RICHARD III'S POWER BASE

Though there is no firm evidence that Richard III lived here as a child, he may have visited as a teenager in the guardianship of 'Warwick the Kingmaker'. But in the 1470s Richard certainly made Middleham the focus of his growing power in the north, taking over the castle after Warwick's death and marrying his daughter Anne. The couple's only son, Edward of Middleham, was born and died here, aged no more than 10.

Enjoy wonderful views over Wensleydale from the keep's viewing platform. In an exhibition about the castle's past you can see a replica of the famous Middleham Jewel, a 15th-century gold and sapphire pendant found nearby. Engraved with religious images and magic words, it may possibly have belonged to Richard's mother-in-law, Anne Beauchamp.

OPENING TIMES

1 Apr-30 Sep, daily	10am-6pm
1 Oct-3 Nov, daily	10am-5pm
4 Nov-31 Mar, Sat-Sun	10am-4pm
24-26 Dec & 1 Jan	Closed

Last entry 30 mins before closing

VISIT US

Direction: Located at Middleham, 2 miles S of Leyburn on A6108

Train: Leyburn (Wensleydale Railway) 2 miles

Bus: Dales & District service 159

Tel: 01969 623899

Local Tourist Information:
Leyburn: 01969 623069

NON-MEMBERS

Adult **£6.60** | Concession **£6.00**
Child **£4.00** | Family **£17.20**

ACQ.1926 🚷 ✕ E f ⚒ ▢ ▣ 🖵 ⚠ OVP

Disabled access (except keep).

MAP PAGE 345 (2F)
OS MAP 99, OL30: SE127876

MOUNT GRACE PRIORY, HOUSE AND GARDENS

With gardens transformed in 2018, now's the time to enjoy a day out at Mount Grace, picturesquely set against the wooded slopes of the Cleveland Hills.

NORTH YORKSHIRE DL6 3JG

At Mount Grace you will find three attractions in one; an Arts and Crafts mansion, 13 acres of rejuvenated gardens, and the most unusual of all our medieval monasteries. There's the brand new Orchard Café and plenty for families to explore together.

Founded in 1398 by Thomas Holland, Duke of Surrey, Mount Grace was the last of the great Yorkshire monasteries. Five centuries later, its ruins were bought by wealthy industrialist Sir Lowthian Bell, patron of the Arts and Crafts movement. Following the movement's principles of craftsmanship, natural materials and simplicity, he refurbished a 17th-century mansion adapted from the priory's guest house, fronting it with terraced gardens.

Now these gardens have been brought back to life by celebrity garden designer Chris Beardshaw. You can wander the terraces, admire richly planted herbaceous borders and spot wildlife on the ponds. We've got individual pamphlets for each season to help green-fingered visitors get the most out of the gardens. Families can collect a children's explorer pack, looking out for the Priory Stoat badges on benches and interpretation panels.

In a quiet woodland corner, you'll discover our new Orchard Café, which is open to all. It's imaginatively designed and built (in the Arts and Crafts spirit) of sustainable timber and recycled slate, with indoor and outdoor seating.

Within the mansion, you'll see how Sir Lowthian Bell sensitively combined 17th-century features with Arts and Crafts remodelling. Rooms have been recreated as they might have appeared in 1901, with wallpapers and fabrics designed by the great Arts and Crafts guru, William Morris. Don't miss the attics, nurseries for the Bell children in the 1920s and 30s; look out for pencilled measurements on a wall, recording their growing heights. Mount Grace was well-loved by the famous adventurer, archaeologist and Middle East diplomat, Sir Lowthian's granddaughter Gertrude Bell.

You'll also find a fascinating display, including site discoveries, telling the intriguing story of medieval Mount Grace Priory, much the best-preserved of the few English Carthusian monasteries. Stepping into its extensive ruins, you'll notice how they differ radically from conventional monasteries. Unlike other monks who lived and worshipped communally, Carthusians were semi-hermits. Each monk lived in solitude in one of the 25 cottage-like cells ranged round the vast Great Cloister, meeting his brethren only for a few hours each week in the small church and refectory.

PLENTY FOR FAMILIES TO EXPLORE

One of these two-storey cells is recreated as it appeared in the late 15th century. It contains a living room, study and bedroom-chapel, with a workshop above. An L-shaped hatch allowed servants to pass in the monk's frugal meat-free meals without seeing the occupant. The little walled garden has covered walkways and a toilet, flushed by an ingenious plumbing system, which chanelled water to each cell. The monk's garden has been newly replanted, and you'll discover what plants it grew for food, cures and contemplation.

Owned by the National Trust, maintained and managed by English Heritage.

🖼 *The Last Knight.*

OPENING TIMES

1 Apr-30 Sep, daily	10am-6pm
1 Oct-3 Nov, daily	10am-5pm
4 Nov-16 Feb, Sat-Sun	10am-4pm
17-23 Feb, daily	10am-4pm
24 Feb-31 Mar, Wed-Sun	10am-4pm
24-26 Dec & 1 Jan	Closed

Last entry 30 mins before closing

During the winter, the attics may close early due to low light levels

VISIT US

Direction: 12 miles N of Thirsk, and 6 miles NE of Northallerton, near A19. **Warning:** take care when turning across the fast dual carriageway. Look out for brown EH direction signs placed approx. ½ mile before the turning

Train: Northallerton 6 miles

Tel: 01609 883494

Local Tourist Information:
Thirsk: 01845 522755

NON-MEMBERS

Adult **£9.90** | Concession **£9.00**
Child **£6.00** | Family **£25.80**

National Trust members admitted free, except on event days

Assistance dogs only.

Parking charges apply to non-members.
Parking free for Members.

MAP PAGE 345 (2G)
OS MAP 99, OL26: SE449985

RICHMOND CASTLE

NORTH YORKSHIRE DL10 4QW

Richmond Castle is impressively sited on a rocky promontory above the River Swale, beside a picturesque Dales market town.

Among the oldest Norman stone fortresses in Britain, it was begun in about 1070 by William the Conqueror's Breton supporter, Alan the Red. The great tower-keep, added about a century later, stands over 30 metres (100 feet) high, and is remarkably complete within.

According to legend, King Arthur and his knights lie sleeping in a cavern beneath the keep, and you can still hear the drumbeats of a drummer-boy lost in a secret passage.

Trace the history of the castle, and discover the poignant graffiti left by the conscientious objectors imprisoned here for refusing to fight in the First World War.

NEW FOR 2019

This summer, vibrant and playful new interpretation will breathe fresh life into Richmond Castle's ancient walls.

The redisplayed museum highlights the people of the fortress, from Alan the Red to First World War conscientious objectors. A new space for reflection will help you discover their story.

Interactive games will tempt families to explore the whole castle, and immerse you in its medieval daily life; try your hand at a medieval play in the secluded cockpit garden.

Enjoy a new illuminated presentation in the keep's great hall. Then climb to the lofty keep roof, where our new orientation tables help you explore breathtaking all round views, the best in the region.

OPENING TIMES

1 Apr-30 Sep, daily	10am-6pm
1 Oct-3 Nov, daily	10am-5pm
4 Nov-16 Feb, Sat-Sun	10am-4pm
17-23 Feb, daily	10am-4pm
24 Feb-31 Mar, Sat-Sun	10am-4pm
24-26 Dec & 1 Jan	Closed

Last entry 30 mins before closing

VISIT US

Direction: In Richmond, just off the market place

Bus: Arriva X26, X27; Dales & District 29, X34, X54, 55, 159; Hodgsons Coaches 79, 79A; Little White Bus service 30, 32, 32A & Richmondshire Rover service; North Yorks CC 31 & 31A

Tel: 01748 822493

NON-MEMBERS

Adult **£7.20** | Concession **£6.50**
Child **£4.30** | Family **£18.70**

Disc parking (2 hours free in market place – not managed by English Heritage).

Disabled parking available at site on request, or in market place.

MAP PAGE 345 (2F)
OS MAP 92, 304: NZ172007

SPOFFORTH CASTLE

NORTH YORKSHIRE – HG3 1DA

The ruined hall and chamber of a fortified medieval manor house of the powerful Percy family, rebuilt in the 15th century. Its undercroft is cut into a rocky outcrop.

Managed by Spofforth-with-Stockeld Parish Council.

OPENING TIMES

1 Apr-30 Sep, daily	10am-6pm
1 Oct-31 Mar, daily	10am-4pm
24-26, 31 Dec & 1 Jan	Closed

VISIT US

Direction: 3½ miles SE of Harrogate, off A661 at Spofforth

Train: Pannal 4 miles

Bus: Transdev Harrogate & District services 70 & 71; Harrogate Coach Travel X70

ACQ.1924 🐕 ⚠

Dogs on leads (restricted areas only).

MAP PAGE 345 (3F)
OS MAP 104, 289: SE36051

STANWICK IRON AGE FORTIFICATIONS

NORTH YORKSHIRE

A reconstructed portion of the ramparts of the huge Iron Age power-centre of the Brigantes, the most important tribe in pre-Roman northern Britain. Its defences were once some 4 miles long. The Brigantian capital later moved to Aldborough Roman Site (see p.219).

STANWICK IRON AGE FORTIFICATIONS

OPENING TIMES

Any reasonable daylight hours

VISIT US

Direction: Located on a minor road off A6274, at Forcett Village

Train: Darlington 10 miles

Bus: Dales & District service 29; Hodgsons 79A (Thu)

ACQ.1953 🐕 ⚠

Dogs on leads (restricted areas only).

MAP PAGE 345 (1F)
OS MAP 92, 304: NZ179124

STEETON HALL GATEWAY

NORTH YORKSHIRE – LS25 5PD

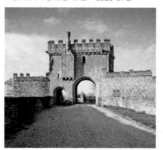

A fine example of a small, well-preserved manorial gatehouse dating from the 14th century.

OPENING TIMES

Exterior only: Any reasonable daylight hours

VISIT US

Direction: Located 4 miles NE of Castleford, on a minor road off A162 at South Milford

Train: South Milford 1 mile

Bus: Arriva Yorkshire 493

ACQ.1948 ♿ 🐕

Dogs on leads (restricted areas only).

MAP PAGE 345 (4G)
OS MAP 105, 290: SE484314

WHARRAM PERCY DESERTED MEDIEVAL VILLAGE

NORTH YORKSHIRE – YO17 9TN

Europe's best-known deserted medieval village, in a remote Wolds valley. Continuously occupied for six centuries, Wharram was abandoned by c. 1527. Above the substantial church ruins and mill pond, the outlines of many houses are traceable on a grassy plateau. Graphic panels recreate their original appearance.

Download a free audio tour from our website.

OPENING TIMES

Any reasonable daylight hours

VISIT US

Direction: 6 miles SE of Malton, on minor road from B1248; ½ mile S of Wharram-le-Street. Park in car park, then ¾ mile walk via uneven track, steep in places. Site also accessible on foot via Wolds Way ramblers' path. Sturdy and waterproof footwear required. Parts of site slope steeply, and farm livestock likely to be present on site and access path

Train: Malton 8 miles

Bus: Stephenson's 190 to Wharram-Le-Street then 1 mile walk

ACQ.1972 🐕 🅿 ⚠

Please note: site is hazardous in snowy conditions

Beware – cattle may be grazing.

MAP PAGE 345 (3H)
OS MAP 100, 300: SE859644

RIEVAULX ABBEY

Rievaulx Abbey offers a host of exciting discoveries. Set in a tranquil wooded valley, the stately ruins are enhanced by many attractions. A welcoming café, site museum, audio tour and engaging family trail help you enjoy the most impressive and extensive monastic remains in Britain.

NORTH YORKSHIRE YO62 5LB

'High hills surround the valley, clothed by trees and encircling it like a crown'; this 12th-century description of Rievaulx's setting still applies today. Here, in 1132, just twelve monks of the new Cistercian order which was revolutionising monasticism in western Europe founded an abbey, 'far from the haunts of men' It became one of the wealthiest monasteries in medieval England. By the 1160s a peak of around 640 monks were living here, attracted by the holiness of Abbot Aelred. After his death the monks successfully sought his canonisation, rebuilding the east end of the church in the new Early English style of Gothic architecture to house his shrine.

Surviving almost to its full height, the east end of this church still serenely dominates the ruins. You can also explore the maze of monastic buildings where the white-robed Cistercian choir monks and their brown-clad lay brothers lived, worked and cared for their sick. The audio tour and pictorial interpretation panels help you find the site's highlights, like the refectory – the finest example in Britain – where the monks ate their largely vegetarian meals. You can also

STAY WITH US

Enjoy the peace and tranquillity of Rievaulx after it closes to the public when you stay in the **Refectory Cottage**. Sleeps 4.

See p.332 for details on staying at **Rievaulx** and our other holiday cottages.

seek out intriguing features like the 'warming-house' sink where the monks did their laundry, the monks' toilets, and the tannery where they prepared leather in vats of urine.

Discover lots more about life at Rievaulx in the must-see museum. Here a wonderful display of artefacts ranges from beautifully carved stonework (including a tiger-hunt using a mirror to distract the prey), via building tools, writing equipment and a 'scourge' whip for monastic penance, to everyday items like 'patten' footwear for muddy weather. A screen presentation illustrates major chapters in Rievaulx's story, including its suppression by Henry VIII in 1538. The 'Shattered Remains' display recalls the wholesale destruction at this time, before Rievaulx's later rebirth as a supremely romantic ruin, a delight to visit.

You can take a break from exploring in the imaginatively designed café. Soak up views of the abbey as you sample a wide range of Yorkshire dishes. There's indoor and outdoor seating, picnic tables, and a big shop offering local products and plants, so allow plenty of time for your visit to Rievaulx Abbey, one of England's most fascinating and atmospheric monastic ruins.

You can also reach Rievaulx from Helmsley Castle (p.223) on foot, via the Cleveland Way. Approx 1½ hours (2½ miles) each way. Strong footwear required. Byland Abbey (p.219), another great Yorkshire Cistercian monastery, is within easy driving distance.

Transformers; The Last Knight.

OPENING TIMES

1 Apr-30 Sep, daily	10am-6pm
1 Oct-3 Nov, daily	10am-5pm
4 Nov-23 Dec, Sat-Sun	10am-4pm
2 Jan-16 Feb, Sat-Sun	10am-4pm
17-23 Feb, daily	10am-4pm
24 Feb-31 Mar, Wed-Sun	10am-4pm
Christmas Opening	
24-25 Dec	Closed
26 Dec-1 Jan, daily	10am-4pm
Last entry 30 mins before closing	

Please note: tearoom closes 30 mins before the abbey

VISIT US

Address: Rievaulx Abbey, Rievaulx, Nr Helmsley, N. Yorks YO62 5LB

Direction: In Rievaulx; 2¼ miles N of Helmsley, on minor road off B1257

Bus: There is no bus service to the Abbey. Nearest location is Helmsley from which it is a 2-mile walk. Stephenson's 31, 31X; Scarborough & District 128 serve Helmsley

Tel: 01439 798228

NON-MEMBERS

Adult **£10.40** | Concession **£9.40**
Child **£6.20** | Family **£27.00**

Parking charges apply to non-members.
Parking free for Members.

MAP PAGE 345 (2G)
OS MAP 100, OL26: SE577850

SCARBOROUGH CASTLE

Battered by siege and attack but still majestic, Scarborough Castle crowns a spectacular headland with a 3,000 year story, amazing views – and 16 acres of history to explore.

NORTH YORKSHIRE YO11 1HY

Soaring between the two bays of the famous seaside resort, with steep drops on three sides, the headland is a natural stronghold, reachable only by a slender neck of land. It attracted prehistoric, Roman, Saxon and perhaps Viking settlers, and the medieval castle made it almost impregnable. As you approach the castle via the strongly-fortified barbican and narrow bridge, the only way in, you'll soon see why it was so hard to attack, defying medieval barons, Tudor rebels and Civil War besiegers. Dominating the fortress stands Henry II's 12th-century Great Tower keep, with one side sheered away by Parliamentarian heavy cannon in 1645. But even then the besiegers couldn't get in, and the garrison had to be starved out.

In the Master Gunner's House, you can trace the headland's long history through site-finds, from a replica Bronze Age sword via Civil War cannonballs to the nose-cap of a shell fired at Scarborough in 1914 during a bombardment by audacious German warships which shocked the whole nation.

Leave plenty of time to explore the vast grassy headland – bigger than 12 football pitches – and discover its many historic features. It's maintained as a gigantic wildflower-meadow, where in high summer you may even spot orchids. On the cliff edge furthest from the keep you'll find the remains of a Roman signal station, one of a chain of beacon-towers which gave warning of Saxon coastal raids in the 4th century AD. An Anglo-Saxon church built on its site may have stood here when the Viking King Harald Hardrada seized the headland in 1066, hurling down blazing timbers to fire the town below.

You can follow the long and many-towered curtain wall which King John built to guard the slope facing towards the harbour. Scarborough was among the busiest east-coast ports in medieval England, making the castle which protected it one of the most important in Yorkshire. Within the ditched Inner Bailey, the heart of the castle, a lofty viewing platform offers you amazing views over the town, the harbour, and the great sweep of South Bay. You'll also get wonderful views – over the narrow castle approach and North Bay – from the platform within the Great Tower, with its tiers of round-topped Norman windows. Dominating the castle and the landscape for miles around, it's one of the finest keeps raised by the champion royal castle-builder King Henry II.

With the finest coastal views in Yorkshire, so much history and such a vast area to explore or play in, Scarborough Castle offers the ideal family day out. Take a break from exploring in our coffee shop.

Guided tours with staff or volunteers are available most weekends throughout the year, at no additional charge. Enquire at the site in advance for details.

OPENING TIMES

1 Apr-30 Sep, daily	10am-6pm
1 Oct-3 Nov, daily	10am-5pm
4 Nov-23 Dec, Sat-Sun	10am-4pm
2 Jan-16 Feb, Sat-Sun	10am-4pm
17-23 Feb, daily	10am-4pm
24 Feb-31 Mar, Wed-Sun	10am-4pm
Christmas Opening	
24-25 Dec	Closed
26 Dec-1 Jan, daily	10am-4pm
Last entry 30 mins before closing	

Please note: coffee shop closes 30 mins before castle. During winter, opening times of coffee shop may vary

VISIT US

Direction: Castle Road, E of the town centre

Train: Scarborough 1 mile

Bus: From surrounding areas to the harbour (not up to the castle)

Tel: 01723 372451

Local Tourist Information:
Scarborough: 01723 383636

NON-MEMBERS

Adult £7.60 | Concession £6.90
Child £4.60 | Family £19.80

ACQ.1920

No public parking (Very limited parking for Blue Badge holders only. Please enquire in advance of visit, especially on event days).

MAP PAGE 345 (2J)
OS MAP 101, 301: TA050892

WHITBY ABBEY

The hauntingly dramatic ruins of Whitby Abbey stand high on the headland above the picturesque fishing port. This year, your experience of visiting them will be transformed by imaginative new developments throughout the headland.

NORTH YORKSHIRE YO22 4JT

The first monastery here was founded in AD 657, headed by the formidable Anglo-Saxon royal princess Abbess Hild. Here Caedmon the cowherd was miraculously transformed into an inspired poet and here the future of the English church was decided by the crucial Synod of Whitby.

The iconic ruins you see today belong to the church of the re-founded medieval abbey, built in the Early English Gothic style during the 13th century. Battered by time, weather and war, these supremely romantic ruins also offer panoramic clifftop views, and it's easy to see how they inspired Bram Stoker's famous Gothic novel, *Dracula*.

They share the headland with Abbey House, the great mansion of the Cholmley family, which now hosts the inspiring new museum. In its courtyard you'll find the famous bronze Gladiator statue and a new metalwork reconstruction revealing what it looked like in its 17th-century heyday.

NEW FOR 2019

We've made momentous changes at Whitby Abbey this year. New developments offer a warmer welcome, and inventive new interpretation helps you discover the headland's 3,000 years of history.

A tree-lined avenue, with scented plants and seating, now guides you towards the visitor centre in Abbey House. There you'll find a spacious new shop and a brand-new atmospheric and dramatically lit museum, where themed displays, building reconstructions and interactives explore the abbey's people and myths. You'll discover how the headland inspired great artists and writers including Turner, Lewis Carroll, and Bram Stoker; how Abbess Hild turned local snakes into ammonites; and how the sea-sunk bells of Whitby Abbey can still allegedly be heard. Look out for surprises.

In the soaring, atmospheric ruins of the great abbey church, discover our interactive new storytelling. Fun learning experiences for all the family now guide you through the abbey's multi-layered history in imaginative new ways.

There's also a new coffee shop, open to all, in the abbey lodge.

If you've never visited Whitby Abbey, now's the time to come. If you've visited before, you'll find the experience of re-discovery greatly enhanced and deepened.

Please note: from the Whitby harbour area, you can reach the abbey directly on foot via the 199 'abbey steps'. Alternatively, a well-signposted road leads from the town outskirts to the clifftop abbey.

OPENING TIMES

1 Apr-30 Sep, daily	10am-6pm
1 Oct-3 Nov, daily	10am-5pm
4 Nov-23 Dec, Sat-Sun	10am-4pm
2 Jan-16 Feb, Sat-Sun	10am-4pm
17-23 Feb, daily	10am-4pm
24 Feb-31 Mar, Wed-Sun	10am-4pm
Christmas Opening	
24-25 Dec	Closed
26 Dec-1 Jan, daily	10am-4pm
Last entry 30 mins before closing	

VISIT US

Address: Whitby Abbey, Abbey Lane, Whitby, North Yorkshire YO22 4JT

Direction: On cliff top, E of Whitby

Train: Whitby ½ mile

Bus: Coastal & Country seasonal town tour services 1 & 1A serve Whitby Abbey. The town is also served by Arriva, Coastal & Country and Yorkshire Coastliner regular services

Tel: 01947 603568

Local Tourist Information: 01723 383636

NON-MEMBERS

Adult £9.80 | Concession £8.80
Child £5.90 | Family £25.50

ACQ.1920

New guidebook.

Disabled access (south entrance parking, charged).

Dogs welcome on leads.

Parking not managed by English Heritage (charge payable).

Toilets situated in the car park are not operated by English Heritage (charge payable).

Tearoom not managed by English Heritage.

MAP PAGE 345 (1H)
OS MAP 94, OL27: NZ903112

WHEELDALE ROMAN ROAD

NORTH YORKSHIRE

A mile-long stretch of enigmatic ancient road – probably Roman but possibly later or earlier – still with its hardcore and drainage ditches. Amid wild and beautiful moorland.

OPENING TIMES

Any reasonable daylight hours

VISIT US

Direction: S of Goathland; W of A169; 7 miles S of Whitby

Train: Goathland (North Yorkshire Moors Rly) (4 miles) or Newtondale Halt (then 3 mile forest walk)

Bus: Yorkshire Coastliner service 840 to Goathland then 4 miles walk. Alternatively alight at Ellerbeck bridge and walk 2½ miles over Howl Moor

Local Tourist Information:
Pickering: 01751 473791

MAP PAGE 345 (2H)
OS MAP 94/100, OL27: SE806977

STAY WITH US

Prior's Lodge sleeps four, with views over the mansion's garden in one direction, the monastic ruins in the other.

See p.332 for details on staying at **Mount Grace** and our other holiday cottages.

YORK COLD WAR BUNKER

NORTH YORKSHIRE – YO24 4HT

For 30 years the volunteers of the Royal Observer Corps watched for nuclear Armageddon here. At a time of crisis 60 men and women would be entombed within 'No 20 Group Control', ready to plot nuclear explosions and radioactive fallout across Yorkshire. Within the brutal concrete exterior is a chilling Cold War time capsule, where original monitoring and communications equipment sit alongside the necessities of life; a canteen, a dormitory and support systems designed to last just 30 days.

Visits are by guided tour, enhanced by a striking 10-minute film (PG rated) telling the story of the Cold War.

OPENING TIMES

1 Apr-30 Sep, Wed-Sun & Bank Hols	10am-6pm
1 Oct-3 Nov, Wed-Sun	10am-5pm
4 Nov-31 Mar, Sat-Sun	10am-4pm
24-26 Dec & 1 Jan	Closed

By tours only, tours every hour. Tours last approximately 1 hour. No need to book. Last tour one hour before closing

Weekdays:
Admission for schools and groups only. Booking 14 days in advance, minimum fee applies

VISIT US

Direction: Monument Close, off Acomb Road (B1224), turning opposite Hobgate, approx. 2 miles from York city centre

Train: York 1¼ miles

Bus: First in York service 1; Connexions service 412

Tel: 01904 797935

Local Tourist Information:
York: 01904 646940

NON-MEMBERS

Adult **£9.20** | Concession **£8.30**
Child **£5.50** | Family **£23.90**

Free parking.

MAP PAGE 345 (3G)
OS MAP 105, 290: SE580515

CONISBROUGH CASTLE

SOUTH YORKSHIRE DN12 3BU

Step into the inspirational setting of Walter Scott's *Ivanhoe* novel. This most unusual medieval fortress has been brought to life by a spectacular and highly imaginative makeover funded by the Heritage Lottery Fund.

The design of Conisbrough Castle's tall cylindrical keep, ringed with six great turret buttresses, is unique in Britain. Probably begun in the 1170s, it was later reinforced by a turreted outer wall. It proclaims the ambition, power and wealth of its builders: Hamelin Plantagenet, illegitimate half-brother of King Henry II, and his wife, the formidable Lady Isabel de Warenne, heiress of Conisbrough.

CLIMBING TO THE ROOF, YOU'LL FIND WONDERFUL ALL-ROUND VISTAS OVER THE SURROUNDING COUNTRYSIDE

You can explore the whole fully roofed and floored keep, with its three big chambers and lovely miniature chapel, guided by larger-than-life wall-projected figures of Hamelin, Isabel and their steward. Climbing to the roof, you'll find wonderful all-round vistas over the surrounding countryside.

'Graphic novel' style interpretation, featuring builders, servants, ladies-in-waiting and squires from the castle's history, offers vivid guidance round the whole fortress. Don't miss the fascinating introductory exhibition, including many excavated site-finds. It traces Conisbrough's history from its beginnings to the present day. A striking cutaway model, with moving figures, offers a virtual tour of the keep if you don't wish to ascend its stairways.

OPENING TIMES

1 Apr-30 Sep, daily	10am-6pm
1 Oct-3 Nov, daily	10am-5pm
4 Nov-31 Mar, Sat-Sun	10am-4pm
24-26 Dec & 1 Jan	Closed
Last entry 30 mins before closing	

VISIT US

Direction: Located NE of Conisbrough town centre off A630; 4½ miles SW of Doncaster

Train: Conisbrough ½ mile

Bus: Stagecoach services 220 & 221; First X78

Tel: 01709 863329

NON-MEMBERS

Adult £6.90 | Concession £6.20
Child £4.10 | Family £17.90

ACQ.1950 🚻 🐕 🎁 🛡 E 🚶 🚼 📷 ⚠ OVP

Dogs on leads (in grounds only).

Disabled parking available outside the visitor centre.

No disabled access to or within the keep, due to steep stairways.

An interactive device is available for visitors unable to access the keep, allowing them to explore the building and meet characters.

Access (limited to some areas).

MAP PAGE 345 (5G)
OS MAP 111, 279: SK515989

BRODSWORTH HALL AND GARDENS

Few places in England can match Brodsworth Hall. In this grand yet gently time-worn Victorian mansion, amid beautiful gardens, you can experience life in a country house as it really was. We're always adding to its attractions, and the newly conserved game larder now joins the restored Victorian garden privy in the grounds.

SOUTH YORKSHIRE DN5 7XJ

'Conserved as found' when English Heritage took over, Brodsworth still reflects its original opulence, but also reveals how its owners and servants weathered the changes and challenges of the 20th century. It's a house full of surprises.

Brodsworth Hall was built in the 1860s by the fabulously wealthy Charles Thellusson, and occupied by his family for over 120 years. The grand rooms on the ground floor recall the house's Victorian heyday, with glittering chandeliers, marble statues, and a billiard room equipped with leather seating.

As you look closer, you can see the changes wrought by time. The last resident, the indomitable Sylvia Grant-Dalton, fought a losing battle against subsidence and leaking roofs. Following her death in 1988, we took the bold decision to conserve the interiors as they were found, rather than restoring them. The house remains as she used it, making do and mending with dwindling funds and ever fewer servants. Her favourite room, the Library, retains its faded Victorian wallpaper and Regency furniture, while Charles Thellusson's woodworking room next door became crowded with delightful clutter. Some of the bedrooms were modernised over the years, and contain furnishings dating from the 1860s to the 1980s. Other rooms fell out of use, though most of the Victorian servants' furnishings have survived.

Downstairs, the cavernous kitchen with its stupendous cooking range was deserted for a cosier room with an Aga range-cooker. Both kitchens remain as they were at the end of Brodsworth's active life. Beside the Aga rests the battered armchair of the last cook-housekeeper, Emily Chester, who spent her entire working life at Brodsworth. Displays reveal more about the Thellusson family, their servants, and how they lived together.

The Award-winning Gardens

Brodsworth's extensive gardens have been restored to their original splendour as 'a collection of grand gardens in miniature', whose character constantly changes at every turn. Romantic views from the restored summerhouse take in both the formal gardens and the pleasure grounds. Stroll through the statue walks, the fern dell grotto and the beautiful wild rose dell.

In spring the snowdrops, bluebells and daffodils put on a fantastic show. The colourful formal bedding is renewed throughout the summer, when hundreds of roses contrast strikingly with the sculptural topiary and ferns. After the brilliant autumn colours, you can admire the extensive collection of Victorian hollies throughout the winter. On summer Sunday afternoons, enjoy the best of Yorkshire's brass bands from the garden terraces.

The Restored Game Larder

We've recently restored our rare Victorian game larder, used to store game shot by the Thellusson family and their guests. Built in the 1860s, it was set under shady trees with louvered sides for ventilation, and positioned so that game could be brought to it up the back drive, and then taken to Brodsworth's nearby kitchen wing. The restoration has included timber repairs, the reinstatement of inner zinc mesh, and replacement of the stones it stands on. Using historic photographs, the gardening team also have reinstated the path to the larder and the original planting scheme.

A Family-friendly Property

The hall and gardens are welcoming whatever your age. We have a new outdoor play area for 2019, and families can make the most of events and activities in the garden. Everyone can enjoy the tearoom in the Servants' Wing, or watch the local croquet club in action. The friendly volunteer room stewards are another unique Brodsworth attraction: many knew the property before English Heritage began caring for it.

Darkest Hour; Testament of Youth; The Thirteenth Tale.

OPENING TIMES

House & Servants' Wing
House open for general admission 1pm-5pm.
(Free guided tours of the house also available at 11am and 12pm, bookable on arrival.)
Non-flash photography allowed

1 Apr-3 Nov, daily	1pm-5pm
4 Nov-31 Mar*	Closed
24-25 Dec	Closed

Garden and Tearooms

1 Apr-30 Sep, daily	10am-6pm
1 Oct-3 Nov, daily	10am-5pm
4 Nov-23 Dec, Sat-Sun*	10am-4pm
26 Dec-1 Jan, daily*	10am-4pm
2 Jan-16 Feb, Sat-Sun*	10am-4pm
17-23 Feb, daily*	10am-4pm
24 Feb-31 Mar, Sat-Sun*	10am-4pm
24-25 Dec	Closed

Last entry 30 mins before closing

*Servants' Wing open weekends and school holidays during this period

Mobility Around the Site
Prams and back carriers for babies are not allowed in the hall, small padded pushchairs and slings are available instead. For visitors with mobility needs or young children, an electric buggy operates a shuttle service from the car park. Benches throughout the gardens, although steps and steep slopes limit access to some areas. The hall has ramps and seats, and a lift to the first floor

VISIT US

Address: Brodsworth Hall and Gardens, Brodsworth, Doncaster, South Yorkshire. **Please note:** some satellite navigation systems give multiple locations for the postcode. To avoid confusion, please follow the brown signs in the local area

Direction: In Brodsworth, 5 miles NW of Doncaster off A635 Barnsley Road; from junction 37 of A1(M)

Train: South Elmsall 4 miles; Moorthorpe 4½ miles; Doncaster 5½ miles; Adwick Le Street 3 miles

Bus: Yorkshire Tiger service 203

Tel: 01302 722598

Local Tourist Information:
Doncaster: 01302 734309

NON-MEMBERS

House and Gardens
Adult £13.00 | Concession £11.70
Child £7.90 | Family £33.90

Winter
Adult £9.20 | Concession £8.30
Child £5.50 | Family £23.90

MAP PAGE 345 (5G)
OS MAP 111, 279: SE506070

MONK BRETTON PRIORY
SOUTH YORKSHIRE – S71 5QD

The substantial ruins of a Cluniac monastery, later absorbed into the Benedictine order, with an unusually well-marked ground plan, almost complete west range and 15th-century gatehouse.

OPENING TIMES

1 Apr-31 Mar, daily	10am-3pm
(managed by a keykeeper)	
24-26, 31 Dec & 1 Jan	Closed

VISIT US

Direction: Located 1 mile E of Barnsley town centre, off A633

Train: Barnsley 2½ miles

Bus: Stagecoach services 26A, 27, 28, 28C, 29, 30, 30A, 32; Watersons 37, 38 all to Cundy Cross from where it is a short walk

NON-MEMBERS

Charge may apply on event days

ACQ.1932

MAP PAGE 345 (5F)
OS MAP 110/111, 278: SE373065

ROCHE ABBEY
SOUTH YORKSHIRE – S66 8NW

The extensive remains of a small Cistercian abbey, in a beautiful setting. The soaring early Gothic transepts of its church were preserved as a 'Romantic eye-catcher' when Capability Brown drastically landscaped their surroundings from the 1760s, covering up other parts of the ruins. These now reveal one of the most complete ground plans of any English Cistercian monastery.

OPENING TIMES

1 Apr-30 Jun, Wed-Sun & Bank Hols	10am-5pm
1 Jul-31 Aug, daily	10am-5pm
1 Sep-3 Nov, Wed-Sun	10am-5pm
4 Nov-31 Mar	Closed

Last entry 30 mins before closing

VISIT US

Direction: 1½ miles S of Maltby, off A634

Train: Conisbrough 7 miles

Bus: First services X1 to Maltby Muglet Lane then 1½ mile walk. Alternatively TM Travel service 20 to Firbeck Village (2 mile walk)

Tel: 01709 812739

NON-MEMBERS

Adult £5.30 | Concession £4.80
Child £3.20 | Family £13.80

ACQ.1921   OVP

MAP PAGE 345 (5G)
OS MAP 111/120, 279: SK544898

COMMA

NDING

Beeston Castle and Woodland Park

Northumberland

Hadrian's Wall

Tyne & Wear

16

9

23

Carlisle

Cumbria

Durham

15

18

Penrith

Workington

17

12

Keswick

10

11

8

21

7

14

5

20

Windermere

22

Ulverston

13

6

North Yorkshire

Barrow-
in-Furness

26

19

Lancaster

Lancashire

25

Blackpool

27

Burnley

Preston

Blackburn

24

West
Yorkshire

Southport

Wigan

Bolton

Oldham

Greater Manchester

South
Yorkshire

Merseyside

St Helens

Liverpool

Manchester

Birkenhead

Warrington

Cheshire

Macclesfield

Chester

2 3

1

4

Crewe

WALES

Derbyshire

Nottinghamshir

TELLING TALES:
THE MYTHS,
LEGENDS AND
FOLKLORE OF
ENGLAND

THE TREASURE OF BEESTON CASTLE

Beeston Castle's 100-metre-deep well is one of the deepest in any English castle, and legends abound about what might lurk at the bottom. Most stories say that it hides the treasure of Richard II – allegedly £66,000 in gold coins – left there in 1399, not long before the king's capture and murder. Others maintain that Royalists hid gold there during the Civil War siege in 1644-5. But be warned – some say that it's guarded by demons, and anyone who seeks the treasure will be struck dumb or driven mad. Archaeologists have explored the well, most recently by camera. One found a mysterious nine-metre tunnel leading off the well shaft, but no treasure – and no demons either.

CUMBRIAN CISTERCIAN WAY

25 miles | 2 days
Piel Island to Grange-over-Sands

A pilgrimage through the calming landscape of South Cumbria. You start with the tiny ferry to Piel Island, owned by the medieval monks of the nearby Furness Abbey – once the second wealthiest and most powerful Cistercian monastery in England. Then you come to Urswick church, with its Arts and Crafts wooden carvings and Saxon 'Tunwini Cross', and over the brow of Birkrigg Common. Its stone circle overlooks Morecambe Bay, which you can cross by train to Cark. Then walk the final stretch to Grange-over-Sands via Cartmel and its magnificent Priory.

View more details and a downloadable version of this route at www.english-heritage.org.uk/pilgrimage

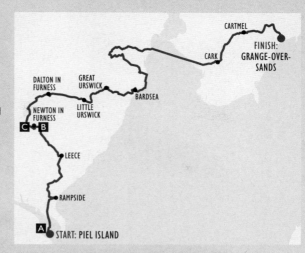

Discover English Heritage sites along the pilgrimage route

A Piel Castle *(p.255)*
B Bow Bridge *(p.248)*
C Furness Abbey *(p.252)*

In partnership with

the
**British
Pilgrimage
Trust**

Piel Castle

BEESTON CASTLE & WOODLAND PARK

Beeston Castle is among the most dramatically sited fortresses in England. It stands on the summit of a sandstone crag towering above the Cheshire Plain, a centre of human activity for over 4,000 years.

CHESHIRE CW6 9TX

The extensive wooded surroundings, rich in wildlife, are fascinating to explore. You can experience some of the best views in Cheshire from the castle.

Defended by steep cliffs on three sides, Beeston's crag attracted prehistoric settlers. There's evidence for Bronze Age metal-working, and it later became an immense Iron Age hillfort.

The 'Castle of the Rock' was begun in the 1220s by Ranulf, Earl of Chester, one of the greatest barons of Henry III's England, as a defence against aristocratic rivals and a proclamation of Ranulf's power. It's approached via a ruined gatehouse in a multi-towered outer wall, defining a huge outer bailey climbing steadily up the hill.

The castle's crowning glory is the inner bailey, defended by a rock-cut ditch and a mighty double-towered gatehouse. From here you can gain astounding views across eight counties, from the Welsh Mountains to the Pennines. It also contains the famous castle well, over 100 metres (328 feet) deep and, according to legend, the hiding place of Richard II's treasure.

Come and see our newly created Bronze Age roundhouse, bringing to life the site's untold prehistoric story. This exciting project involved a team of volunteers working with experts to understand and practice the methods used to construct a roundhouse. It will be an atmospheric place for school groups and visitors to explore a different aspect of Beeston's history.

Please check our website for the latest updates.

OPENING TIMES

1 Apr-30 Sep, daily	10am-6pm
1 Oct-3 Nov, daily	10am-5pm
4 Nov-23 Dec, Sat-Sun	10am-4pm
2 Jan-16 Feb, Sat-Sun	10am-4pm
17-23 Feb, daily	10am-4pm
24 Feb-31 Mar, Wed-Sun	10am-4pm
Christmas Opening	
24-25 Dec	Closed
26 Dec-1 Jan, daily	10am-4pm

Last entry 30 mins before closing

VISIT US

Address: Beeston Castle, Chapel Lane, Beeston, Cheshire

Direction: Located 11 miles SE of Chester, on minor road off A49

Train: Chester 14 miles or Crewe 15 miles

Bus: D&G service 83 (Tue) to Beeston; otherwise D&G service 56 (Thu & Sat) to Bunbury Heath (then 1 mile walk) or Arriva service 84 to Tarporley (2½ miles)

Tel: 01829 260464

Local Tourist Information:
Chester: 01244 402111

NON-MEMBERS

Adult £8.80 | Concession £8.00
Child £5.30 | Family £22.90

Warning: Steep ascent to inner bailey (no disabled access to the top of the hill). Boots or sturdy footwear recommended for Woodland Walk.

Parking charges apply to non-members.
Parking free for Members.

MAP PAGE 344 (6D)
OS MAP 117, 257/258: SJ537593

Beeston experienced a final blaze of glory as an important English Civil War stronghold, finally surrendering to Parliament in November 1645 after a long and eventful siege.

ASTOUNDING VIEWS ACROSS EIGHT COUNTIES, FROM THE WELSH MOUNTAINS TO THE PENNINES

Set in 40 acres of woodland, Beeston Castle is a paradise for walkers, nature lovers and adventurous children. A circular Woodland Walk winds around the base of the crag through wildlife-thronged woods. Offering glimpses of the castle above, it leads to Beeston's sandstone caves (external viewing only). You can also reach the caves directly from the visitor centre, where the 'Castle of the Rock' display draws you into Beeston's long story.

The Sandstone Café offers hot and cold snacks and drinks. No indoor seating, but picnic tables are available outside.

CHESTER CASTLE: AGRICOLA TOWER AND CASTLE WALLS

CHESHIRE – CH1 2DN

The original gateway to Chester Castle, this 12th-century tower houses a chapel with traces of wall-paintings of c. 1220, rediscovered in the 1980s.

OPENING TIMES

See website for details

VISIT US

Direction: Access via Assizes Court car park on Grosvenor St

Train: Chester 1 mile

Bus: Arriva 1, 3, 3A, 4, 4S, 10A, X1, X4, DB2 pass close to the site

ACQ. 1912 🐕

MAP PAGE 344 (6C)
OS MAP 117, 266: SJ405657

CHESTER ROMAN AMPHITHEATRE

CHESHIRE – CH1 1RE

The largest Roman amphitheatre in Britain, used by the 20th Legion, based at the fortress of 'Deva' (Chester). Excavations revealed two successive stone-built amphitheatres with wooden seating. The two buildings differed from all other British amphitheatres, underlining the importance of Roman Chester.

Managed by Cheshire West and Chester Council.

CHESTER ROMAN AMPHITHEATRE

OPENING TIMES

Any reasonable daylight hours

VISIT US

Direction: On Vicars Lane, beyond Newgate, Chester

Train: Chester ¾ mile

Bus: From surrounding areas

ACQ.1964 ♿ 🐕

Disabled access (no access to amphitheatre floor).

MAP PAGE 344 (6C)
OS MAP 117, 266: SJ408662

SANDBACH CROSSES

CHESHIRE – CW11 1AT

Dominating Sandbach market square, these are among the finest surviving Anglo-Saxon high crosses. Probably dating from the 9th century, and originally painted as well as elaborately carved.

OPENING TIMES

Any reasonable daylight hours

VISIT US

Direction: Market Sq, Sandbach

Train: Sandbach 1½ miles

Bus: D&G Travel 32, 38 (Sun), 78, SB1, SB2, SB3; Arriva 37, 37E, 38; Tomlinson 319

ACQ.1937 ♿ 🐕

MAP PAGE 344 (6D)
OS MAP 118, 268: SJ759608

AMBLESIDE ROMAN FORT

CUMBRIA

Foundations of a 2nd to 4th-century Roman fort, in a meadow beside Windermere. Possibly a supply base for Lake District patrols.

Managed by the National Trust.

OPENING TIMES

Any reasonable daylight hours

VISIT US

Direction: In Borrans Field, beside A5075 on south-western outskirts of Ambleside. 182 metres W of Waterhead car park

Train: Windermere 5 miles

Bus: Stagecoach Cumbria 505, 516, 555 & 599 then ½ mile walk

ACQ.1978 🐕 ⚠

Beware – cattle may be grazing.

No parking at site. Stout footwear advised.

MAP PAGE 346 (6D)
OS MAP 90, OL7: NY372034

BOW BRIDGE   CUMBRIA

This narrow 15th-century stone bridge across Mill Beck carried an old packhorse route to nearby Furness Abbey (see p.252).

OPENING TIMES

Any reasonable daylight hours

VISIT US

Direction: Located ½ mile N of Barrow-in-Furness, on minor road off A590; near Furness Abbey

Train: Barrow-in-Furness 1½ miles

Bus: Stagecoach in Cumbria service 6 & X6 to within 1 mile

ACQ.1950 🐕 ⚠

Beware – livestock may be grazing on site.

MAP PAGE 346 (7D)
OS MAP 96, OL6: SD224715

BROUGH CASTLE

CUMBRIA – CA17 4EJ

On a ridge commanding Stainmore Pass. Frequently the target of Scots raids, its towering keep dates from c. 1200. Like many other castles hereabouts, Brough was restored in the 17th century by Lady Anne Clifford, whose additions are still visible.

OPENING TIMES

1 Apr-30 Sep, daily	10am-5pm
1 Oct-31 Mar, daily	10am-4pm
24-26, 31 Dec & 1 Jan	Closed

VISIT US

Direction: 8 miles SE of Appleby

Train: Kirkby Stephen 10 miles

Bus: Stagecoach Cumbria 502; Cumbria Classic Bus 571 (Mon), 572 (Wed); 574 (Tue)

ACQ. 1919

Please note: approach may be muddy, stout footwear recommended.

Beware – livestock may be grazing on site.

Guidebook available at Brougham Castle.

MAP PAGE 347 (6F)
OS MAP 91, OL19: NY791141

CASTLERIGG STONE CIRCLE

CUMBRIA

Among the most dramatically sited prehistoric stone circles in Britain, surrounded by a panorama of Lakeland fells. Probably raised in c. 3000 BC, thirty-three of its close-set stones still stand.

Managed by the National Trust.

OPENING TIMES

Any reasonable daylight hours

VISIT US

Direction: 1½ miles E of Keswick. Signposted from A66 and A591

Train: Penrith 16 miles

Bus: Stagecoach 'Caldbeck Rambler' service 73A (Summer, Sat) passes the site. Otherwise Stagecoach 555 to Castle Lane (1 mile walk)

ACQ. 1883

Limited parking in lay-by.

Beware – livestock may be grazing on site.

Sturdy footwear is recommended.

MAP PAGE 346 (5D)
OS MAP 89/90, OL4: NY291236

BROUGHAM CASTLE   CUMBRIA – CA10 2AA

In a picturesque setting beside the River Eamont, near the site of a Roman fort, red sandstone Brougham Castle was founded in the early 13th century by Robert de Vieuxpont. His tall keep largely survives amid many later buildings added by the powerful Clifford family. These include the unusual double gatehouse and impressive 'Tower of League'. A formidable barrier against Scots invaders and a proclamation of baronial splendour, the castle welcomed Edward I in 1300. Falling into decay after James I's visit in 1617, Brougham was restored by the indomitable Lady Anne Clifford. She often visited with her travelling 'court', and died here in 1676.

There's a lot to explore at Brougham, and you can climb the spiral stairs to the keep top for panoramic views over the Eden Valley.

OPENING TIMES

1 Apr-30 Sep, daily	10am-6pm
1 Oct-3 Nov, daily	10am-4pm
4 Nov-31 Mar, Sat-Sun	10am-4pm
24-26 Dec & 1 Jan	Closed

Last entry 30 mins before closing

VISIT US

Direction: 1½ miles SE of Penrith, off A66

Train: Penrith 2 miles

Bus: Stagecoach Cumbria service 104, 506 and 563 pass the castle on the A66, but the nearest official stop is at Whinfell Park (about 1 mile east). Alternatively Stagecoach 106, 508 or Fellrunner 132 (Fri) or 562 (Tue) to Eamont Bridge and walk c. 1 mile

Tel: 01768 862488

Local Tourist Information:
Penrith: 01768 867466;
Rheged: 01768 860034

NON-MEMBERS

Adult **£6.30** | Concession **£5.70**
Child **£3.80** | Family **£16.40**

ACQ. 1920

Please note: Car parking limited, in 'no through road' opposite castle entrance.

There is good wheelchair access to most of the site (excluding the keep).

MAP PAGE 346 (5E)
OS MAP 90, OL5: NY537290

CARLISLE CASTLE

The storm-centre of many famous sieges, Carlisle Castle was for centuries the flashpoint of frontier warfare, as well as a notorious prison. Trace its long and sometimes grim history.

CUMBRIA CA3 8UR

Carlisle Castle remains a dominating presence in the city it has watched over for nine centuries. You can witness its rich and varied story in a vividly retold exhibition celebrating Carlisle's fame as the most besieged town in Britain.

The medieval castle was built on the site of an important Roman fortress. The commanding keep was begun during the 12th century by King Henry I of England and completed by King David I of Scotland. It's a reminder that Carlisle Castle was for centuries a disputed frontier fortress, guarding the especially turbulent western end of the Anglo-Scottish border. It triumphantly repelled a siege by King Robert Bruce of Scotland in 1315, after a great Scots siege engine got stuck fast in mud.

The castle's violent history also included skirmishes with Elizabethan Border Reivers, a Civil War siege – the longest siege of a town in English history – and Bonnie Prince Charlie's Jacobite Rising of 1745-46. Carlisle was then the very last English fortress ever

to suffer a siege. Overwhelmed by the Duke of Cumberland's Hanoverian army, its Jacobite defenders were imprisoned in the keep's dank basement. Today you can see the legendary 'licking stones', which they supposedly licked for moisture. Unique carvings on the keep's second floor were probably cut in the 1460-70s.

By the time Mary Queen of Scots was imprisoned here in 1568, Henry VIII's updating for heavy artillery had left its mark on the fortress, including the Half Moon Battery defending the Captain's Tower gatehouse. You can explore both the Tudor Battery and the 12th-century gatehouse, one of the best preserved in England.

Discover more highlights in 'Besieged', a display which includes examples of the weapons used during Carlisle's many sieges, a reconstruction graphic of the keep, a retelling of the daring rescue of a Border Reiver, and a 360-degree virtual tour of the castle.

MEMBERS GET FREE ENTRY TO CUMBRIA'S MUSEUM OF MILITARY LIFE

Unusually, the medieval castle remained an operational fortress well into the 20th century. From 1873 to 1959 it was the regimental headquarters of Cumbria's Infantry Regiment. English Heritage Members get free entry into Cumbria's Museum of Military Life within the castle, where the regiment's 300-year history is brought to life. There's a café in the museum, which also hosts a programme of temporary exhibitions. Separate opening times apply. Please visit www.cumbriasmuseumofmilitarylife. org for details.

OPENING TIMES

1 Apr-30 Sep, daily	10am-6pm
1 Oct-3 Nov, daily	10am-5pm
4 Nov-9 Feb, Sat-Sun	10am-4pm
10-23 Feb, daily	10am-4pm
24 Feb-31 Mar, Sat-Sun	10am-4pm
24-26 Dec & 1 Jan	Closed

Last entry 30 mins before closing

VISIT US

Address: Carlisle Castle, Castle Way, Carlisle, Cumbria

Direction: In Carlisle city centre. Follow Castle Street, past Carlisle Cathedral on left. At main road, take underpass to the castle

Train: Carlisle ½ mile

Bus: Nearest stop is West Tower Street. Buses operated by Stagecoach and Reay's both stop here

Tel: 01228 591922

Local Tourist Information: Carlisle: 01228 598596

NON-MEMBERS

Adult £8.30 | Concession £7.50
Child £5.00 | Family £21.60

ACQ.1963

Disabled access (limited).

Dogs on leads (restricted areas only).

Guided tours available to pre-book at a small extra charge.

Parking (disabled only, but signposted city centre car parks nearby).

Cumbria's Museum of Military Life café not managed by EH.

MAP PAGE 346 (4D)
OS MAP 85, 315: NY396562

FURNESS ABBEY CUMBRIA – LA13 0PJ

The North West's grandest and most extensive monastic ruins, set in a lovely wooded valley. Furness Abbey was founded by Stephen, later King of England, becoming the second richest Cistercian abbey in England. Dating principally from the 12th and 13th centuries, its imposing red sandstone ruins reflect its prosperity. They include the east end of the great church and its western tower. You can also explore the chapter house, with its fine carved decoration, and almost the entire east range of the cloister.

A visitor centre exhibition reveals the abbey's history and a large collection of sculpture from the ruins, including striking effigies of knights. The beautiful 12th-century 'Furness Crozier', a silver-gilt abbot's staff-head from an abbey grave, is on permanent display.

Combine your visit with a venture across to Piel Castle (p.255), the abbey's island fortress.

OPENING TIMES

1 Apr-30 Sep, daily	10am-6pm
1 Oct-4 Nov, daily	10am-4pm
5 Nov-31 Mar, Sat-Sun	10am-4pm
24-26 Dec & 1 Jan	Closed

Last entry 30 mins before closing

VISIT US

Direction: Located 1½ miles N of Barrow-in-Furness, off A590

Train: Dalton and Roose 2 miles; Barrow-in-Furness 2 miles

Bus: Stagecoach in Cumbria service 6 & X6 to within 1 mile

Tel: 01229 823420

NON-MEMBERS

Adult **£6.60** | Concession **£6.00**
Child **£4.00** | Family **£17.20**

Dogs on leads (restricted areas only).

MAP PAGE 346 (7D)
OS MAP 96, OL6: SD218717

CLIFTON HALL CUMBRIA

The well-preserved early Tudor tower of an otherwise vanished manor house, now surrounded by a busy working farmyard. Graphic panels reveal its history, and you can climb the spiral stairs to look into the kitchen and private chambers it contained, with a fine king-post roof.

OPENING TIMES

Any reasonable daylight hours

24-26 Dec & 1 Jan	Closed

Key available from farmhouse if tower is locked

VISIT US

Direction: In Clifton, 2 miles S of Penrith; signposted from A6 in village

Train: Penrith 2½ miles

Bus: Stagecoach service 106 & Fellrunner service 562 (Tue)

ACQ.1973

Please park in the village and walk to the site.

Beware – livestock may be grazing on site.

Farmyard may be muddy: stout footwear recommended.

MAP PAGE 346 (5E)
OS MAP 90, OL5: NY530271

COUNTESS PILLAR, BROUGHAM
CUMBRIA

A monument erected in 1656 by Lady Anne Clifford of nearby Brougham Castle, to commemorate her final parting here from her mother, 40 years earlier. Sundials are carved on three faces, and on the low stone beside it money was given to the poor on each anniversary of their parting.

COUNTESS PILLAR, BROUGHAM

OPENING TIMES

Any reasonable daylight hours

VISIT US

Direction: ¼ mile E of Brougham. A new access route has also been created, which runs from the B6262 (to Brougham) and starts near the junction with the A66

Train: Penrith 2½ miles

Bus: Stagecoach Cumbria service 104, 506 and 563 pass the castle on the A66, but the nearest official stop is at Whinfell Park (about 1 mile east). Alternatively Stagecoach 106, 508 or Fellrunner 132 (Fri) or 562 (Tue) to Eamont Bridge and walk c. 1 mile

ACQ.1977 ✉

Warning: site on a very busy main road. Parking on B6262, close to the junction with A66. Safe access by footpath.

MAP PAGE 346 (5E)
OS MAP 90, OL5: NY546289

HARDKNOTT ROMAN FORT

CUMBRIA

Among the remotest and most spectacularly sited Roman forts in England, guarding a Roman road across the high fells. Its complete perimeter walls, headquarters building and nearby bath-house and 'sauna' are clearly visible.

Managed by the National Trust.

OPENING TIMES

Any reasonable daylight hours

VISIT US

Direction: 9 miles NE of Ravenglass; at W end of Hardknott Pass, via short uphill path from unclassified road

Train: Dalegarth (Ravenglass & Eskdale) 3 miles or Ravenglass 10 miles

Bus: Muncaster Microbus, a demand responsive service, covers the area and operates the Whitehaven Wanderer service on Tue & Fri only. Tel: 01229 717229 for details

ACQ.1949 ✉ P ⚠

Very limited parking in lay-by. More parking at Jubilee Bridge, ½ mile to west. Access hazardous in winter months or bad weather. Stout footwear essential.

HARDKNOTT ROMAN FORT

Beware – livestock may be grazing on site.

Visitors are strongly advised to approach from the western (Eskdale) direction: the road from Ambleside over the Wrynose and Hardknott passes is hazardous in poor weather, with hairpin bends and 1-in-3 gradients. Not accessible by coaches.

MAP PAGE 346 (6D)
OS MAP 89/90, OL6: NY218015

KING ARTHUR'S ROUND TABLE

CUMBRIA – CA10 2BX

Grassy banks of a late Neolithic earthwork henge, dating from c. 2000-1000 BC, but much later believed to be King Arthur's jousting arena. Mayburgh Henge is nearby.

OPENING TIMES

Any reasonable daylight hours

VISIT US

Direction: At Eamont Bridge, 1 mile S of Penrith. Signposted from A6 at S end of village

Train: Penrith 1½ miles

Bus: Stagecoach service 106 & 508 and Fellrunner services 111 (Thu), 132 (Fri) & 562 (Tue)

ACQ.1884 ✉ ⚠

No parking at site. Park at Mayburgh Henge (400 metres away).

Beware – cattle may be grazing.

MAP PAGE 346 (5E)
OS MAP 90, OL5: NY523284

MAYBURGH HENGE

CUMBRIA – CA10 2BX

Among the biggest and most impressive prehistoric henges in northern England, dating from the late Neolithic period. Unusually constructed from river boulders, its enormous circular bank still stands over 3 metres (10 feet) high. Near its centre is a single standing stone, sole survivor of eight stones recorded here. King Arthur's Round Table is nearby.

OPENING TIMES

Any reasonable daylight hours

MAYBURGH HENGE

VISIT US

Direction: At Eamont Bridge, 1 mile S of Penrith. Signposted from A6 at S end of village

Train: Penrith 1½ miles

Bus: Stagecoach service 106 & 508 and Fellrunner services 111 (Thu), 132 (Fri) & 562 (Tue)

ACQ.1884 ✉ ⚠

Roadside parking by site entrance.

Beware – cattle may be grazing.

Steep banks: sturdy and waterproof footwear required.

MAP PAGE 346 (5E)
OS MAP 90, OL5: NY519284

PENRITH CASTLE

CUMBRIA

Begun in the later 14th century and subsequently transformed into a luxurious residence by Richard, Duke of Gloucester (afterwards Richard III). Surviving in places to its full height.

OPENING TIMES

Park:
Summer	7.30am-9pm
Winter	7.30am-4.30pm

VISIT US

Direction: Opposite Penrith railway station

Train: Penrith (adjacent)

Bus: From surrounding areas

ACQ.1913 ✉ ⚕ ⚥ ⚠

MAP PAGE 346 (5E)
OS MAP 90, OL5: NY513299

LANERCOST PRIORY

──────── CUMBRIA CA8 2HQ ────────

The tranquil setting of Augustinian Lanercost Priory belies an often troubled history.

Less than half a mile from Hadrian's Wall, it suffered frequent attacks during the long Anglo-Scottish wars. The mortally sick King Edward I rested here for five months in 1306-07, shortly before his death on his final campaign.

There is still a great deal for you to see in one of Cumbria's best-preserved monasteries. The east end of the noble 13th-century church survives to its full height and you can admire some fine monuments within its dramatic triple tier of arches. The nave, with its lofty west front, is still in full use as the parish church.

LANERCOST'S IMPRESSIVE REMAINS OFFER AN UNFORGETTABLE VISIT

Lanercost's cloisters include a beautiful vaulted 13th-century refectory undercroft. Converted into the Tudor mansion of the Dacre family, they also include the Dacre Tower, adapted from the monastic kitchen, and the Dacre Hall (used as the village hall, so not often open to the public). The Dacre Hall displays fragments of 16th-century wall-painting and a splendid Jacobean chimneypiece, recently returned here.

Set beside an ancient vicarage, and 'vicar's pele tower' (exterior viewing only), Lanercost Priory's extensive remains offer an unforgettable visit.

Nearby farm buildings have been converted into a visitor centre, with a restaurant/tearoom and display about Hadrian's Wall. The parish church, Dacre Hall, tearoom and visitor centre are not managed by English Heritage.

OPENING TIMES

1 Apr-30 Sep, daily	10am-6pm
1 Oct-4 Nov, daily	10am-5pm
5 Nov-16 Feb, Sat-Sun	10am-4pm
17-23 Feb, daily	10am-4pm
24 Feb-31 Mar, Sat-Sun	10am-4pm
24-26 Dec & 1 Jan	Closed

Last entry 30 mins before closing

VISIT US

Direction: Off the minor road through Lanercost, next to the church; 2½ miles NE of Brampton

Train: Brampton 3 miles

Bus: Border Rambler BR3 (Wed) passes site; otherwise Stagecoach/Arriva service 685 to Naworth Parks, which is within 1½ mile walk

Tel: 01697 73030

NON-MEMBERS

Adult **£5.80** | Concession **£5.20**
Child **£3.50** | Family **£15.10**

ACQ.1930 🍴 f P 📷 ⚠ OVP

Please note: no toilet facilties available at site.

Lanercost tearoom and Visitor Information Centre is open every day except 25 and 26 Dec. www.lanercost.co.uk Tel: 01697 741267 (not managed by English Heritage).

MAP PAGE 346 (4E)
OS MAP 86, 315: NY556637

PIEL CASTLE

CUMBRIA – LA13 0QN

Accessible only via small boat ferry, this 14th-century island fortress was built by Furness Abbey (p.252) as a refuge from pirates and Scots raiders. It shares its little island in Barrow harbour with a famous pub. Lambert Simnel, pretender to Henry VII's throne, landed here in 1487.

OPENING TIMES

Any reasonable daylight hours. Access by ferry boat not managed by English Heritage

VISIT US

Direction: Via ferry from Roa Island, accessible by road 3¼ miles SE of Barrow-in-Furness

By Small Boat: From Easter until September, approx. 11am until 6pm daily, a ferry service operates from Roa Island to Piel Island (subject to tides and weather). Call in advance Alan Cleasby on 07798 794550. There is a charge for the ferry

Train: Barrow-in-Furness 4 miles

Bus: Blueworks Taxis service 11 Barrow-in-Furness – Ulverston Roa Island and then ferry to Piel Castle

ACQ.1973 ⚐ ⚠

Beware – livestock may be grazing on site.
Public house refreshments (not managed by EH).

MAP PAGE 346 (7D)
OS MAP 96, OL6: SD233636

RAVENGLASS ROMAN BATH HOUSE · CUMBRIA

Among the tallest surviving Roman structures in northern Britain, the walls of this bath-house stand up to 4 metres (13 feet) high, complete with remains of plasterwork and elegant niches for statues. It served Ravenglass Roman fort, which guarded a useful harbour and was garrisoned by troops from Hadrian's fleet.

OPENING TIMES

Any reasonable daylight hours

VISIT US

Direction: ½ mile SE of Ravenglass station, via signposted footpath from village car park and then private road. No vehicular access or parking at site

Train: Ravenglass (adjacent)

Bus: Muncaster Microbus, a demand responsive service, covers the area and operates the Whitehaven Wanderer service on Tue & Fri only. Tel: 01229 717229 for details

ACQ.1980 ⚐ ⚐

MAP PAGE 346 (6C)
OS MAP 96, OL6: SD088959

SHAP ABBEY

CUMBRIA – CA10 3NB

The impressive full-height 15th-century tower and other remains of a remote abbey of Premonstratensian 'white canons'.

Information panels guide you round the abbey and illustrate daily monastic life.

OPENING TIMES

Any reasonable daylight hours

VISIT US

Direction: 1½ miles W of Shap, on the bank of the River Lowther

Train: Penrith 10 miles

SHAP ABBEY

Bus: Fellrunner service 111 (Tue) passes the approach road. Otherwise Stagecoach service 106 Penrith-Kendal passes within 1½ miles

ACQ.1948 ⚐ ⚐ P

Disabled access (limited views from outside the site).

Steep access road may be hazardous in wintry weather.

MAP PAGE 346 (5E)
OS MAP 90, OL5: NY548152

WETHERAL PRIORY GATEHOUSE

CUMBRIA

Well-preserved early 16th-century gatehouse, the sole survivor of a small Benedictine priory. A miniature 'pele tower' containing two storeys of comfortable rooms, it later became a fortified vicarage, a defence against border raiders.

OPENING TIMES

1 Apr-30 Sep, daily	10am-5pm
1 Oct-31 Mar, daily	10am-4pm
24-26, 31 Dec & 1 Jan	Closed

VISIT US

Direction: Near Wetheral village; 6 miles E of Carlisle, on B6263

Train: Wetheral ½ mile

Bus: Reay's services 74 & 75 to Wetheral then short walk

ACQ.1978 ⚐

MAP PAGE 346 (4D)
OS MAP 86, 315: NY468541

STOTT PARK BOBBIN MILL

CUMBRIA LA12 8AX

Experience the Industrial Revolution vividly brought to life at Stott Park. A new woodland walk now enhances your visit to one of our most unusual and fascinating attractions.

In a lovely wooded setting near Lake Windermere, this fully-working mill is the only survivor of the Lakeland mills which turned bobbins for the Lancashire textile industry. It operated from 1835 until 1971, diversifying into products from cotton reels to toggles for Second World War duffel coats.

It was powered first by water, then by a magnificent steam engine – still operating on working steam weekends – and finally by electricity. Much of its clattering belt-driven machinery remains in full working order, and close-up demonstrations of the fascinating process of bobbin-making feature in the guided tour. Entry to the mill is by guided tour only, with seven guided tours per day; the first starts at 10.30am, the last at 4.30pm.

Displays tell the stories of the people who worked the mill, and take you on a self-guided tour of its picturesque surroundings. A hands-on family trail with children's dressing up clothes helps you imagine what it was like to work at the mill.

Please visit our website or call 01539 531087 for details of steam weekends throughout the season.

NEW FOR 2019

This year we're adding a new dimension to Stott Park. A new footbridge over the mill stream and a 200-metre walk will let you explore our previously inaccessible woodland, carpeted with bluebells in spring and rich in wildlife all year round. We're re-introducing coppicing of this woodland, which once provided timber for the mill's bobbins.

OPENING TIMES

3 Apr-30 Jun, Wed-Sun & Bank Hols	10am-5pm
1 Jul-31 Aug, daily	10am-5pm
1 Sep-3 Nov, Wed-Sun	10am-5pm
4 Nov-31 Mar	Closed

Last entry one hour before closing

Please call for details of steam days

VISIT US

Direction: Located 1½ miles N of Newby Bridge, off A590

Train: Grange-over-Sands 8 miles; Lakeside Station (Lakeside & Haverthwaite railway) ¾ mile

Bus: Stagecoach service 6 to Newby Bridge and then 1½ mile walk. Lakeside and Haverthwaite Railway's Lakeside terminus is ¾ mile walk from the mill

Boat: Windermere Lake Cruises from Ambleside or Bowness to Lakeside, then ¾ mile walk

Tel: 01539 531087

Local Tourist Information:
Hawkshead: 01539 436946

NON-MEMBERS

Adult **£9.30** | Concession **£8.40**
Child **£5.60** | Family **£24.20**

Disabled access (ground floor only. Specific interpretation for visually impaired visitors).

Lower car park for disabled parking (short downhill path to mill). Upper car park for general parking.

Disabled visitors can be dropped off at the mill entrance (with level access to site) before cars are parked. Please phone site in advance to arrange.

Dogs welcome on leads.

Parking charges apply for non-members. Parking free for Members.

MAP PAGE 346 (6D)
OS MAP 96/97, OL7: SD372881

GOODSHAW CHAPEL

LANCASHIRE

English Heritage's only Nonconformist place of worship, this atmospheric Baptist chapel displays a complete set of Georgian box-pews, galleries and pulpit.

OPENING TIMES

Please call the keykeeper for details
Tel: 01706 227333

VISIT US

Direction: In Crawshawbooth, 2 miles N of Rawtenstall via A682 (in Goodshaw Ave – turning off A682 opp. Alderson & Horan). Chapel approx. 1½ miles from main road

Train: Burnley Manchester Road 4½ miles

Bus: Transdev Burnley & Pendle 'Witch Way' service X43; alight at Crawshawbooth, Alderson & Horan, then short walk

ACQ.1976

MAP PAGE 344 (4D)
OS MAP 103, OL21: SD814261

SAWLEY ABBEY

LANCASHIRE

Riverside remains of a Cistercian abbey founded in 1148. Its monks briefly returned during the Pilgrimage of Grace, but the insurrection collapsed and their abbot was executed.

OPENING TIMES

1 Apr-31 Oct, daily	10am-5pm
1 Nov-31 Mar, daily	10am-4pm
24-26, 31 Dec & 1 Jan	Closed

VISIT US

Direction: Located at Sawley; 3½ miles N of Clitheroe, off A59

Train: Clitheroe 4 miles

Bus: Pilkington Bus service 7A serves Sawley Village then ¾ mile walk; Preston Transport service 280 to Smithies Bridge on the A59 and then ½ mile walk

ACQ.1951

MAP PAGE 344 (3D)
OS MAP 103, OL41: SD777464

WARTON OLD RECTORY

LANCASHIRE

A rare survival of a large 14th-century stone house with great hall and chambers. It served as a residence and courthouse for the wealthy and powerful rectors of Warton.

WARTON OLD RECTORY

OPENING TIMES

1 Apr-30 Sep, daily	10am-6pm
1 Oct-31 Mar, daily	10am-4pm
24-26, 31 Dec & 1 Jan	Closed

VISIT US

Direction: At Warton; 1 mile N of Carnforth, on minor road off A6

Train: Carnforth 1 mile

Bus: Stagecoach Lancashire 55 or 55X to The George Washington public house Warton then short walk

ACQ.1969

MAP PAGE 344 (3C)
OS MAP 97, OL7: SD499723

WHALLEY ABBEY GATEHOUSE

LANCASHIRE – BB7 9TN

The 14th-century gatehouse of the nearby Cistercian abbey, the second wealthiest monastery in Lancashire, beside the River Calder. The first floor was probably a chapel.

OPENING TIMES

Any reasonable daylight hours. No access to first floor

VISIT US

Direction: In Whalley; 6 miles NE of Blackburn, on minor road off A59

Train: Whalley ¼ mile

Bus: From surrounding area

ACQ.1971

MAP PAGE 344 (4D)
OS MAP 103, 287: SD729362

RING

HADRIAN'S WALL

HOUSESTEADS ROMAN FORT

- The best-preserved Roman fort anywhere in Britain.
- A dramatic hilltop setting with panoramic views.
- The famous Roman public loos.
- Outstanding interactive displays revealing life on the Wall.

See feature on page 266

BIRDOSWALD ROMAN FORT

- A great place to start your Hadrian's Wall adventure.
- Admire the longest continuous stretch of the Wall visible today.
- Experience our new hands-on displays tracing the story of the Wall.
- Enjoy this outstandingly family-friendly site.

See feature on page 263

Where next?
Chesters is only 8 miles away*

 Where next?
Housesteads is only 12½ miles away*

CHESTERS ROMAN FORT & MUSEUM

- Find out about the lives of Roman cavalry soldiers.
- Explore a nearly complete Roman bath-house.
- Enjoy a charming Victorian-style museum packed with finds from the Wall.
- Admire the beautiful riverside setting.

See feature on page 268

 Where next?
Corbridge is only 8 miles away*

HADRIAN'S WALL HIGHLIGHTS

Marching 73 miles from sea to sea across some of the wildest and most dramatic country in England, this famous World Heritage Site was the north-west frontier of the Roman Empire.

CHESTERS ROMAN FORT & MUSEUM 16

HOUSESTEADS ROMAN FORT 12 13 14 15

1 2 3 7 8 9 10 11 17 18 19

CUMBRIA

4 5 6

BIRDOSWALD ROMAN FORT

NORTHUMBERLAND

CARLISLE

CORBRIDGE ROMAN TOWN

- Explore the impressive remains of the most northerly town in the Roman Empire.
- Walk down a Roman high street.
- View the Wall's biggest collection of archaeological finds, highlighting Roman social life.
- Discover the internationally important Corbridge Hoard.

See feature on page 271

Where next?

Housesteads is only 16 miles away*

CARING FOR THE HADRIAN'S WALL WORLD HERITAGE SITE AND NATIONAL TRAIL

When planning your holiday or visit, please remember to observe 'Every Footstep Counts' – the World Heritage Site's own country code. As you will appreciate, Hadrian's Wall is a fragile environment and the archaeology is easily damaged. **You can help us to protect this great Wonder of the World by ensuring you:**

- Always keep to the signed paths.
- Visit the organised paying sites, which are more robust and can accommodate visitors. Also please avoid walking alongside the Wall when the ground is very wet. The buried archaeology underfoot is particularly vulnerable to damage in the wet winter months between November and April.
- Avoid walking on the Wall as this may cause it to collapse.
- Avoid walking in a single file.
- Respect livestock and land.
- Keep dogs on a lead and under close control.
- Use public transport whenever you can.
- Note that Hadrian's Wall Path National Trail is a footpath only. Please cycle on legal routes only, i.e. bridgeways, byways, roads and cyclepaths.

*All distances between sites are using most direct routes.

NEWCASTLE-UPON-TYNE

21

22
23

20 CORBRIDGE ROMAN FORT

TYNE AND WEAR

DURHAM

MAKE A DAY OF IT

Make the most of your day. Discover more of the Wall by visiting all our major forts, a short drive away from each other.

1 HARE HILL

A short length of Wall still stands 2.7 metres (8ft 10in) high.

VISIT US

Direction: ¾ mile NE of Lanercost

ACQ.1972

OS MAP 86, 43: NY564646

2 BANKS EAST TURRET

Imposing and well-preserved turret with adjoining stretches of Hadrian's Wall.

VISIT US

Direction: On minor road E of Banks village; 3½ miles NE of Brampton

ACQ.1934 P ♿ ⚠

OS MAP 86, 315: NY575647

3 PIKE HILL SIGNAL TOWER

The remains of one of a network of signal towers predating Hadrian's Wall, Pike Hill was later joined to the Wall at an angle of 45 degrees.

VISIT US

Direction: On minor road E of Banks village

ACQ.1971 P

OS MAP 86, 315: NY577648

4 LEAHILL TURRET & PIPER SIKE TURRET

Turrets west of Birdoswald: Piper Sike has a cooking-hearth.

VISIT US

Direction: On minor road 2 miles W of Birdoswald Fort

ACQ.1952

OS MAP 86, OL43/315: NY586652

5 BIRDOSWALD ROMAN FORT

See feature opposite.

STAY WITH US

Wake up and go to bed in a Roman Fort. The **Bunkhouse** at Birdoswald is perfect for residential educational visits and large groups, sleeping up to 36 persons in 7 bedrooms.

Call our customer services team on 0370 333 1187 to book.

6 HARROWS SCAR MILECASTLE & WALL

A mile-long section of the Wall, rebuilt in stone later in Hadrian's reign. It's linked to Birdoswald Roman Fort (see opposite).

VISIT US

Direction: ¼ mile E of Birdoswald, on minor road off B6318

ACQ.1946 P

Parking at Birdoswald.

OS MAP 86, OL43: NY620664

🅕 🅣 FOR UPDATES ON HADRIAN'S WALL, DON'T FORGET TO FOLLOW US ON FACEBOOK AND TWITTER.

SCOTLAND

CUMBRIA

CARLISLE

NORTHUMBERLAND

BIRDOSWALD ROMAN FORT

CUMBRIA CA8 7DD

5

New developments have transformed days out at Birdoswald Roman Fort. Imaginative hands-on interpretation and new family-friendly features make this the perfect place to begin your journey into Roman Britain.

Just outside the fort, you'll find the longest continuous stretch of Hadrian's Wall visible today. Once inside, our brand-new interactive displays help you discover how and why the Wall was built, who built it, and how it was defended for nearly 300 years. You can create a model of the Wall with Lego bricks, use a crane to assemble an arch, experiment with Roman signalling techniques and get a soldier's-eye view over the original 5-metre height of the Wall. A great experience to share with children and adults alike, the displays are a must if you want to discover the full history of the Wall.

Fresh interpretation also guides you round the big fort. One of 16 major bases along the Wall, it was garrisoned by up to 1,000 Roman soldiers – for most of its history a unit originally raised in Romania, later joined by troops from northern Holland. Clues and puzzles lead families on the hunt for a spy, taking in the three main gates and the view over the ravine of the River Irthing. You'll also discover another unique feature of Birdoswald; how it was continuously occupied for sixteen centuries after the collapse of Roman rule – by Dark Age warlords, medieval and Elizabethan landowners and Victorian farmers.

We've made Birdoswald more family friendly. There's a generously sized room where visitors with younger children can park buggies, wash, hang coats and boots, play Wall-related games and even try on a Roman toga.

Now also equipped with an education room and new café, Birdoswald makes an ideal base for exploring the wild and beautiful surrounding countryside. The fort stands on the Hadrian's Wall Path National Trail, making it a perfect stopping place for ramblers and cyclists.

OPENING TIMES

1 Apr-30 Sep, daily	10am-6pm
1 Oct-3 Nov, daily	10am-5pm
4 Nov-23 Dec, Sat-Sun	10am-4pm
2 Jan-16 Feb, Sat-Sun	10am-4pm
17-23 Feb, daily	10am-4pm
24 Feb-31 Mar, Wed-Sun	10am-4pm
Christmas Opening 24-25 Dec	Closed
26 Dec-1 Jan, daily	10am-4pm
Last entry 30 mins before closing	

VISIT US

Direction: 4 miles west of Greenhead off B6318. Signposted from A69 Carlisle – Hexham road at Brampton roundabout

Train: Haltwhistle 7 miles

Bus: Go NE Tyndale Link service 185. Border Rambler service BR3 (Wed) also passes the site. Otherwise nearest bus service is Stagecoach/Arriva 685 to Low Row from where it is a c. 2½ mile walk

Tel: 01697 747602

Local Tourist Information: Haltwhistle: 01434 321863

NON-MEMBERS

Adult **£9.50** | Concession **£8.60**
Child **£5.80** | Family **£24.80**

Please note: Short uphill walk from car park to fort.

Disabled access (to visitor centre, toilets, shop, tearoom and part of site. Disabled parking on site).

Parking charges apply to non-members. Parking free for Members.

MAP PAGE 346 (4E)
OS MAP 86, OL43: NY615663

7 WILLOWFORD WALL, TURRETS AND BRIDGE

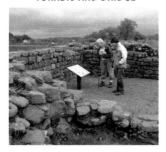

A fine 914-metre (2,999-foot) stretch of Wall, including two turrets and impressive bridge remains beside the River Irthing. Linked by a bridge to Birdoswald Roman Fort (see p.263).

VISIT US

Direction: W of minor road, ¾ mile W of Gilsland

ACQ.1946 ⚠

Beware – livestock may be grazing on site.

OS MAP 86, OL43: NY627664

DID YOU KNOW …

We've recently made big changes at **Birdoswald Roman Fort** and **Corbridge Roman Town**, offering you even more to enjoy along the Wall in 2019.

8 POLTROSS BURN MILECASTLE

One of the best-preserved milecastles on Hadrian's Wall, Poltross includes an oven, a stair to the rampart walk, and the remains of its north gateway. Known locally as 'the King's Stables'.

VISIT US

Direction: On minor road E of Banks village. Immediately SW of Gilsland village, by old railway station

ACQ.1938 **P**

Parking (follow brown signs).

OS MAP 86, OL43: NY634662

9 WALLTOWN CRAGS

One of the best places of all to see the Wall, dramatically snaking and diving along the crags of the Whin Sill.

VISIT US

Direction: 1 mile NE of Greenhead, off B6318

ACQ.1939

OS MAP 86/87, 43: NY674663

10 CAWFIELDS MILECASTLE

A fine stretch of Hadrian's Wall on a steep slope, with turrets and an impressive milecastle, probably built by the Second Legion.

VISIT US

Direction: 1¼ miles N of Haltwhistle, off B6318

ACQ.1960 🚹 🚹 **P**

Parking not operated by EH. Parking charge applies (payable to Northumberland National Park).

OS MAP 86/87, OL43: NY716667

11 WINSHIELDS WALL

The highest point on the Wall, in rugged country with spectacular views.

VISIT US

Direction: W of Steel Rigg car park; on minor road off B6318

ACQ.1937

OS MAP 86/87, 43: NY742676

SCOTLAND

CUMBRIA

CARLISLE

NORTHUMBERLAND

12 HOUSESTEADS ROMAN FORT

See feature on p.266

13 SEWINGSHIELDS WALL

A length of Wall with milecastle remains, impressively sited along the Whin Sill. It commands fine views of many prehistoric and later earthworks to the north.

VISIT US

Direction: N of B6318; 1½ miles E of Housesteads Fort

ACQ.1946

OS MAP 86/87, OL43: NY805702

14 TEMPLE OF MITHRAS, CARRAWBURGH

Just below Carrawburgh Roman fort (accessible, but not in our care) hides a little stone temple to the eastern soldiers' god Mithras, with facsimiles of altars found during excavation. Built in around AD 200, it was eventually desecrated, probably by Christians. Nearby, but no longer visible, was the popular shrine of the water-nymph Coventina. Finds from here are at Chesters Roman Fort (p.268).

VISIT US

Direction: 3¾ miles W of Chollerford, on B6318

ACQ.1953 **P**

Parking charge payable to Northumberland National Park.

OS MAP 87, 43: NY859711

15 BLACK CARTS TURRET

A 460-metre (1,509-foot) length of Hadrian's Wall including one turret. Please note: no visitor parking available.

VISIT US

Direction: On minor road E of Banks village; 3½ miles NE of Brampton

ACQ.1970

OS MAP 86, 315: NY575647

16 CHESTERS ROMAN FORT & MUSEUM

See feature on p.268

17 CHESTERS BRIDGE ABUTMENT

Close to Chesters Roman Fort are the remains of a bridge which carried Hadrian's Wall across the North Tyne. Visible on both river banks, but best viewed from the Roman fort.

VISIT US

Direction: ½ mile S of Low Brunton, on A6079

ACQ.1946

OS MAP 87, 43: NY914701

NEWCASTLE-UPON-TYNE

TYNE AND WEAR

DURHAM

20 21 22 23

AD122 Bus information is subject to change.

Please check **http://jplanner.travelinenortheast.info** before starting your journey.

HOUSESTEADS ROMAN FORT

Set high on a wild hilltop with panoramic views, Housesteads is the most complete example of a Roman fort anywhere in Britain. Discover the stories of the fort and its people in the interactive exhibition.

NORTHUMBERLAND NE47 6NN

Among the most popular sites on Hadrian's Wall, this famous fort stands on the Whin Sill escarpment, flanked by dramatic stretches of the Wall. Hadrian's Wall Trail runs just above it. The site museum houses an outstanding exhibition, vividly interpreting life here on the northern edge of the Roman Empire.

Begun in about AD 124 as one of 16 permanent forts supporting Hadrian's frontier system, Housesteads was known as Vercovicium. It was garrisoned by around 1,000 infantry – from a unit originally raised in what's now eastern Belgium – later reinforced by cavalry. The 5-acre fort displays the remains of gateways and a turreted wall: within are a host of clearly traceable buildings, including the commandant's house, hospital and the renowned multi-seater communal lavatories.

The Roman south gate was much later adapted into a 'bastle' farmhouse, fortified against the 'rank robbers hereabouts': the Border Reivers. Outside the fort wall are the excavated foundations of the Roman civilian settlement. One of the houses here produced evidence of a gruesome Roman double murder.

AN OUTSTANDING EXHIBITION

Visit the museum to witness the story of Housesteads and its people retold in a multimedia display. A short film traces the history of the fort and recreates its original appearance. Every aspect of Roman life here – what the soldiers wore, the tools and weapons they used, how they were cared for when sick, and deities they worshipped, including 'Hooded Gods' – is illuminated by displays. These feature many fascinating objects from the fort, most strikingly a winged Victory statue. Children can enjoy a dressing-up 'Discovery Box', and touchable replicas of Roman objects set at child-height, explained by Felix the Roman soldier. You can also follow Felix in the panels that guide you round the fort.

The fort and museum stand uphill from the car park (via a fairly strenuous 10-minute walk). The National Trust visitor centre by the car park offers a welcome and introduction to the site and an indoor café with outdoor seating for warm days.

Owned by the National Trust and managed by English Heritage.

OPENING TIMES

1 Apr-30 Sep, daily	10am-6pm
1 Oct-3 Nov, daily	10am-5pm
4 Nov-31 Mar, daily	10am-4pm
24-25 Dec	Closed

Last entry 45 mins before closing

VISIT US

Address: Housesteads Roman Fort, Haydon Bridge, Hexham, Northumberland

Direction: Bardon Mill 4 miles

Bus: AD122 Hadrian's Wall Bus Hexham ⊞ – Haltwhistle (14 Apr-1 Oct). Otherwise nearest bus is Stagecoach 685 to Bardon Mill then c. 3½ miles walk

Tel: 01434 344363

Local Tourist Information: Hexham: 01434 652220

NON-MEMBERS

Adult £9.00 | Concession £8.10
Child £5.40 | Family £23.40

Free to National Trust members

Disabled access to the museum (companion recommended). Limited access to site. 750-metre walk up a steep gradient. Disabled parking available at the top of the hill. Please enquire at the visitor centre in the roadside car park to arrange disabled parking. Assistance dogs only in the museum.

Car park not operated by English Heritage (charge payable to Northumberland National Park).

MAP PAGE 347 (4F)
OS MAP 86/87, OL43: NY790688

CHESTERS ROMAN FORT AND MUSEUM

Set in the beautiful valley of the River North Tyne, Chesters is the best-preserved Roman cavalry fort in Britain, with the finest surviving Roman bath-house complex and a unique Victorian-style museum.

NORTHUMBERLAND NE46 4EU

Imaginative interpretation throughout the site, including a family trail, helps you explore the fort and its links with John Clayton, 'Saviour of the Wall'.

Known as Cilurnum, Chesters was positioned to defend the vulnerable section of Hadrian's Wall where it crossed the river. Around 500 cavalry troops – the elite of the Roman auxiliary forces – were based here. From the late 2nd century the garrison was a regiment originating from Asturias in northern Spain.

Pictorial panels guide you round the many clearly marked features of the fort, including its four gates, a barrack block which cavalrymen shared with their horses, the headquarters building with its underground strongroom and the commanding officer's mansion with its private baths.

Armed with the 'Chesters Fort Takeover' trail leaflet, children can seek out the 'rubbing stones' concealed among the buildings, collecting tips to help them in their chosen roles of commander, trooper, guard, messenger, musician, or commander's dog. Two viewfinders reveal how parts of the fort once appeared.

Between the fort and the river, the garrison's bath-house survives to above head height, the finest example of a military bath-house in Britain. It's easy to imagine how the soldiers enjoyed this 'spa' complex of cold, warm and hot 'sauna' baths, together with a big changing-room-cum-clubhouse, still equipped with niches, which probably housed bathers' clothes.

All this was rediscovered by John Clayton, the wealthy Victorian landowner whose mansion stands within sight of the west gate. His ground-breaking excavations here, and lifelong fascination with the Wall – sections of which he bought and safeguarded – played a crucial role in saving Hadrian's great frontier system for us to enjoy today.

His single-minded vision – and the help he got from family, friends and staff – is celebrated in the unique Clayton Museum, an absolute must-see for all visitors to Chesters. Packed with hundreds of fascinating finds from the central section of the Wall, it preserves its traditional Victorian layout and atmosphere. Sensitive re-ordering and creative storytelling, including Kindles disguised as Victorian books, help visitors today to explore museum treasures – from statues of gods to a tiny dog figurine – at their chosen level of detail.

Take a break from your journey of discovery in the Chesters Tearoom with its indoor and outdoor seating. Contact the site for details of hands-on 'Archaeology Detectives' children's activities during school holidays.

OPENING TIMES

1 Apr-30 Sep, daily	10am-6pm
1 Oct-3 Nov, daily	10am-5pm
4 Nov-23 Dec, Sat-Sun	10am-4pm
2 Jan-16 Feb, Sat-Sun	10am-4pm
17-23 Feb, daily	10am-4pm
24 Feb-31 Mar, Wed-Sun	10am-4pm
Christmas Opening	
24-25 Dec	Closed
26 Dec-1 Jan, daily	10am-4pm

Last entry 30 mins before closing

VISIT US

Direction: ¼ mile W of Chollerford, on B6318

Train: Hexham 5½ miles

Bus: Hadrian's Wall bus service AD122 Haltwhistle – Hexham ▣ (April – end Sep). Otherwise nearest bus service is Go North East 680 to Chollerford (then 1½ miles walk)

Tel: 01434 681379

Local Tourist Information: Hexham: 01434 652220

NON-MEMBERS

Adult **£8.00** | Concession **£7.20**
Child **£4.80** | Family **£20.80**

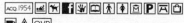

Disabled access (companion recommended). Disabled parking and toilets.

Dogs on leads (some areas only).

Tearoom.

Parking charges apply to non-members. Parking free for Members.

MAP PAGE 347 (4F)
OS MAP 87, OL43: NY912702

18 BRUNTON TURRET

Wall section and a surviving piece of turret 2.5 metres (8ft 2in) high, built by men of the Twentieth Legion.

VISIT US

Direction: ¼ mile S of Low Brunton, off A6079

ACQ.1947

No dogs allowed.

OS MAP 87, OL43: NY922698

19 PLANETREES ROMAN WALL

A 15-metre (49-foot) length of narrow Wall on broad foundations, reflecting a change of policy concerning the thickness of the Wall during construction.

VISIT US

Direction: 1 mile SE of Chollerford on B6318

ACQ.1945

OS MAP 87, OL43: NY929696

20 CORBRIDGE ROMAN TOWN
See feature opposite.

21 HEDDON-ON-THE-WALL

A consolidated stretch of Wall, up to 2 metres (6ft 6in) thick in places.

VISIT US

Direction: Immediately E of Heddon village, S of A69

ACQ.1935

OS MAP 88, 316: NZ137669

22 DENTON HALL TURRET

The foundations of a turret and a 65-metre (213-foot) length of Wall.

VISIT US

Direction: 4 miles W of Newcastle-upon-Tyne city centre, located immediately SE of A69

ACQ.1934

OS MAP 88, 316: NZ198655

23 BENWELL ROMAN TEMPLE

The remains of a small temple to the native god 'Antenociticus', in the 'vicus' (civilian settlement), which stood outside Benwell Fort.

VISIT US

Direction: Temple located immediately SE of A69, at Benwell in Broomridge Ave; Vallum Crossing in Denhill Park

ACQ.1936

OS MAP 88, 316: NZ217647

BENWELL VALLUM CROSSING

A stone-built causeway, where the road from the south crossed the Vallum earthwork on its way to Benwell Fort.

ACQ.1934

Viewing only – no access to the Vallum.

OS MAP 88, 316: NZ216646

NEWCASTLE-UPON-TYNE

TYNE AND WEAR

NORTHUMBERLAND

DURHAM

CORBRIDGE ROMAN TOWN

NORTHUMBERLAND NE45 5NT

20

Our lavishly revamped museum offers you unique insights into Roman social life at Corbridge, the only place in Britain where you can walk the high street of a Roman town.

Beginning as a series of forts, Corbridge was founded well before Hadrian began his Wall, 2½ miles away. It later developed into a prosperous town, the most northerly in the whole Roman Empire, providing goods and services for the Wall garrisons and far beyond. You can still walk the original surface of its Roman main street, flanked by the impressive excavated remains of granaries, a fountain, mansions, markets and workshops.

Excavation also produced an internationally important collection of around 150,000 individual finds. We have redisplayed the museum to showcase the highlights, many previously unseen, illuminating as never before the social and working life of a Roman town. You'll discover how Corbridge's people originated from all over the Roman Empire, ranging from Syrians, Africans and Germans to local Brigantian tribesmen. Thematically displayed tools, weapons, jewellery and personal possessions mingle with grave-finds and altars and images of the town's many gods, and you'll also trace Corbridge's links with 'the African Emperor', Septimius Severus. A pictorial timeline leads you through Corbridge's development from its foundation until the collapse of Roman rule and the move to the site of the present town, clearly visible from the ruins.

Don't miss the iconic Corbridge Lion sculpture, the poignant monuments to Corbridge children, or the Corbridge Hoard, one of the most important finds from Roman Britain. Now explored in a touchscreen display, this extraordinary collection of weapons, tools and personal possessions was buried in the early 2nd century and rediscovered in 1964. It crucially included articulated Roman armour, allowing archaeologists to reconstruct for the first time how this complex armour actually worked.

For a really in-depth look at how people lived, worked and worshipped in a Roman town near Hadrian's Wall, Corbridge is the place to visit.

OPENING TIMES

1 Apr-30 Sep, daily	10am-6pm
1 Oct-3 Nov, daily	10am-5pm
4 Nov-16 Feb, Sat-Sun	10am-4pm
17-22 Feb, daily	10am-4pm
23 Feb-31 Mar, Sat-Sun	10am-4pm
24-26 Dec & 1 Jan	Closed

Last entry 30 mins before closing

VISIT US

Direction: ½ mile NW of Corbridge, on minor road, then signposted

Train: Corbridge 1¼ miles

Bus: Go North East service 686 passes Roman Town entrance. Alternatively Go North East 10, X84 & X85; Arriva/Stagecoach in Cumbria services 685; Wrights summer service 888 to Corbridge then 10-minute walk

Tel: 01434 632349

Local Tourist Information:
Corbridge: 01434 632815

NON-MEMBERS

Adult **£8.70** | Concession **£7.90**
Child **£5.20** | Family **£22.60**

Dogs on leads (restricted areas only).

Disabled access (parking, toilet, audio tour, access to the museum and perimeter of site).

Please note: We don't have a tearoom, but you'll find plenty of refreshment spots in Corbridge.

MAP PAGE 347 (4F)
OS MAP 87, OL43: NY982648

ICAL

Belsay Hall, Castle and Gardens

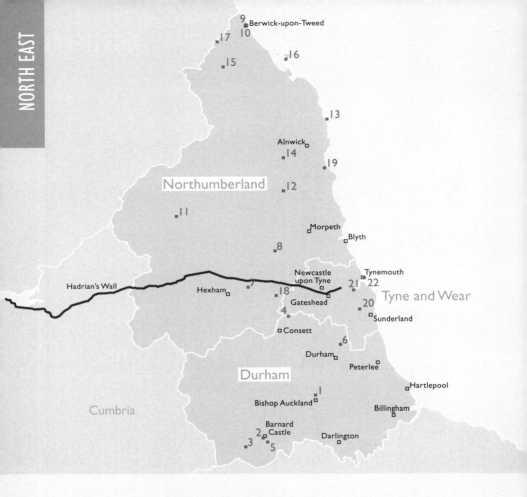

9 Berwick-upon-Tweed
.17 10
.15 .16

.13

Alnwick
.14

.19

Northumberland .12

.11

.8

Morpeth

Blyth

Hadrian's Wall

Hexham

.7

.18

Newcastle upon Tyne

Tynemouth

21 22

Tyne and Wear

Gateshead

20

4

Sunderland

Consett

.6

Durham

Peterlee

Durham

Hartlepool

Cumbria

Bishop Auckland

.1

Billingham

Barnard Castle

2

.3

5

Darlington

TELLING TALES:
THE MYTHS, LEGENDS AND FOLKLORE OF ENGLAND

THE SAINTLY CONSERVATIONIST

Saint Cuthbert of **Lindisfarne**, born a shepherd boy, was Northumbria's greatest and most beloved holy man. Among countless tales told of him, many emphasise his love of and power over wild creatures. After he'd prayed standing in the sea, two young otters dried his feet with their fur; an eagle caught a salmon and dropped it for him to eat; and his horse (which he called his comrade) miraculously found bread and meat for him hidden in the thatch of a house. But his greatest love was for the eider ducks which shared his lonely Farne Island retreat, which he tamed and decreed should be protected forever. Today it's a bird sanctuary, still inhabited by 'Cuddy's ducks', the eiders named after him.

FINCHALE CAMINO INGLÉS

20 miles | 3 days | Escomb Church to Finchale Priory, via Durham Cathedral

You begin at the Saxon church of Escomb before reaching Bishop Auckland. Walk through the Weardale valley before arriving at Durham Cathedral, the shrine of St Cuthbert, and hear its choir sing Evensong. From Durham walk the Weardale Way to the spectacular ruins of Finchale Priory, where the 12th-century hermit Godric lived for 50 years, and from where he made one of the earliest recorded pilgrimages from England to Santiago in Northern Spain. This route is a recognised English section of the Camino de Santiago, starting at the port city of A Coruña, where medieval pilgrims arrived from England.

View more details and a downloadable version of this route at www.english-heritage.org.uk/pilgrimage

Auckland Castle Deer House   Finchale Priory

Discover English Heritage sites along the pilgrimage route

A Auckland Castle Deer House *(p.276)*

B Finchale Priory *(p.277)*

In partnership with

AUCKLAND CASTLE DEER HOUSE

DURHAM – DL14 7QJ

A Gothic Revival 'eyecatcher' of 1760. A deer-shelter with facilities for picnics and enjoying the view.

Managed by The Auckland Project.

OPENING TIMES

Park

1 Apr-30 Sep, daily	10am-6pm
1 Oct-31 Mar, daily	10am-4pm
24-26 Dec & 1 Jan	Closed

VISIT US

Direction: Located in Auckland Park, Bishop Auckland; N of town centre on A68

Train: Bishop Auckland 1 mile

Bus: Arriva service 6 & 56; Go Ahead 18, X21; Scarlet Band 104 & 113 pass closest to the castle gates

ACQ.1952

MAP PAGE 347 (5G)
OS MAP 93, 305: NZ216304

BARNARD CASTLE

DURHAM – DL12 8PR

Spectacularly set high above the River Tees, on the fringe of an attractive market town, this imposing fortress takes its name from its 12th-century founder, Bernard de Balliol. Later developed by Richard III.

OPENING TIMES

1 Apr-30 Sep, daily	10am-6pm
1 Oct-3 Nov, daily	10am-5pm
4 Nov-31 Mar, Sat-Sun	10am-4pm
24-26 Dec & 1 Jan	Closed

Last entry 30 mins before closing

VISIT US

Direction: In Barnard Castle town

Bus: Arriva services 6, X75, X76; Cumbria Classic service 572 (Wed); Scarlet Band services 70, 71, 72, 74, 83, 84, 85, 95 & 96; Hodgsons 73 & 79; Jim Hughes Coaches B66

Tel: 01833 638212

NON-MEMBERS

Adult **£6.50** | Concession **£5.90**
Child **£3.90** | Family **£16.90**

ACQ.1952

Parking (pay and display in town centre).

MAP PAGE 347 (5F)
OS MAP 92, OL31: NZ049165

BOWES CASTLE

DURHAM – DL12 9LG

Impressive ruins of Henry II's 12th-century keep, on the site of a Roman fort guarding strategic Stainmore Pass over the Pennines.

OPENING TIMES

Any reasonable daylight hours

VISIT US

Direction: In Bowes Village off A66; 4 miles W of Barnard Castle town

Bus: Scarlet Band 72; Cumbria Classic 572 (Wed); Jim Hughes Coaches summer service B66

ACQ.1931

MAP PAGE 347 (6F)
OS MAP 92, OL30/31: NY992135

DERWENTCOTE STEEL FURNACE

DURHAM – NE17 7RS

Built in the 1730s, Derwentcote is the last surviving cementation steel-making furnace in Britain. It produced high-grade steel for springs and cutting tools.

OPENING TIMES

Any reasonable daylight hours (Grounds only)

24-26 Dec & 1 Jan	Closed

New woodland walk due in 2019. For information on this, and to arrange access to the furnace, please see English Heritage website and **www. landofoakandiron.org.uk** for up-to-date opening information

DERWENTCOTE STEEL FURNACE

VISIT US

Direction: 10 miles SW of Newcastle, on A694; between Rowland's Gill and Hamsterley

Train: MetroCentre, Gateshead, 7 miles

Bus: Go North East Red Kite services 45/6 Newcastle-upon-Tyne – Consett

Tel: 01661 881636 (Sat-Sun)

ACQ.1985 🐕 P

Dogs on leads (restricted areas only).

Parking across main road from site.

MAP PAGE 347 (4G)
OS MAP 88, 307: NZ130566

EGGLESTONE ABBEY

DURHAM – DL12 9TN

Ruins of a Premonstratensian monastery, picturesquely sited by the River Tees. Remains include parts of the 13th-century church and living quarters.

Egglestone Abbey can be reached by a short walk from Barnard Castle (p.276).

OPENING TIMES

1 Apr-31 Mar, daily	10am-6pm
24-26, 31 Dec & 1 Jan	Closed

VISIT US

Direction: 1 mile S of Barnard Castle, on a minor road off B6277

Bus: Hodgsons service 79 to Abbey Bridge then short (¼ mile) walk

ACQ.1925 ♿ 🐕 P 🎏

Limited free parking available.

MAP PAGE 347 (5G)
OS MAP 92, OL31: NZ062151

FINCHALE PRIORY DURHAM – DH1 5SH

Extensive ruins of a 13th-century priory, on the site of the hermitage of retired merchant adventurer St Godric. Beautifully positioned by the River Wear, with riverside walks nearby.

OPENING TIMES

1 Apr-30 Sep, daily	10am-5pm
1 Oct-31 Mar, daily	10am-4pm
24-26, 31 Dec & 1 Jan	Closed

VISIT US

Direction: 3 miles NE of Durham; on minor road off A167

Train: Durham 5 miles

Bus: Arriva 62 from Durham to HMP Frankland and then a short walk

ACQ.1916 🐕 🏠 🚹 🎏 🌳 P ⚠

Car park (fees apply – not managed by EH).

MAP PAGE 347 (4G)
OS MAP 88, 308: NZ296471

AYDON CASTLE NORTHUMBERLAND – NE45 5PJ

An outstandingly complete defensible medieval manor house in a secluded and beautiful woodland setting, very near Hadrian's Wall. By 1315 Aydon had been fortified against the Scots. The 'castle' served as a farmhouse until 1966, yet remains remarkably unchanged. Explore the fully-roofed hall and chambers, mount the battlements and picnic in the orchard.

A short drive from Corbridge Roman Town (p.271) and Chesters Roman Fort (p.268), and under a mile from Hadrian's Wall Trail.

OPENING TIMES

1 Apr-30 Sep, Wed-Sun & Bank Hols	10am-6pm
1 Oct-3 Nov, Wed-Sun	10am-4pm
4 Nov-31 Mar	Closed

Last entry 30 mins before closing

VISIT US

Direction: 3 mile NE of Corbridge, on minor road off B6321 or A68

Train: Corbridge 4 miles

Bus: Use Go North East services to Corbridge

Tel: 01434 632450

NON-MEMBERS

Adult **£6.30** | Concession **£5.70**
Child **£3.80** | Family **£16.40**

ACQ.1966 ♿ 🐕 🍴 f 🏠 🚹 🎏 P
🎏 📷 ⚠ OVP

Disabled access (ground floor only).

Dogs on leads (restricted areas only).

Short walk from car park.

Accessible parking outside castle gate.

Parking charges apply for non-members. Parking free for Members.

MAP PAGE 347 (4F)
OS MAP 87, 316: NZ001663

The remains of a medieval castle crucial in Anglo-Scottish warfare, superseded by the most complete and impressive bastioned town defences in England. The defences, mainly Elizabethan but updated in the 17th and 18th centuries, surround the whole historic town and you can walk their entire circuit.

OPENING TIMES

Any reasonable daylight hours.
Please note: Steep hidden drops. Dangerous after dark

VISIT US

Direction: The castle is adjacent to Berwick-upon-Tweed railway station. The ramparts surround the town (accessed at various points)

Train: Berwick-upon-Tweed (adjacent)

Bus: Arriva services X15 & X18; Border Buses services B1, B2; Berwick Hoppa 60, 67, 235, 253, 267, 464, 477; Travelsure 32, 34, 87, 236, 260, 418

ACQ.1931 🔥 👁 **P** ⚠️

Disabled access (Ramparts).

Dogs on leads.

Parking: pay and display (in town).

Among the first purpose-built English barracks, begun in 1717, it houses an exhibition telling the story of British infantrymen.

Within the gates you'll discover Berwick's turbulent past. Three separate museums paint a picture of military life and work in the border town.

The Main Guard is managed by Berwick Civic Society.

OPENING TIMES

Barracks

1 Apr-30 Sep, daily	10am-6pm
1 Oct-3 Nov, daily	10am-4pm
4 Nov-31 Mar	Closed

Main Guard
Please call for details

Last entry 30 mins before closing

VISIT US

Direction: On the Parade, off Church St in town centre

Train: Berwick-upon-Tweed ¼ mile

Bus: Arriva services X15 & X18; Border Buses services B1, B2; Berwick Hoppa 60, 67, 235, 253, 267, 464, 477; Travelsure 32, 34, 87, 236, 260, 418

Tel: 01289 304493

NON-MEMBERS

Barracks
Adult **£5.80** | Concession **£5.20**
Child **£3.50** | Family **£15.10**

ACQ.1981 🔥 🐾 **E** 🔥 ✋ 🖥 🚹 🚻
🔥 📷 ♿ OVP

The grounds (i.e. the Barracks square) are accessible to wheelchairs, but the museums are not.

Dogs on leads.

Parking: pay and display (in town).

MAP PAGE 347 (1F)
OS MAP 75, 346
BARRACKS: NU001531
MAIN GUARD: NU000525

MAP PAGE 347 (1F)
OS MAP 75, 346
CASTLE: NT993534
RAMPARTS: NU003530

A fortified farmhouse with thick walls and living quarters only accessible at first floor level. Characteristic of the troubled 16th-century Anglo-Scottish borders.

OPENING TIMES

Any reasonable daylight hours

VISIT US

Direction: 180 metres N of minor road, 7 miles NW of Bellingham; or along a minor road from A68

Bus: Nearest bus service is Go North East service 680 which links Hexham and Bellingham. Bellingham is about 6 miles from the property

ACQ.1978

MAP PAGE 347 (3F)
OS MAP 80, OL42: NY773900

While in the area, why not visit The Alnwick Garden. See p.311 for details.

The beautiful church of Augustinian Brinkburn Priory, built in the Early English style, survives as completely roofed and restored in Victorian times. The church and adjoining Manor House are picturesquely set by the River Coquet, and reached by a scenic 10-minute walk from the car park.

OPENING TIMES

1 Apr-30 Sep, Wed-Sun & Bank Hols	10am-6pm
1-27 Oct, Sat-Sun	10am-4pm
28 Oct-3 Nov, daily	10am-4pm
4 Nov-31 Mar	Closed

Last entry 30 mins before closing

VISIT US

Direction: 4½ miles SE of Rothbury, off B6344

Train: Morpeth 12 miles, Acklington 10 miles

Bus: Arriva service X14 Morpeth-Thropton (passing Morpeth ≥). Nearest stop Weldon Bridge then about 1½ miles walk

Tel: 01665 570628

NON-MEMBERS

Adult **£5.80** | Concession **£5.20**
Child **£3.50** | Family **£15.10**

ACQ.1965

MAP PAGE 347 (3G)
OS MAP 92, 325: NZ116983

BELSAY HALL, CASTLE AND GARDENS

Belsay has something for everyone. Twenty acres of outstanding gardens make a wonderful setting for a succession of fascinating buildings: a fine medieval castle, enlarged into a Jacobean mansion, and the elegant Greek Revival-style home that succeeded it.

NORTHUMBERLAND NE20 0DX

The whole ensemble is the creation of the Middleton family over more than seven centuries. The castle, dominated by its massive 14th-century 'pele tower', was mainly built for defence, but also to impress, and you can still trace its elaborate medieval wall-paintings. In more peaceful times a Jacobean mansion wing was added, where the family lived until they moved into Belsay Hall.

Belsay Hall is an elegant Classical Greek Revival villa. Begun in 1807, it was designed by Sir Charles Monck (formerly Middleton), a man inspired by Ancient Greece and the buildings he'd seen on his honeymoon in Athens. Despite its austere façade, it had a comfortable interior, arranged round an amazing central 'Pillar Hall'. It's displayed without furnishings, so you can admire the fine craftsmanship of its construction.

The vast gardens, which provide a magnificent setting for the castle and hall, are also largely Sir Charles's work. Explore his romantic Quarry Garden, created where stone was cut for his hall, with ravines and sheer rock faces inspired by Sicilian quarries. His grandson Sir Arthur Middleton, likewise a pioneering plantsman, further embellished the quarry with exotic species which you can now see in full maturity. He also added the Winter Garden, Yew Garden, and Magnolia Terrace.

INTRIGUING BUILDINGS IN A MAGICAL GARDEN SETTING

GARDEN HIGHLIGHTS

SPRING: A white carpet of snowdrops, followed by a riot of colour from daffodils, spring snowflakes and dog's tooth violets.

SUMMER: Spectacular rhododendrons flower (May & June). Giant Himalayan lilies up to 2.7 metres (8ft 10in) tall. A NCCPG National Collection of iris.

AUTUMN: The foliage produces a dazzling canopy of russet and gold.

WINTER: Rhododendrons add a splash of colour to the Quarry Garden. Scented viburnums and jasmines in the Winter Garden.

OPENING TIMES

1 Apr-30 Sep, daily	10am-6pm
1 Oct-3 Nov, daily	10am-5pm
4 Nov-23 Dec, Sat-Sun	10am-4pm
2 Jan-16 Feb, Sat-Sun	10am-4pm
17-23 Feb, daily	10am-4pm
24 Feb-31 Mar, Sat-Sun	10am-4pm
Christmas Opening 24-25 Dec	Closed
26 Dec-1 Jan, daily	10am-4pm
Last entry 45 mins before closing	

VISIT US

Address: Belsay Hall, Castle & Gardens, Belsay, Northumberland

Direction: In Belsay; 14 miles NW of Newcastle, on A696

Train: Morpeth 10 miles

Bus: Peter Hogg service 131 (Kelso – Newcastle) and the limited PCL Travel service 808 (Otterburn – Newcastle) pass the main gate

Tel: 01661 881636

Local Tourist Information: Morpeth: 01670 500700

NON-MEMBERS

Adult **£11.00** | Concession **£9.90**
Child **£6.60** | Family **£28.60**

Disabled access (grounds, tearoom and ground floor of hall and castle; toilets).

Dogs on leads (grounds only).

Tearoom (open daily Apr-Oct, weekends Nov-Mar).

MAP PAGE 347 (3G)
OS MAP 88, 316: NZ086785

DUNSTANBURGH CASTLE

NORTHUMBERLAND NE66 3TT

Take a bracing coastal walk to Dunstanburgh Castle, a spectacularly sited fortress with a rich history.

Defending a headland jutting from the rugged Northumberland coast, the castle was begun in 1313 by Earl Thomas of Lancaster, cousin and leading baronial enemy of Edward II. He built on a grand scale, perhaps to underline his rivalry with the crown. The castle's most striking feature is the great double-towered gatehouse. It imitated the new royal castles – such as Harlech – built in Wales.

When his rebellion faltered in 1322, Lancaster may have hoped to take refuge in his remote fortress. But before reaching it, he was defeated, captured and beheaded. Later the castle was inherited by John of Gaunt, Richard II's powerful but unpopular uncle. Gaunt strengthened it against Scots attacks during the 1380s, converting the gatehouse into a strong keep.

A GREAT DOUBLE-TOWERED GATEHOUSE

Dunstanburgh's strength made it a target for both sides during the Wars of the Roses, when it saw fierce fighting. It changed hands at least three times, once after a siege by 10,000 Yorkists in 1462.

Today it's a peaceful place, though still remote and reachable only on foot. You can explore its circuit of walls and strong towers, and look into the rocky cove it once protected. This is a famous place for seabirds, and you may be lucky enough to spot eider ducks – 'Saint Cuthbert's ducks' – an iconic bird of this wild and dramatic coast.

Owned by the National Trust, maintained and managed by English Heritage.

OPENING TIMES

1 Apr-1 Sep, daily	10am-6pm
2-30 Sep, daily	10am-5pm
1 Oct-3 Nov, daily	10am-4pm
4 Nov-23 Dec, Sat-Sun	10am-4pm
26 Dec-1 Jan, daily	10am-4pm
2 Jan-16 Feb, Sat-Sun	10am-4pm
17-23 Feb, daily	10am-4pm
24 Feb-31 Mar, Sat-Sun	10am-4pm
24-25 Dec	Closed

Last entry one hour before closing

VISIT US

Direction: 8 miles NE of Alnwick; on footpaths from Craster or Embleton – 1½ miles rugged coastal walk

Train: Alnmouth, 7 miles from Craster; Chathill (not Sun), 5 miles from Embleton; 7 miles from Castle

Bus: Arriva service X18 or Travelsure (Mon-Sat) 418. Alight Craster and take coast walk, 1½ miles

Tel: 01665 576231

Local Tourist Information:
Craster: 01665 576007

NON-MEMBERS

Adult **£6.30** | Concession **£5.70**
Child **£3.80** | Family **£16.40**

Free to National Trust members

ACQ.1929 🦮 ⬛ 🅿️ 📷 ⚠️ OVP

Parking (in Craster village; approx. 1½ miles walk. A charge is payable).

Nearest toilets located at car park in Craster Village.

MAP PAGE 347 (2G)
OS MAP 75, 332: NU257219

EDLINGHAM CASTLE
NORTHUMBERLAND

The tower and other remains of a fortified medieval manor house, in a remote and beautiful setting.

Managed by the Edlingham Community Association.

OPENING TIMES

Any reasonable daylight hours

VISIT US

Direction: Accessible via a short path from Edlingham church, on a minor road off B6341; 6 miles SW of Alnwick

Train: Alnmouth 9 miles

Bus: Closest bus is PCL Travel 473 service to Banktop (2 miles)

Note: Waterproof footwear recommended. Guide pamphlet available in church.

MAP PAGE 347 (2G)
OS MAP 81, 332: NU116092

NORHAM CASTLE
NORTHUMBERLAND

Besieged at least 13 times by the Scots, this important medieval border castle was called 'the most dangerous place in the country'.

Recaptured after falling to James IV in 1513, it was rebuilt as an artillery fortress.

NORHAM CASTLE

Download a free audio tour from the English Heritage website.

OPENING TIMES

1 Apr-30 Sep, daily	10am-6pm
1-31 Oct, daily	10am-4pm
1 Nov-31 Mar, Sat-Sun	10am-4pm

VISIT US

Direction: In Norham village; 6 miles SW of Berwick-upon-Tweed, on minor road off B6470 (from A698)

Train: Berwick-upon-Tweed 7½ miles

Bus: Border Buses service 67 Berwick-upon-Tweed – Galashiels

Disabled access (excluding keep).

MAP PAGE 347 (1F)
OS MAP 74/75, 339: NT906476

ETAL CASTLE NORTHUMBERLAND – TD12 4TN

Etal Castle was begun in the early 14th century as a tower house, in a strategic position by a ford on the Anglo-Scottish border. Vulnerable to raiders, it was soon reinforced by a curtain wall with corner towers and a gatehouse.

In 1513 the castle was suddenly thrust into the forefront of history, when King James IV of Scotland invaded with the largest Scots army ever to attack England. He quickly captured Etal

Castle, but was soon afterwards defeated at the nearby Battle of Flodden, the greatest-ever English victory over the Scots. King James was killed along with nine Scots earls, fourteen lords, and thousands of his men.

Leave time to explore the story of Flodden and Anglo-Scottish border warfare in an exhibition. You can also visit the nearby Flodden battlefield.

OPENING TIMES

1 Apr-30 Sep, Wed-Sun & Bank Hols	10am-6pm
1 Oct-3 Nov, Wed-Sun	10am-4pm
4 Nov-31 Mar	Closed

Last entry 30 mins before closing

VISIT US

Direction: In Etal village, 10 miles SW of Berwick-upon-Tweed

Train: Berwick-upon-Tweed 10½ miles

Bus: Border Buses service 267 Berwick-upon-Tweed – Wooler

Tel: 01890 820332

NON-MEMBERS

Adult **£6.30** | Concession **£5.70**
Child **£3.80** | Family **£16.40**

Dogs on leads.

Toilets (in car park).

MAP PAGE 347 (1F)
OS MAP 74/75, 339: NT925393

LINDISFARNE PRIORY

Serene and remote, the Holy Island of Lindisfarne has drawn visitors to it for over thirteen centuries. It still retains powerful memories of the monks and saints of Anglo-Saxon and medieval Northumbria.

NORTHUMBERLAND TD15 2RX

Founded by the Irish monk St Aidan in AD 635 and still a place of pilgrimage today, Lindisfarne Priory was one of the most important centres of early Christianity in Anglo-Saxon England. The dramatic approach to the island across the causeway only emphasises the tranquil appeal of this atmospheric site.

St Cuthbert, Prior of Lindisfarne, is the most celebrated of the priory's many holy men. After ten years seeking peace as a hermit on lonely Inner Farne Island, he reluctantly became Bishop before retiring to die on Inner Farne in 687. Eleven years after his burial at the monastery, his coffin was opened and his body found to be undecayed – a sure sign of sanctity. His remains were then transferred to a pilgrim shrine.

But the rich monastery was easy prey for raiders, suffering a devastating raid by Viking pirates in 793 – the first significant Viking attack in western Europe. In 875 the monks left, carrying Cuthbert's remains, which after long wanderings were enshrined in Durham

Coastguard's Cottage on Holy Island sleeps six, with an accessible en-suite bedroom. Enjoy the private gardens overlooking the castle.

See p.332 for details on staying at **Lindisfarne** and our other holiday cottages.

OPENING TIMES

1 Apr-30 Sep, daily	10am-6pm
1 Oct-3 Nov, daily	10am-5pm
4 Nov-16 Feb, Sat-Sun	10am-4pm
17-23 Feb, daily	10am-4pm
24 Feb-31 Mar, Wed-Sun	10am-4pm
Christmas Opening 24-26 Dec & 1 Jan	Closed

Last entry 30 mins before closing. Opening times can vary at short notice due to tidal restrictions

The causeway floods at high tide so it is very important to check the tide times before crossing

VISIT US

Address: Lindisfarne Priory, Holy Island, Berwick-upon-Tweed, Northumberland

Direction: On Holy Island, only reached at low tide across causeway; tide tables at each end, or from Tourist Information Centre

Train: Berwick-upon-Tweed 14 miles, via causeway

Bus: Border Buses service 477 from Berwick-upon-Tweed (passes close Berwick-upon-Tweed ⊠). Times vary with tides

Tel: 01289 389200

Tourist Information Centre: 01289 330733

NON-MEMBERS

Adult £8.00 | Concession £7.20
Child £4.80 | Family £20.80

ACQ.1913 ♿ 🦮 🔇 🛡 f 🌳 ▢ ▢ 🎒 📷 ⚠ OVP

Dogs on leads (restricted areas only).

Parking and toilets in the village. Parking pay and display operated by Northumberland County Council.

Access (limited in some areas of priory grounds).

MAP PAGE 347 (1G)
OS MAP 75, 340: NU126417

Cathedral in 1104, where they still rest. Only after that time did Durham monks re-establish a priory on Lindisfarne. Today you can see the evocative ruins of the richly decorated priory church they built in c. 1150, with their famous 'rainbow arch' – a vault-rib of the now-vanished crossing tower.

The priory is likewise renowned for the Lindisfarne Gospels, among England's greatest artistic and religious treasures. They were produced here in the late 7th or early 8th century by Bishop Eadfrith, possibly in honour of St Cuthbert's transference to his pilgrim shrine.

The same Lindisfarne artists may well have produced the 14 extraordinary 'name stones' discovered around the site. Carved and originally painted and possibly bejewelled versions of the Gospels' manuscript pages, these delicate stones commemorate people who may have known Cuthbert and Eadfrith. Visit the site museum to explore the 'Inscribed in Stone' display, which celebrates these rare survivals of 8th-century craftsmanship, unique links with the vanished Saxon monastery.

WARKWORTH CASTLE AND HERMITAGE

Among the biggest, strongest and most impressive medieval fortresses in northern England, Warkworth Castle was the favourite home of the powerful and turbulent Percy family, Earls of Northumberland. Today you can explore its almost complete Great Tower and elaborate defences, and venture out to the atmospheric riverside 'Hermitage'.

NORTHUMBERLAND NE65 0UJ

Warkworth Castle straddles the neck of a tight loop in the River Coquet, guarding an attractive stone-built town. Its still-complete circuit of towered walls, including the powerful gatehouse and formidable Grey Mare's Tail tower, took shape during the 13th century, and the fortress repelled a Scots siege in 1327.

But Warkworth attained its greatest glory under the Percy family, who wielded almost kingly power in the North during the later Middle Ages. The Percy lion badge proudly adorns the Great Tower, the castle's most outstandingly distinctive feature. Built on top of an earlier mound, this ingeniously-planned 'keep' houses everything a medieval baron could desire. Ground floor wine-cellars and stores; first floor kitchens, great hall, chapel and great chamber and second floor bedchambers are interconnected by completely separate systems of passages and stairways for servants and masters, so food and wine could appear in the lord's state rooms, without being seen on their way.

Cleverly lit by a central light-well, this masterpiece of medieval design for gracious living is an intriguing place to explore. On selected days you can also view the second-floor 'Duke's Rooms', restored in the 1850s and equipped with antique-style Victorian furniture.

The Great Tower was built after 1377 for the first Percy Earl of Northumberland, who along with his famous son Harry 'Hotspur' – hero of many Border ballads as the bane of the Scots – helped depose Richard II and set Henry IV on the throne, only to rebel against him in turn. Both were killed in battle, as were the second and third earls. Then the fourth earl remodelled Warkworth's courtyard, adding a complete new set of state rooms – entered via the still-impressive Lion Tower, bedecked with Percy heraldry – before himself being murdered by an angry mob in 1489.

A MASTERPIECE OF MEDIEVAL DESIGN

A delightful riverside walk and a rowing-boat ferry take you to a contrastingly tranquil feature of Warkworth, the supremely atmospheric 'Hermitage' hewn into a sandstone cliff. (Open selected days). Here a priest said prayers for the Percy family's souls. Within its tiny unlit chapel you can still trace worn carvings of a Nativity scene. Even tinier 'closets' provided views of the altar for worshippers, and yew trees now grow amid the ruins of the priest's house. Take time to quietly experience this extraordinary survival from medieval England, featured in Robson Green's 'Tales from Northumberland'.

OPENING TIMES

Castle

1 Apr-30 Sep, daily	10am-6pm
1 Oct-3 Nov, daily	10am-5pm
4 Nov-23 Dec, Sat-Sun	10am-4pm
2 Jan-16 Feb, Sat-Sun	10am-4pm
17-23 Feb, daily	10am-4pm
24 Feb-31 Mar, Wed-Sun	10am-4pm

Christmas Opening

24-25 Dec	Closed
26 Dec-1 Jan, daily	10am-4pm

The Duke's rooms are open on Sun, Mon and Bank Hols from 1 Apr to 30 Sep

Hermitage

1 Apr-30 Jun, Sun, Mon & Bank Hols	11am-4pm
1 Jul-31 Aug, Fri-Mon	11am-4pm
1 Sep-3 Nov, Sun-Mon	11am-4pm
4 Nov-31 Mar	Closed

Last entry 30 mins before closing

VISIT US

Direction: In Warkworth; 7½ miles S of Alnwick, on A1068. Access to Hermitage is via an approx. 15-minute riverside walk from the castle, including some slopes, and rowing-boat ferry (included in entry charge). Staff will give directions. The Hermitage is reached by uneven steps, and unlit within

Train: Alnmouth 3½ miles

Bus: Arriva X18 & X20 Newcastle – Alnwick

Tel: 01665 711423

NON-MEMBERS

Castle
Adult £8.00 | Concession £7.20
Child £4.80 | Family £20.80

Hermitage
Adult £5.30 | Concession £4.80
Child £3.20 | Family £13.80

Castle and Hermitage Joint Ticket
Adult £11.30 | Concession £10.20
Child £6.80 | Family £29.40

Disabled access: Limited access in castle: steps to and within Great Tower. Disabled access to Hermitage is difficult.

Dogs on leads welcome in most areas.

Parking charges apply for non-members.
Parking free for Members.

MAP PAGE 347 (2G)
OS MAP 81, 332: NU247058

PRUDHOE CASTLE NORTHUMBERLAND – NE42 6NA

Guarding a strategic crossing of the River Tyne, impressive Prudhoe Castle was a vital bastion against Scots invaders. After resisting two Scots sieges during the 1170s – when King William the Lion lamented 'as long as Prudhoe stands, we shall never have peace' – it was given its tall keep, and later reinforced by towered walls. In the late 14th century it became a stronghold of the locally all-powerful Percy family, Earls of Northumberland.

You'll witness Prudhoe's great strength as you approach via the barbican, passing the picturesque mill pond and crossing the inner ditch to the powerful gatehouse. You can climb the steps to the atmospheric gatehouse chapel, explore the inner and outer baileys and look up at the towering keep. There's also a fine 'Regency Gothic' mansion within the walls, built by the Percys in the early 1800s as a 'gentleman's residence' for their land agent. Its elegant unfurnished rooms house family-friendly displays tracing the long history of this formidable fortress, continuously occupied for over nine centuries. There's an array of site-finds and a children's activity room with games.

Hadrian's Wall is a short drive away.

OPENING TIMES

1 Apr-30 Sep, Wed-Sun & Bank Hols	10am-6pm
1 Oct-3 Nov, Wed-Sun	10am-4pm
4 Nov-31 Mar	Closed
Last entry 30 mins before closing	

VISIT US

Direction: In Prudhoe, on minor road off A695

Train: Prudhoe ¼ mile

Bus: Go North East 10, 10B, 10X, 686

Tel: 01661 833459

NON-MEMBERS

Adult **£6.50** | Concession **£5.90**
Child **£3.90** | Family **£16.90**

ACQ.1966

Dogs on leads (restricted areas only).

Toilets with disabled access on site.

MAP PAGE 347 (4G)
OS MAP 88, 316: NZ091634

HYLTON CASTLE
TYNE AND WEAR – SR5 3PA

The heraldry-bedecked gatehouse-tower of a castle built by Sir William Hylton c. 1400.

OPENING TIMES

1 Apr-31 Mar, daily	10am-4pm
24-26, 31 Dec & 1 Jan	Closed

An exciting HLF-funded project at Hylton Castle is due to complete, and the castle itself is due to open, in Spring 2019. Please see **hyltoncastle. org.uk** for additional information

VISIT US

Direction: 3¾ miles W of Sunderland

Train: Seaburn Metro (2½ miles) then bus 99; Pallion Metro then bus 29, 29A, 39 or 39A

Bus: Stagecoach services 3, 12, 13; Go North East services 56

ACQ.1950 Dogs on leads.
Disabled access (grounds only).

MAP PAGE 347 (4H)
OS MAP 88, 308: NZ358588

ST PAUL'S MONASTERY, JARROW
TYNE AND WEAR

Home of the Venerable Bede, chronicler of early English Christianity. The Anglo-Saxon church, founded AD 685, partly survives as the parish church's chancel. Download a free audio tour from our website.

OPENING TIMES
Monastery ruins any reasonable daylight hours

VISIT US

Direction: In Jarrow, on minor road N of A185; follow signs for Bede's World

Metro: Bede ¾ miles

Bus: Go North East The Crusader services 27

Tel: 0191 489 7052

ACQ.1956

MAP PAGE 347 (4G)
OS MAP 88, 316: NZ339652

TYNEMOUTH PRIORY AND CASTLE

TYNE AND WEAR NE30 4BZ

From fortified medieval monastery and Tudor stronghold to gun battery in both World Wars, Tynemouth Priory and Castle have exciting stories to reveal.

Set at the mouth of the river Tyne, it offers impressive views of the coastline and beaches below. Explore the castle defences, stunning priory ruins and underground batteries.

A 7th-century Anglian monastery, burial place of Oswin, sainted King of Northumbria, originally stood here. After its destruction by Vikings, the present Benedictine priory was founded on its site in c. 1090.

The towering east end of the priory church, built in c. 1200, still survives almost to its full height, dominating the headland.

IMPRESSIVE VIEWS OF THE COASTLINE

Beyond it you can explore a small but exceptionally well-preserved chapel, with a rose window and an ornately sculpted roof vault. This was built in the mid-15th century as a chantry for the souls of the powerful Percy family, Earls of Northumberland.

When the priory surrendered to Henry VIII in 1539, it was immediately adopted as a royal castle. After that the fortress-headland continued to play a vital role in coastal defence from Elizabethan times until the end of the Second World War.

The interactive 'Life in the Stronghold' exhibition takes you on a journey from Tynemouth's beginnings to its importance as a coastal gun battery in both World Wars.

OPENING TIMES

1 Apr-30 Sep, daily	10am-6pm
1 Oct-3 Nov, daily	10am-5pm
4 Nov-16 Feb, Sat-Sun	10am-4pm
17-23 Feb, daily	10am-4pm
24 Feb-31 Mar, Sat-Sun	10am-4pm
24-26 Dec & 1 Jan	Closed

Last entry 30 mins before closing

Gun Battery: Access limited, please ask site staff for details

VISIT US

Direction: In Tynemouth, near North Pier

Metro: Tynemouth ½ mile

Bus: Arriva Northumbria service 306 stops close to the entrance; Go North East services 1 & 1A also stop nearby

Tel: 0191 257 1090

NON-MEMBERS

Adult £7.00 | Concession £6.30
Child £4.20 | Family £18.20

ACQ 1969   ♿ 🐕 🏛 😊 f ♿ ☐ ☂ 🧍 🚶 ⛺ ☐

⚠ OVP

Dogs on leads.

Disabled access (priory only). Toilets with disabled access on site. Limited disabled parking available.

MAP PAGE 347 (4H)
OS MAP 88, 316: NZ373694

St Mary of the Angels, Brownshill, Gloucestershire, © Andy Marshall

THE FRIENDS OF FRIENDLESS CHURCHES

FRIENDS
OF
FRIENDLESS
CHURCHES

The Friends own redundant but beautiful places of worship that would otherwise have been demolished or left to ruin.

The Friends now own 50 former churches saved from destruction. We are a small, voluntary organisation that works in partnership, sharing an office and staff with the Ancient Monuments Society, a statutory consultee on listed building consent in England and Wales.

We warmly welcome visitors to our churches, but do not claim sophistication in terms of parking, toilets, attendants or shops, and access may require approach to a key-holder. Our churches are places for quiet study and contemplation, preserved for posterity as beautiful historic buildings.

We have been very grateful for substantial English Heritage (Historic England) grants over the years, especially for Boveney, near Windsor, St John the Baptist at Matlock Bath and Mundon in Essex, which we could not have otherwise saved. These and all the other vestings are described and illustrated on the website.

THE FRIENDS OF FRIENDLESS CHURCHES

St Ann's Vestry Hall, 2 Church Entry, London EC4V 5HB
T. 020 7236 3934 E. office@friendsoffriendlesschurches.org.uk
www.friendsoffriendlesschurches.org.uk Registered charity no: 1113097

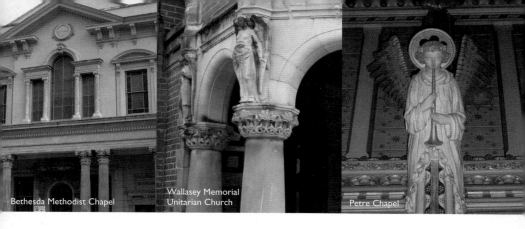

Bethesda Methodist Chapel

Wallasey Memorial
Unitarian Church

Petre Chapel

HISTORIC CHAPELS TRUST

An Important Story of Dissent and Faith.

The Historic Chapels Trust rescues non-Anglican places of worship in England that are no longer in use by their congregations. We aim to hand them on to future generations in good condition, as the physical record of religious life and a vital strand of our history.

Since 1993 we have rescued a remarkable collection of Non-conformist chapels, meeting houses and Catholic churches. Together, they are the evidence of a remarkable story of dissent from the Established Church and of self-determination and autonomy by people of faith, courage and social vision.

VISIT OUR CHAPELS AND CHURCHES

All our sites are Listed Grade II* or Grade I. Some are important for their architecture, some as rare survivals, some for their history, some for what the architectural historian John Summerson described as 'endearing simplicity'. All of them are worth visiting.

To visit our chapels and churches please arrange a time with our local keyholders at the site first. Details of how to find the buildings and our keyholders are on our website.

EVENTS IN OUR CHAPELS

Many of our chapels can be hired for concerts or other events. Some provide interesting venues for marriages or commemorative events. If you are interested in using one of our buildings look for details on our website.

Historic Chapels Trust gratefully acknowledges financial support from Historic England.

HISTORIC CHAPELS TRUST

Society Building, 8 All Saints St, London N1 9RL
T. 020 7481 0533 E. chapels@hct.org.uk
www.hct.org.uk UK Registered charity no: 1017321

Evesham Discover. Photo: © Ian Tustin

THE CHURCHES CONSERVATION TRUST

THE CHURCHES
CONSERVATION TRUST

Open a church door to discover 1,000 years of England's history.

Whether Anglo-Saxon carvings, medieval stained glass, grand Victorian architecture or proximity to the stories of our past, our collection of historic churches provides wonder and beauty in places you know and in those you don't.

We are the national charity protecting historic churches at risk. We've saved more than 350 beautiful buildings, enjoyed by almost 2 million visitors a year. Scattered the length and breadth of England in town and country, and ranging from ancient, rustic buildings to others of great richness and splendour, each has been saved because it represents something remarkable.

With our help and with your support they are kept open and in use – living once again in the heart of their communities. Entry is free, so push open the door and 1,000 years of history awaits you.

Discover more and see what's on near you at www.visitchurches.org.uk

---

THE CHURCHES CONSERVATION TRUST

Society Building, 8 All Saints Street, London N1 9RL
T. 0845 303 2760 E. central@thecct.org.uk
www.visitchurches.org.uk Registered charity no: 258612

ASSOCIATED ATTRACTIONS
—— IN ENGLAND ——

Discount applies to: | KEY | ⊞ MEMBERS | 📷? NO. OF MEMBER'S CHILDREN

Terms and conditions may apply, so make sure you check the details on our website or call the individual property for more information.

ASSOCIATED ATTRACTIONS: LONDON

CUTTY SARK London SE10 9HT   ⊞

Visit the celebrated *Cutty Sark*; delve into the ship's extraordinary history, meet the crew and discover what life was like on board the fastest ship of its day.

*Offer redeemable in person on production of Membership card. Senior and Student tickets available weekdays only. Under 4s free.

25%
DISCOUNT ON
ADULT, CHILD,
SENIOR AND
STUDENT TICKETS*

www.rmg.co.uk/cuttysark

Tel: 020 8312 6608

DANSON HOUSE Kent DA6 8HL   ⊞ 📷 6

Set overlooking the award-winning Danson Park, this beautiful Grade I listed Palladian villa was officially re-opened by HM Queen Elizabeth II in July 2005.

*Discount applies for English Heritage Members. November-February: open Thursdays, 10am-4pm. March-October: open Sundays, 10am-4pm. Last admission 3.15pm.

50%
DISCOUNT
ON ENTRY*

www.bexley.gov.uk

Tel: 0300 041 1103

DULWICH PICTURE GALLERY London SE21 7AD   ⊞

The world's first purpose-built public art gallery, today a vibrant hub hosting some of the UK's leading exhibitions alongside its collection of Baroque masterpieces including Rembrandt's *Girl at a Window*.

*Children free. Collection only. Not valid for exhibitions.

2 for 1
ENTRY*

www.dulwichpicturegallery.org.uk

Tel: 020 8693 5254

BENJAMIN FRANKLIN HOUSE
London WC2N 5NF
www.benjaminfranklinhouse.org

2 FOR 1 ENTRY on Adult tickets.
Children under 16 free.

⊞

Tel: 020 7925 1405

Use your membership to get discounted entry at these independent attractions. Please remember to show your card as proof of membership.

THE ROYAL MEWS, BUCKINGHAM PALACE London SW1W 1QH

Buckingham Palace's working royal stables. Discover the Gold State Coach and other historic carriages, meet the Mews horses and take part in fun family activities.

*Offer applies to all ticket types, including children's tickets for children under age 17 and in the family group. Under 5s free. Please note the Royal Mews is closed in December and January.

20%

DISCOUNT ON ENTRY*

www.rct.uk/royalmews

Tel: 0303 123 7302

STRAWBERRY HILL HOUSE & GARDEN London TW1 4ST

Strawberry Hill House & Garden is internationally famous as Britain's best example of Georgian Gothic revival architecture. It has been meticulously restored to ensure visitors enjoy the theatrical experience Horace Walpole intended.

*Offer cannot be used in conjunction with any other offer or on a guided tour.

2 for 1

ENTRY ON STANDARD ADULT SELF-GUIDED TICKET*

www.strawberryhillhouse.org.uk

Tel: 020 8744 1241

GREENWICH ROYAL TOURS
London SE7 7BA

10% OFF advance bookings for all tours. Children 6 and under free. Bookings must be made 10 days in advance. Minimum 2 persons booking.

www.greenwichroyaltours.com

Tel: 0800 180 4565

GUNNERSBURY PARK MUSEUM London W5 4NH | FREE ENTRY

www.visitgunnersbury.org/visit

Tel: 020 3961 0280

HOGARTH'S HOUSE London W4 2QN | FREE ENTRY

www.hounslow.gov.uk/hogarthshouse

Tel: 020 8994 6757

ASSOCIATED ATTRACTIONS: SOUTH EAST

ANNE OF CLEVES HOUSE MUSEUM East Sussex BN7 1JA

Discover how the Tudors and Elizabethans lived, worked and relaxed at home. This 15th-century Wealden hall-house displays authentically furnished rooms, traditional planted gardens and local museum.

*Not valid for family tickets.

50%

DISCOUNT ON ENTRY*

www.sussexpast.co.uk/anneofcleves

Tel: 01273 474610

Discount applies to:

KEY | ⊞ MEMBERS | 👪? NO. OF MEMBER'S CHILDREN

Terms and conditions may apply, so make sure you check the details on our website or call the individual property for more information.

ASSOCIATED ATTRACTIONS: SOUTH EAST *CONTINUED*

BIGGIN HILL MEMORIAL MUSEUM Kent TN16 3EJ ⊞

Visit to discover Britain's most famous fighter station, and the inspiring stories of the brave people and technical innovations that shaped our world today.

*Offer redeemable in person on production of Membership card. Under 5s free.

10%
DISCOUNT ON ENTRY*

www.bhmm.org.uk

Tel: 020 8313 4916

BLENHEIM PALACE Oxfordshire OX20 1UL ⊞ 👪 6

The birthplace of Sir Winston Churchill, Blenheim Palace is a UNESCO World Heritage Site offering an awe-inspiring experience for visitors.

*Not valid on special event days – please call or check the website before visiting. Cannot be combined with any other offer. Under 5s free.

30%
OFF PALACE, PARK AND GARDENS TICKETS*

www.blenheimpalace.com

Tel: 01993 810530

BLETCHLEY PARK Buckinghamshire MK3 6EB ⊞

Once the top-secret home of the World War Two codebreakers. Bletchley Park is now a vibrant heritage attraction and a place of exceptional historical importance.

*Not valid on group or education bookings. Offer not valid with other offers. Under 12s free.

20%
DISCOUNT ON ADULT, CONCESSION AND CHILD TICKETS*

www.bletchleypark.org.uk

Tel: 01908 640404

BRITISH AIRWAYS i360 Brighton & Hove BN1 2LN ⊞ 👪 6

Take to the skies to see Brighton and the beautiful south coast as you've never seen them. Gently glide to 450ft in our futuristic glass viewing pod, which was conceived and designed by Marks Barfield Architects, creators of the London Eye.

*Cheapest ticket free. Offer valid on walk-up tickets only. Not valid for special events.

2 for 1
ENTRY ON STANDARD ADULT AND CHILD TICKETS*

britishairwaysi360.com

Tel: 0333 772 0360

Use your membership to get discounted entry at these independent attractions.
Please remember to show your card as proof of membership.

BUTSER ANCIENT FARM Hampshire PO8 0BG

Experimental archaeological site in the South Downs, displaying ancient buildings from Stone Age, Iron Age, Romans and Saxons, prehistoric crops and rare breed animals.
*Cheapest ticket free. Not applicable for any special events or with any other offer. Under 3s free. Dogs welcome.

2 for 1
ENTRY ON ADULT, CONCESSION AND FULL PRICE CHILD ADMISSIONS*

www.butserancientfarm.co.uk

Tel: 023 9259 8838

CANTERBURY TALES Kent CT1 2TG

Become immersed in Chaucer's brilliant tales! Watch each one spring to life before your eyes in this unique and charming recreation of medieval life.

*Not bookable online, drop in only. Must present an English Heritage membership card at admissions. Valid for up to 4 people. Not valid on special event days.

20%
DISCOUNT ON ENTRY*

www.canterburytales.org.uk

Tel: 01227 696002

CHILTERN OPEN AIR MUSEUM Buckinghamshire HP8 4AB

An eclectic selection of over 30 reconstructed historic buildings including Victorian toll house, 1940s prefab, Nissen huts, tin chapel, blacksmith's forge and Iron Age roundhouse.
*Cheapest ticket free. Not to be used in conjunction with any other offer. Excludes evening and special fundraising events.
Museum open 1 April-31 October 2019.

2 for 1
ENTRY ON ADULT AND FULL PRICE CHILD ADMISSION TICKETS*

www.coam.org.uk

Tel: 01494 871117

EASTGATE HOUSE Kent ME1 1EW

In the heart of historic Rochester, visitors can learn about the house, including its time as an Elizabethan Home and a Victorian School.

*Standard admission ticket including child, adult, and over 60s. Open Wednesday-Sunday, 10am-5pm.
Image © Simon Kelsey.

20%
DISCOUNT ON ENTRY*

www.visitmedway.org

Tel: 01634 332700

Terms and conditions may apply, so make sure you check the details on our website or call the individual property for more information.

ASSOCIATED ATTRACTIONS: SOUTH EAST *CONTINUED*

EMIRATES SPINNAKER TOWER Hampshire PO1 3TT ⊞

Experience the South Coast's most spectacular view at Emirates Spinnaker Tower, with our thrilling glass sky walk, VR experience, café in the clouds, and open air sky garden.
*Not valid in conjunction with any other discounted or promotional ticket. Not available to book online. 20% off for EH member and up to 6 accompanying guests. Children under 4 free.

20%
DISCOUNT
ON STANDARD
WALK UP TICKET*

www.spinnakertower.co.uk

Tel: 023 9285 7520

FISHBOURNE ROMAN PALACE & GARDENS West Sussex PO19 3QR ⊞

Explore the largest collection of early mosaic floors in Britain and recreated Roman garden. Join inspiring guided tours and look behind the scenes in the Collections Discovery Centre.

*Not valid for family tickets.

50%
DISCOUNT
ON ENTRY*

www.sussexpast.co.uk/fishbourne

Tel: 01243 785859

THE HISTORIC DOCKYARD CHATHAM Kent ME4 4TE ⊞ 👪2

Climb aboard three historic warships, discover where rigging for HMS Victory was made and where rope is still made today, plus so much more!

*Not valid on special event days.
Child price applies to age 5-15. Under 5s free.

15%
DISCOUNT
ON ENTRY*

www.thedockyard.co.uk

Tel: 01634 823800

LEWES CASTLE & BARBICAN HOUSE MUSEUM East Sussex BN7 1YE ⊞

This 950-year-old Norman castle offers stunning panoramic views across Sussex. The adjoining Barbican House museum is home to the Museum of Sussex Archaeology.

*Not valid for family tickets.

50%
DISCOUNT
ON ENTRY*

www.sussexpast.co.uk/lewescastle

Tel: 01273 486290

Use your membership to get discounted entry at these independent attractions. Please remember to show your card as proof of membership.

MICHELHAM PRIORY HOUSE & GARDENS East Sussex BN27 3QS ⊞

England's longest medieval moat encircles a site with over 800 years of history. The picturesque island boasts a Tudor mansion, 14th-century gatehouse, watermill, forge and much more.

*Not valid for family tickets.

50%
DISCOUNT
ON ENTRY*

www.sussexpast.co.uk/michelham

Tel: 01323 844224

MILTON'S COTTAGE Buckinghamshire HP8 4JH ⊞ ⫴ 6

The only surviving residence (Grade I listed) of the great poet and parliamentarian John Milton, with museum and Grade 2 registered literary garden.

*Groups out of normal hours and disabled access by prior arrangement. Please see website for details. Accompanied children under 16 free.

33%
OFF ADULT AND
CONCESSION
ENTRY*

www.miltonscottage.org

Tel: 01494 872313

OXFORD CASTLE & PRISON Oxfordshire OX1 1AY ⊞

Oxford Castle & Prison reveals Oxford's lesser known history, one that's rich with tales of great escapes, betrayals and even romance – 1,000 years of history, all within the site.

*Discount only applicable to daily standard tours on site. Not valid on special event days.

25%
DISCOUNT
ON ENTRY*

www.oxfordcastleandprison.co.uk

Tel: 01865 260666

THE ROYAL PAVILION Brighton & Hove BN1 1EE ⊞ ⫴ 2

Discover the magnificent seaside residence of King George IV. The Indian architecture contrasts with interiors inspired by China. Regency gardens, tearoom and gift shop.

*Valid on full adult admission only. Not available on concession prices, promotions or other discounted tickets.

20%
DISCOUNT
OFF FULL ADULT
ADMISSION ONLY*

www.brightonmuseums.org.uk

Tel: 0300 029 0900

Terms and conditions may apply, so make sure you check the details on our website or call the individual property for more information.

ASSOCIATED ATTRACTIONS: SOUTH EAST *CONTINUED*

RYCOTE CHAPEL Oxfordshire OX9 2PE   ⊞ 👥 6

15th-century chapel with original furniture, including exquisitely carved and painted woodwork. Also restored Capability Brown Ice House.

Managed by the Rycote Buildings Charitable Foundation.

50%
DISCOUNT ON ENTRY

rycote.bodleian.ox.ac.uk   Tel: 01844 214468

WATTS GALLERY – ARTISTS' VILLAGE Surrey GU3 1DQ   ⊞ 👥 6

A unique gem nestled in the Surrey Hills, The Artists' Village is the home, studios, gallery, chapel and joint architectural legacy of artist G F Watts and renowned designer Mary Watts.
*Valid on standard admission to the Artists' Village. Does not apply to Limnerslease tour tickets. Not valid on special event days. Children under 16 free.

20%
OFF STANDARD ADULT ADMISSION TICKETS*

www.wattsgallery.org.uk   Tel: 01483 810235

CHIDDINGSTONE CASTLE
Kent TN8 7AD

20% DISCOUNT ON ENTRY
Adult admission only. Not to be used on special event days, or in conjunction with any other voucher or offer.   ⊞

www.chiddingstonecastle.org.uk   Tel: 01892 870347

COGGES MANOR FARM
Oxfordshire OX28 3LA

2 FOR 1 ENTRY Please see website for opening times. Under 3s free. Only available during Cogges' open season mid-March to early November.   ⊞

www.cogges.org.uk   Tel: 01993 772602

LULLINGSTONE CASTLE &
THE WORLD GARDEN Kent DA4 0JA

2 FOR 1 ADULT ENTRY Not valid on event days or for single adult entry. Please check website for details.   ⊞

www.lullingstonecastle.co.uk   Tel: 01322 862114

MARLIPINS MUSEUM West Sussex BN43 5DA | **20% DISCOUNT ON ENTRY** Not valid on family tickets.

www.sussexpast.co.uk/marlipins   Tel: 01273 462994

NEWPORT ROMAN VILLA Isle of Wight PO30 1HA | **20% DISCOUNT ON ENTRY** 👥 3

www.iwight.com/museums   Tel: 01983 529720

Use your membership to get discounted entry at these independent attractions.
Please remember to show your card as proof of membership.

**PENSHURST PLACE
& GARDENS** Kent TN11 8DG

www.penshurstplace.com

FREE UPGRADE TO HOUSE ENTRY When grounds ticket purchased. ▦ ♦♦♦ 6
Offer only applicable upon presentation of an official English Heritage membership card.
This offer is not available to third party English Heritage partnerships.

Tel: 01892 870307

THE PRIEST HOUSE West Sussex RH19 4PP | **20% DISCOUNT ON ENTRY** Not valid on family tickets. ▦

www.sussexpast.co.uk/priesthouse

Tel: 01342 810479

ASSOCIATED ATTRACTIONS: SOUTH WEST

ARTHURIAN CENTRE / THE VALE OF AVALON Cornwall PL32 9TT ▦ ♦♦♦ 4

Beautiful walks past an archaeological site to the River Camel, Camlann – King Arthur's last battlefield, 6th-century inscribed memorial, 18th-century garden, exhibition, gifts and tearoom.
*Cannot be used in conjunction with any other offer or promotion. Offer not valid for senior, student, or other discounted rates.

20%
DISCOUNT
OFF ADULT AND
FAMILY TICKETS*

www.arthur-online.co.uk

Tel: 01840 213947

EXETER CATHEDRAL Devon EX1 1HS ▦ ♦♦♦ 6

Exeter Cathedral is a remarkable feat of engineering, design and craftsmanship, sitting on a site that has maintained a Christian presence for nearly 1,000 years.

*Offer applicable during normal opening hours, and does not apply to any special events or tours.

25%
DISCOUNT
ON ENTRY*

www.exeter-cathedral.org.uk

Tel: 01392 285983

THE JANE AUSTEN CENTRE Bath BA1 2NT ▦ ♦♦♦ 6

Situated in an original Georgian townhouse, The Jane Austen Centre tells the story of Jane's time in Bath, including the effect that living in this magnificent city had on her life and writing.

*Discount does not apply to group bookings.

40%
DISCOUNT
ON ENTRY*

www.janeausten.co.uk

Tel: 01225 443000

Terms and conditions may apply, so make sure you check the details on our website or call the individual property for more information.

ASSOCIATED ATTRACTIONS: **SOUTH WEST** *CONTINUED*

LULWORTH CASTLE & PARK Dorset BH20 5QS ⊞ 👪 6

Discover the story of this former family home and 17th-century hunting lodge, set within extensive parkland with woodlands and walks. Explore the notable Roman Catholic chapel and Anglican church, also in the grounds. Castle Tearoom serves cream teas, cakes and ice creams.

FREE ENTRY
TO THE CASTLE*

*Please check website for accepted memberships and opening times

www.lulworth.com

Tel: 01929 400352

PENCARROW HOUSE & GARDENS Cornwall PL30 3AG ⊞ 👪 6

Beautiful Georgian house and Grade II listed gardens. Café, children's play area, gift and plant shop, free parking. Dogs welcome in gardens.

*Applies to House & Gardens only (not Gardens only visits). Check website for opening times before visiting.

2 for 1
ENTRY*

www.pencarrow.co.uk

Tel: 01208 841369

POWDERHAM CASTLE Devon EX6 8JQ ⊞ 👪 2

Over 600 years of history can be discovered within the walls of one of Devon's oldest family homes.

Enjoy two unique guided tour experiences around this spectacular castle.

*Dogs welcome (additional £1 admission fee per dog).

20%
DISCOUNT OFF ENTRY ON FULL PRICED TICKETS*

www.powderham.co.uk

Tel: 01626 890243

THE SALISBURY MUSEUM Wiltshire SP1 2EN ⊞ 👪 4

Located in the medieval King's House within the glorious setting of Salisbury Cathedral Close. Nationally important archaeology collections and exciting temporary exhibitions.

*Day ticket only.

50%
DISCOUNT ON STANDARD MUSEUM DAY TICKET*

www.salisburymuseum.org.uk

Tel: 01722 332151

Use your membership to get discounted entry at these independent attractions.
Please remember to show your card as proof of membership.

SHERBORNE CASTLE & GARDENS Dorset DT9 5NR

Built by Sir Walter Raleigh in 1594 and home to the Digby family since 1617. The Castle has magnificent staterooms, Raleigh's kitchen and a museum. Breathtaking landscaped garden by Capability Brown.

*Discount applies to gardens only, Castle upgrades are available. This offer does not apply to special event days. Please check the website for details of events.

£1.50
OFF GARDEN
TICKETS*

www.sherbornecastle.com

Tel: 01935 812072

WEST SOMERSET RAILWAY Somerset TA24 5BG

Enjoy a steam-hauled train journey along the longest heritage railway in England. Board at Bishops Lydeard, near Taunton M5, J25. Alight at Washford for the short walk to Cleeve Abbey or continue along the coast to Minehead Bay.

*Purple and Pink operating days excluded. Not to be used in conjunction with any other offer.

£3
OFF FAMILY TICKET*
£1
OFF ADULT TICKET*

www.west-somerset-railway.co.uk

Tel: 01643 704996

WILTSHIRE MUSEUM Wiltshire SN10 1NS

Award-winning galleries telling Wiltshire's story and featuring prehistoric gold from the time of Stonehenge. Nationally important collections include objects that belonged to the chieftains and priests buried close to Stonehenge. Located in Devizes, mid-way between Stonehenge and Avebury.

2 for 1
ENTRY ON
STANDARD
TICKET*
*Under 16s are free.

www.wiltshiremuseum.org.uk

Tel: 01380 727369

AVON VALLEY RAILWAY
South Gloucestershire BS30 6HD

2 FOR 1 TRAIN RIDES Lowest price goes free. Valid on operation dates with Timetables A, B & D only. Not valid with family tickets or on Dining or Santa trains. Under 5s free.

www.avonvalleyrailway.org

Tel: 0117 932 5538

EDEN PROJECT
Cornwall PL24 2SG

10% OFF ENTRY FOR MEMBER + 1
Adult and Child tickets only.

www.edenproject.com

Tel: 01726 811911

KENTS CAVERN PREHISTORIC CAVES
Devon TQ1 2JF

50% DISCOUNT ON ENTRY For daytime cave tours.
Only valid for Adults, Seniors and Students.

www.kents-cavern.co.uk

Tel: 01803 215136

Terms and conditions may apply, so make sure you check the details on our website or call the individual property for more information.

ASSOCIATED ATTRACTIONS: **SOUTH WEST** *CONTINUED*

SOMERSET COALFIELD LIFE AT RADSTOCK MUSEUM Somerset BA3 3EP

£1 TEAROOM VOUCHER with each Adult/Concession ticket purchased. ⊞
£2 TEAROOM VOUCHER with each Family ticket purchased.
Offer not applicable to children's tickets or group prices and may not be used with any other discount offer. Under 6s free.

www.radstockmuseum.co.uk

Tel: 01761 437722

STEAM – MUSEUM OF THE GREAT WESTERN RAILWAY Wiltshire SN2 2EY

25% OFF ENTRY ⊞ 👪 1
Not valid on special event days.

www.steam-museum.org.uk

Tel: 01793 466646

SUDELEY CASTLE Gloucestershire GL54 5JD

10% DISCOUNT ON ENTRY Discount can only be redeemed on general ⊞
admission tickets in person at the Visitor Centre and not online. Discount cannot be used in conjunction with any other offers or reduced ticket prices.

www.sudeleycastle.co.uk

Tel: 01242 604244

WILTON HOUSE Wiltshire SP2 0BJ

2 FOR 1 ENTRY Joint House & Gardens tickets only. ⊞
Not available on special event days. Offer applies to English Heritage Members only.

www.wiltonhouse.com

Tel: 01722 746728

WOODCHESTER MANSION Gloucestershire GL10 3TS

£1 DISCOUNT ON STANDARD ADMISSION PRICE ⊞
Children under 14 years are admitted free when accompanied by an adult.

www.woodchestermansion.org.uk

Tel: 01453 861541

ASSOCIATED ATTRACTIONS: EAST OF ENGLAND

HEDINGHAM CASTLE Essex CO9 3DJ ⊞ 👪 6

The 900-year-old keep of Hedingham Castle contains five floors of unique Norman architecture, set in 160 acres of landscaped grounds and woodland.

*Not valid on special event days.

2 for 1
ENTRY*

www.hedinghamcastle.co.uk

Tel: 01787 460261

HOLKHAM HALL Norfolk NR23 1AB ⊞ 👪 3

18th-century stately home with stunning architecture, art and classical statuary, 'Field to Fork' experience, 6-acre walled garden, children's woodland play area, cycle and boat hire.

*Valid on standard admission only during visitor season. Not valid for events or to be used with any other offer.

20%
DISCOUNT TO HALL, FIELD TO FORK & WALLED GARDEN, OR FIELD TO FORK & WALLED GARDEN*

www.holkham.co.uk

Tel: 01328 713111

Use your membership to get discounted entry at these independent attractions.
Please remember to show your card as proof of membership.

ASSOCIATED ATTRACTIONS: EAST OF ENGLAND *CONTINUED*

STOW MARIES AERODROME Essex CM3 6RJ ⊞

Set in the Essex Countryside, this is the last operating First World War aerodrome in the world. Explore the history of the Great War through its three exhibitions, see period aircraft and learn about the men and women who ruled the air. Café, shop and free parking.

*Offer not valid for events.

2 for 1
ENTRY ON
ADULT TICKETS
ONLY*

www.stowmaries.org.uk

Tel: 01245 329358

WOBURN ABBEY & GARDENS Bedfordshire MK17 9WA ⊞

The Earls and Dukes of Bedford have been at the centre of historical events for nearly 400 years. Discover more about their lives, world-renowned art and antiquities, Repton inspired gardens and 3,000-acre deer-park.

*Not valid on weekend or event days and valid for combined house and garden ticket only.

15%
DISCOUNT ON
HOUSE & GARDEN
TICKETS*

www.woburnabbey.co.uk

Tel: 01525 290333

ASSOCIATED ATTRACTIONS: EAST MIDLANDS

THE 1620s HOUSE & GARDENS AT DONINGTON LE HEATH Leicestershire LE67 2FW ⊞ 👪2

Step back in time to discover and explore our early 17th-century house and gardens and see how people lived and worked 400 years ago.

*A current English Heritage card must be produced for each Member. Offer includes up to 2 children per Member. Offer excludes all special events and activities.

20%
DISCOUNT
ON ENTRY*

www.doningtonleheath.org.uk

Tel: 01455 290429

BOSWORTH BATTLEFIELD HERITAGE CENTRE AND COUNTRY PARK Leicestershire CV13 0AD ⊞ 👪2

Discover the drama and excitement of the Battle of Bosworth (1485) at one of the UK's leading and multi-award-winning attractions, set in spectacular countryside.
*A current English Heritage card must be produced for each Member. Offer includes up to 2 children per Member. Offer excludes all special events including the August Bosworth Medieval Festival Weekend.

20%
DISCOUNT
ON ENTRY*

www.bosworthbattlefield.org.uk

Tel: 01455 290429

Terms and conditions may apply, so make sure you check the details on our website or call the individual property for more information.

ASSOCIATED ATTRACTIONS: EAST MIDLANDS *CONTINUED*

CRESWELL CRAGS MUSEUM AND PREHISTORIC GORGE Derbyshire S80 3LH ⊞ 👪 4

Calling all intrepid explorers: delve deep into Ice Age Man's northern frontier. Venture into a hyena den and discover Britain's 13,000-year-old Ice Age cave art.

*Timed cave tours. Advance booking recommended.

50%
DISCOUNT OFF FULL PRICE ADULT CAVE TOUR AND MUSEUM TICKETS*

www.creswell-crags.org.uk

Tel: 01909 720378

KING RICHARD III VISITOR CENTRE Leicestershire LE1 5DB ⊞

Discover the incredible story of King Richard III's life, death and discovery and see the place where his remains lay undiscovered for over 500 years.

*Offer applies when an adult or over 60s ticket is purchased. Children under 16 must be accompanied by an adult. Offer is valid on all days the Centre is open until 31 March 2020.

2 for 1
ENTRY*

www.kriii.com

Tel: 0300 300 0900

LINCOLN CASTLE Lincolnshire LN1 3AA ⊞

Built in 1068, Lincoln Castle has stood as a symbol of power and seat of justice. Discover 1,000 years of history – where it happened.

*Castle Day Pass tickets – Adult, Concession, Child and Family. Check website for castle opening dates and times.

10%
DISCOUNT ON ENTRY*

www.lincolncastle.com

Tel: 01522 554559

NATIONAL CIVIL WAR CENTRE Nottinghamshire NG24 1JY ⊞ 👪 6

Plunge deep into the heart of Britain's deadliest conflict with fantastic galleries, HD cinema, fascinating objects and costumes and armour for all to try!

*Valid on day passes only.

2 for 1
ENTRY*

www.nationalcivilwarcentre.com

Tel: 01636 655765

Use your membership to get discounted entry at these independent attractions.
Please remember to show your card as proof of membership.

ASHBY DE LA ZOUCH MUSEUM Leicestershire LE65 1HU | FREE ENTRY

www.ashbymuseum.org.uk

Tel: 01530 560090

THE CHARLES RENNIE MACKINTOSH HOUSE, 78 DERNGATE Northamptonshire NN1 1UH | **15% DISCOUNT ON ADULT ENTRY**
Excludes corporate membership, current EH Membership cards to be shown on entry.

www.78derngate.org.uk

Tel: 01604 603407

CRICH TRAMWAY VILLAGE | **2 FOR 1 ON FULL PRICE TICKETS** Cheapest ticket free.
Derbyshire DE4 5DP | Not valid for Second World War/1940s events, or between 14-17 June 2019.

www.tramway.co.uk

Tel: 01773 854321

GRIMSTHORPE CASTLE PARK & GARDENS | **£2 OFF** Full Adult ticket price.
Lincolnshire PE10 0LY | **£1 OFF** Adult garden ticket price.

www.grimsthorpe.co.uk

Tel: 01778 591205

PAPPLEWICK PUMPING STATION | **25% DISCOUNT**
Nottinghamshire NG15 9AJ | Steam events only.

www.papplewickpumpingstation.org.uk

Tel: 0115 963 2938

PEAK RAIL | **10% DISCOUNT**
Derbyshire DE4 3NA | Not valid at special events. Please see website for details.

www.peakrail.co.uk

Tel: 01629 580381

ASSOCIATED ATTRACTIONS: WEST MIDLANDS

BRITISH MOTOR MUSEUM Warwickshire CV35 0BJ

Discover the world's largest collection of historic British cars. Experience sights, sounds and stories of our motor industry. A great day out with the family.

*Can only be redeemed with an English Heritage Membership card. Cannot be used on 5 show days per year or in conjunction with any other offer – see website for full details.

£2
OFF ENTRY
PER PERSON FOR
UP TO 5 PEOPLE*

www.britishmotormuseum.co.uk

Tel: 01926 641188

ROYAL SHAKESPEARE COMPANY Warwickshire CV37 6BB

The RSC's award-winning exhibition, *The Play's The Thing*. See costumes, props and a copy of Shakespeare's First Folio. Get hands-on with digital and interactive exhibits.

*Cheapest ticket free. Children must be accompanied by an adult. Under 5s free.

2 for 1
ENTRY*

www.rsc.org.uk/the-plays-the-thing

Tel: 01789 403493

Discount applies to: **KEY** ⊞ MEMBERS 👪? NO. OF MEMBER'S CHILDREN

Terms and conditions may apply, so make sure you check the details on our website or call the individual property for more information.

ASSOCIATED ATTRACTIONS: **WEST MIDLANDS** *CONTINUED*

SHAKESPEARE'S SCHOOLROOM & GUILDHALL Warwickshire CV37 6HB ⊞ 👪6

Discover where William Shakespeare was educated and inspired to become the world's greatest playwright.

Winner – *Best Visitor Attraction Coventry & Warwickshire Tourism & Heritage Awards 2017.*

*Discount applies to all ticket types.

50%
DISCOUNT
ON ENTRY*

www.shakespearesschoolroom.org

Tel: 01789 203170

SHREWSBURY FLAXMILL MALTINGS VISITOR CENTRE Shropshire SY1 2SX ⊞

Industrial site of international importance and home of the world's first iron-framed building. Centre tells the story of the site and its uses since construction in 1797.

*Open 1 day a week over winter and 3 days a week during the summer. Check website for full details and tour booking instructions.

FREE ENTRY*

www.flaxmill-maltings.co.uk

Tel: 01743 360213

WARWICK CASTLE Warwickshire CV34 4QU ⊞ 👪2

Celebrate over 1,100 years of history at Warwick Castle and Knight's Village Lodges! Open 364 days a year, guests can enjoy shows and attractions that bring history vividly to life!

*Castle entry only (excluding entry to The Castle Dungeon and evening events). Cannot be booked online or in advance. English Heritage card must be presented to receive discount. Car parking charges apply.

50%
DISCOUNT
OFF ENTRY ON
ADULT AND UP TO
2 CHILD TICKETS*

www.warwick-castle.com

Tel: 01926 495421

WORLD OF WEDGWOOD Staffordshire ST12 9ER ⊞ 👪6

Discover 260 years of heritage and craftsmanship, explore the V&A Museum collection, award-winning factory tour and creative studios, and enjoy our restaurants and retail stores.

*Available Monday-Friday only, Factory closed at weekends. Museum free entry for everyone, every day including children's trails. Free factory tour for children under 12.

25%
DISCOUNT ON THE
DISCOVERY EXPERIENCE
TICKET, FACTORY
TOUR AND MUSEUM*

www.worldofwedgwood.com

Tel: 01782 282986

Use your membership to get discounted entry at these independent attractions.
Please remember to show your card as proof of membership.

ASSOCIATED ATTRACTIONS: **WEST MIDLANDS** *CONTINUED*

EASTNOR CASTLE
Herefordshire HR8 1RL

www.eastnorcastle.com

50% DISCOUNT ON GATE ENTRY TICKETS
Not valid for Chilli Festival, Deer Park events or Theatre Performances.

Tel: 01531 633160

IRONBRIDGE GORGE MUSEUMS
Shropshire TF8 7DQ

www.ironbridge.org.uk

15% DISCOUNT OFF Annual Passport tickets only.
Annual Family Passport Ticket is valid for 1 or 2 adults and all of their children.

Tel: 01952 433424

THE SHAKESPEARE FAMILY HOMES
Warwickshire CV37 6QW

www.shakespeare.org.uk

20% DISCOUNT ON FULL STORY TICKETS
Applies to EH Members and their children when they buy
individual Full Story tickets – see website for details.

Tel: 01789 204016

STONELEIGH ABBEY
Warwickshire CV8 2LF

www.stoneleighabbey.org

2 FOR 1 ON ENTRY WITH A HOUSE TOUR
Valid with a house tour entry only.

Tel: 01926 858535

ASSOCIATED ATTRACTIONS: YORKSHIRE AND THE HUMBER

BARLEY HALL North Yorkshire YO1 8AR

Barley Hall is a stunning medieval
townhouse. Lovingly restored to its original
splendour showcasing stunning high ceilings,
beautiful exposed timber frames and
possibly the only horn window in England.

*Not valid on Joint tickets.

www.barleyhall.co.uk

15%
DISCOUNT
ON STANDARD
TICKET*

Tel: 01904 615505

CASTLE HOWARD North Yorkshire YO60 7DA

Magnificent 18th-century house built by
Sir John Vanbrugh for the 3rd Earl of
Carlisle, set within spectacular parkland.
With exhibitions, events, adventure
playground, shops and cafés.

*Offer valid when house open.

www.castlehoward.co.uk

DISCOUNTED
ADMISSION RATE
£15.50 ADULT*
£7.50 CHILD*
£37.50 FAMILY*

Tel: 01653 648333

Discount applies to: | KEY | ⊞ MEMBERS | 👨‍👧❓ NO. OF MEMBER'S CHILDREN

Terms and conditions may apply, so make sure you check the details on our website or call the individual property for more information.

ASSOCIATED ATTRACTIONS: YORKSHIRE AND THE HUMBER *CONTINUED*

DIG: AN ARCHAEOLOGICAL ADVENTURE North Yorkshire YO1 8NN ⊞ 👨‍👧 6

DIG: An Archaeological Adventure offers you a unique adventure to get you on your way to becoming a real archaeologist.

*Not valid on Joint tickets.

2 for 1
ENTRY ON
STANDARD
TICKETS*

www.digyork.com

Tel: 01904 615505

FOUNTAINS ABBEY & STUDLEY ROYAL WATER GARDEN North Yorkshire HG4 3DY ⊞ 👨‍👧 6

Spectacular World Heritage Site including 12th-century abbey ruins and stunning Georgian water garden.

*Offer applies to normal admission to the whole estate. Not valid for special events. Please note offer doesn't apply to education or corporate members.

**FREE ADMISSION
ON STANDARD
TICKET***

www.nationaltrust.org.uk/fountainsabbey

Tel: 01765 608888

JORVIK VIKING CENTRE North Yorkshire YO1 9WT ⊞ 👨‍👧 6

JORVIK Viking Centre is now open daily, following a multi-million pound re-imagining. Discover the sights, sounds, and, of course, smells of Viking-age York.

*Not valid on Joint tickets.

15%
DISCOUNT
ON STANDARD
ENTRY*

www.jorvikvikingcentre.co.uk

Tel: 01904 615505

MERCHANT ADVENTURERS' HALL North Yorkshire YO1 9XD ⊞ 👨‍👧 6

The Merchant Adventurers' Hall is one of York's medieval marvels, constructed in 1357. Discover this stunning building and its unique collections.

*Accompanied children go free.

50%
DISCOUNT
ON ENTRY*

www.merchantshallyork.org

Tel: 01904 654818

Use your membership to get discounted entry at these independent attractions.
Please remember to show your card as proof of membership.

ASSOCIATED ATTRACTIONS: YORKSHIRE AND THE HUMBER *CONTINUED*

NORTH YORKSHIRE MOORS RAILWAY North Yorkshire YO18 7AJ

Visit one of the world's greatest heritage railway experiences, with thrills and family fun at its heart. Climb on board a steam or heritage diesel train and experience 24 miles of Yorkshire's amazing scenery.
*Not valid on special event days, gold timetable, Pullman Dining Train, annual membership, other NYMR tickets, or with any other offer. Expires 01/01/20.

£4 OFF FULL PRICE ADULT TICKET ON THE PICKERING TO WHITBY SERVICE*

www.nymr.co.uk

Tel: 01751 472508

RICHARD III & HENRY VII EXPERIENCE North Yorkshire YO1 6JX

Explore the lives of two of England's most famous medieval monarchs, and how their reigns impacted the city of York.

*Not valid on Joint tickets.

15% DISCOUNT ON STANDARD TICKET*

www.richardiiiexperience.com

Tel: 01904 615505

YORK'S CHOCOLATE STORY North Yorkshire YO1 7LD

Discover York's Chocolate heritage. A fully guided tour and three floors of interactive exploration take you on a journey through the city where chocolate made history.

*Not valid on family tickets or special event days. Check www.yorkschocolatestory.com for full terms and conditions.

25% DISCOUNT ON ENTRY*

www.yorkschocolatestory.com

Tel: 01904 527765

THE GEORGIAN THEATRE ROYAL RICHMOND
North Yorkshire DL10 4DW

20% OFF ADMISSION
To The Georgian Theatre Experience.

www.georgiantheatreroyal.co.uk

Tel: 01748 823710

THE GREEN HOWARDS MUSEUM
North Yorkshire DL10 4QN

2 FOR 1 ENTRY
Adult and concession admissions. Under 16s free.

www.greenhowards.org.uk

Tel: 01748 826561

Discount applies to: **KEY**   ⊞ MEMBERS   🛈❓ NO. OF MEMBER'S CHILDREN

Terms and conditions may apply, so make sure you check the details on our website or call the individual property for more information.

ASSOCIATED ATTRACTIONS: NORTH WEST

NORTON PRIORY MUSEUM & GARDENS Cheshire WA7 1BD   ⊞

Norton Priory is the most excavated monastic site in Europe. A 12th-century undercroft and 18th-century walled garden sit among acres of woodland and a museum telling the 900-year history of the site.

2 for 1
ENTRY ON
ADULT DAY
TICKET

www.nortonpriory.org   Tel: 01928 569895

SMITHILLS HALL Greater Manchester BL1 7NP   ⊞

Set in over 2,200 acres of woodland, Smithills Hall is one of the oldest and best preserved manor houses in the North West.

20%
DISCOUNT
FROM GOODS
BOUGHT IN THE
MUSEUM SHOP

www.boltonlams.co.uk   Tel: 01204 332377

LOWTHER CASTLE AND GARDENS
Cumbria CA10 2HH
www.lowthercastle.org

20% DISCOUNT ON STANDARD ENTRY   ⊞
Cannot be used in conjunction with any other offers or special events.

Tel: 01931 712192

ASSOCIATED ATTRACTIONS: NORTH EAST

THE ALNWICK GARDEN Northumberland NE66 1YU   ⊞

One of the world's most contemporary gardens, The Alnwick Garden's enchanting landscape offers adventure and intrigue in the heart of Northumberland.

20%
DISCOUNT
ON GATE RATE
ENTRY*

*Not available in conjunction with any other offer.

www.alnwickgarden.com   Tel: 01665 511350

ALNWICK CASTLE
Northumberland NE66 1NG
www.alnwickcastle.com

15% DISCOUNT on gate rate entry. Please show EH card to redeem offer.   ⊞
Available during Alnwick Castle open season 1 Apr-27 Oct 2019.

Tel: 01665 511100

Use your membership to get discounted entry at these independent attractions.
Please remember to show your card as proof of membership.

ASSOCIATED ATTRACTIONS: NORTH EAST

THE AUCKLAND PROJECT County Durham DL14 7NP

The Auckland Project – beautiful artworks, stunning landscapes and engrossing stories. Centred in and around Auckland Castle, featuring galleries, historic parkland and gardens.

*Not available in conjunction with any other offer.

www.aucklandproject.org

15%
DISCOUNT
ON ENTRY*

Tel: 01388 743750

BESSIE SURTEES HOUSE Tyne and Wear NE1 3JF

Jacobean home with a romantic history, Bessie Surtees House now contains offices, an exhibition space and splendid period interiors that are open to the public and free to visit.

FREE ENTRY

www.historicengland.org.uk/bsh

Tel: 0191 269 1255

THE BOWES MUSEUM County Durham DL12 8NP

The Bowes Museum houses a collection of outstanding European fine and decorative arts, offers an acclaimed exhibition programme, its own bistro, shop and beautiful parkland.

*Not applicable when an additional cost is applied to special exhibitions and events.

10%
DISCOUNT ON
ADMISSION*

www.thebowesmuseum.org.uk

Tel: 01833 690606

ASSOCIATED ATTRACTIONS: HADRIAN'S WALL

SENHOUSE ROMAN MUSEUM
Cumbria CA15 6JD

2 FOR 1 ENTRY Valid on full price adult tickets only. Allows the cardholder to take either one free adult or one free child, per full paying adult.

www.senhousemuseum.co.uk

Tel: 01900 816168

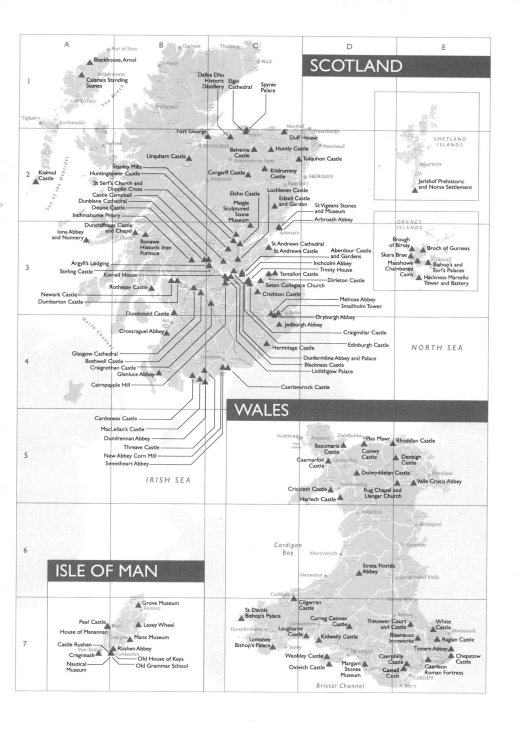

SCOTLAND

A — Port of Ness
Blackhouse, Arnol
Stornoway
Calanais Standing Stones
Tarbert
Durness — Thurso — Wick
Scourie
Dallas Dhu Historic Distillery — Elgin Cathedral — Spynie Palace
Tighnabruaich
Lochmaddy
Uig — Portree
Fort George
Macduff — Fraserburgh
Duff House — Peterhead
INVERNESS — Elgin
Balvenie Castle — Huntly Castle
Urquhart Castle — Grantown-on-Spey — Tolquhon Castle
Kisimul Castle
Stanley Mills
Huntingtower Castle
St Serf's Church and Dupplin Cross
Castle Campbell
Dunblane Cathedral
Doune Castle
Inchmahome Priory
Corgarff Castle — Kildrummy Castle — ABERDEEN
Kingussie
Elcho Castle — Lochleven Castle
Meigle Sculptured Stone Museum — Edzell Castle and Garden
St Vigeans Stones and Museum
Arbroath Abbey
Arbroath
Dunstaffnage Castle and Chapel
Iona Abbey and Nunnery
Oban
Bonawe Historic Iron Furnace
Argyll's Lodging
Stirling Castle
Kinneil House
Rothesay Castle
Newark Castle
Dumbarton Castle
North Channel
Dundonald Castle
Ayr
Crossraguel Abbey
Glasgow Cathedral
Bothwell Castle
Craignethan Castle
Glenluce Abbey
Cairnpapple Hill
Dumfries
St Andrews Cathedral
St Andrews Castle
Aberdour Castle and Gardens
Inchcolm Abbey
Trinity House
Tantallon Castle
Dirleton Castle
Seton Collegiate Church
Crichton Castle
Melrose Abbey
Smailholm Tower
Dryburgh Abbey
Jedburgh Abbey
Craigmillar Castle
Hermitage Castle
Edinburgh Castle
Dunfermline Abbey and Palace
Blackness Castle
Linlithgow Palace
Caerlaverock Castle

SHETLAND ISLANDS
Lerwick
Jarlshof Prehistoric and Norse Settlement

ORKNEY ISLANDS
Brough of Birsay
Skara Brae
Maeshowe Chambered Cairn
Kirkwall
Broch of Gurness
Bishop's and Earl's Palaces
Hackness Martello Tower and Battery

NORTH SEA

WALES

Cardoness Castle
MacLellan's Castle
Dundrennan Abbey
Threave Castle
New Abbey Corn Mill
Sweetheart Abbey

IRISH SEA

Holyhead — Llandudno
Anglesey
Plas Mawr — Rhuddlan Castle
Beaumaris Castle
Caernarfon Castle
Conwy Castle
Denbigh Castle
Dolwyddelan Castle
Wrexham
Criccieth Castle
Rug Chapel and Llangar Church
Valle Crucis Abbey
Harlech Castle

Cardigan Bay
Aberystwyth
Strata Florida Abbey
Llandrindod Wells

ISLE OF MAN

Ramsey
Grove Museum
Peel Castle
Peel
Laxey Wheel
House of Mananan
Douglas
Manx Museum
Castle Rushen
Cregneash
Rushen Abbey
Castletown
Old House of Keys
Old Grammar School
Nautical Museum

St Davids Bishop's Palace
Cilgerran Castle
Carmarthen
Carreg Cennen Castle
Tretower Court and Castle
White Castle
Laugharne Castle
Kidwelly Castle
Blaenavon Ironworks
Raglan Castle
Lamphey Bishop's Palace
SWANSEA
Caerphilly Castle
Tintern Abbey
Weobley Castle
Margam Stones Museum
Castell Coch
Caerleon Roman Fortress
Chepstow Castle
Oxwich Castle
CARDIFF
Bristol Channel
Barry

CADW

Conwy Castle

English Heritage members can gain half price admission to Cadw attractions during the first year of membership and free entry in subsequent years.

Beaumaris Castle, Anglesey LL58 8AP **T.** 01248 810361

Blaenavon Ironworks*, Nr Pontypool, Torfaen NP4 9RQ **T.** 01495 792615

Caerleon Roman Fortress*, Caerleon, Newport NP18 1AE **T.** 01633 422518

Caernarfon Castle, Caernarfon, Gwynedd LL55 2AY **T.** 01286 677617

Caerphilly Castle, Caerphilly CF83 1JD **T.** 029 2088 3143

Carreg Cennen Castle, Nr Trapp, Carmarthenshire SA19 6UA **T.** 01558 822291

Castell Coch, Cardiff CF15 7JS **T.** 029 2081 0101

Chepstow Castle, Chepstow, Monmouthshire NP16 5EY **T.** 01291 624065

Cilgerran Castle, Nr Cardigan, Pembrokeshire SA43 2SF **T.** 01239 621339

Conwy Castle, Conwy LL32 8AY **T.** 01492 592358

Criccieth Castle, Criccieth, Gwynedd LL52 0DP **T.** 01766 522227

Denbigh Castle, Denbigh LL16 3NB **T.** 01745 813385

Dolwyddelan Castle, Dolwyddelan, Gwynedd LL25 0JD **T.** 01690 750366

Ewloe Castle*, Ewloe, Flintshire, CH5 3BZ **T.** 03000 256000

Harlech Castle, Harlech, Gwynedd LL46 2YH **T.** 01766 780552

Kidwelly Castle, Kidwelly, Carmarthenshire SA17 5BQ **T.** 01554 890104

Lamphey Bishop's Palace*, Lamphey, Pembroke SA71 5NT **T.** 03000 256000

Laugharne Castle, Laugharne, Carmarthenshire SA33 4SA **T.** 01994 427906

Margam Stones Museum, Margam, Port Talbot SA13 2TA **T.** 01639 871184

Oxwich Castle, Oxwich, Swansea SA3 1ND **T.** 01792 390359

Plas Mawr, Conwy LL32 8DE **T.** 01492 580167

Raglan Castle, Raglan, Monmouthshire NP15 2BT **T.** 01291 690228

Rhuddlan Castle, Rhuddlan, Denbighshire LL18 5AD **T.** 01745 590777

Rug Chapel and Llangar Church, Corwen, Denbighshire LL21 9BT **T.** 01490 412025

Segontium Roman Fort*, Caernarfon, Gwynedd, LL55 2LN **T.** 01286 677617

St Davids Bishop's Palace, St Davids, Pembrokeshire SA62 6PE **T.** 01437 720517

St Dogmael's Abbey*, The Coach House, Shingrig, St. Dogmaels, Pembrokeshire SA43 3DX **T.** 01239 615389

Strata Florida Abbey, Pontrhydfendigaid, Ceredigion SY25 6ES **T.** 01974 831261

Tintern Abbey, Tintern, Monmouthshire NP16 6SE **T.** 01291 689251

Tretower Court and Castle, Tretower, Powys NP8 1RD **T.** 01874 730279

Valle Crucis Abbey, Nr Llangollen, Denbighshire LL20 8DD **T.** 01978 860326

Weobley Castle, Nr Llanrhidian, Swansea SA3 1HB **T.** 01792 390012

White Castle*, Nr Abergavenny, Monmouthshire NP7 8UD **T.** 03000 256000

*Entry to these sites is free.

PLAS CAREW

Unit 5/7 Cefn Coed Parc, Nantgarw, Cardiff CF15 7QQ **T.** 03000 256000 **W.** www.gov.wales/cadw

Peel Castle   Laxey Wheel   Cregneash Village

All images © Manx National Heritage

MANX NATIONAL HERITAGE

Manx National Heritage welcomes members of English Heritage with FREE* admission to all its heritage attractions on presentation of a valid membership card.

ISLE OF MAN

EAST OF THE ISLAND

Douglas
Manx Museum

SOUTH OF THE ISLAND

Ballasalla
Rushen Abbey

Castletown
Castle Rushen
Nautical Museum
Old Grammar School
Old House of Keys

Cregneash
Cregneash Village

NORTH OF THE ISLAND

Ramsey
Grove Museum

Laxey
Laxey Wheel

WEST OF THE ISLAND

Peel
House of Manannan
Peel Castle

Admission charges may apply for some special events. Travel connections between the Isle of Man heritage sites are available on Victorian Steam Railway, Manx Electric Railway and Bus Vannin.

*Free admission applies to the member only and children aged 4 years and under.

MANX NATIONAL HERITAGE

Kingswood Grove, Douglas, Isle of Man IM1 3LY
T. 01624 648000 W. www.manxnationalheritage.im

HISTORIC SCOTLAND

Stirling Castle

English Heritage members can gain half price admission to Historic Scotland attractions during the first year of membership and free entry in subsequent years.

Valid membership cards must be shown at Historic Scotland sites for entry.

Aberdour Castle and Garden,
Aberdour, Fife
T. 01383 860519

Arbroath Abbey, Angus
T. 01241 878756

Argyll's Lodging, Stirling
T. 01786 450000 (Stirling Castle)

Balvenie Castle, Dufftown,
Grampian
T. 01340 820121

The Bishop's and Earl's Palaces,
Kirkwall, Orkney
T. 01856 871918

The Black House, Arnol, Lewis,
Western Isles
T. 01851 710395

Blackness Castle, Firth of Forth,
Edinburgh and Lothians
T. 01506 834807

Bonawe Historic Iron Furnace,
Taynuilt, Argyll
T. 01866 822432

Bothwell Castle, Bothwell,
Greater Glasgow
T. 01698 816894

Broch of Gurness, Aikerness,
Orkney
T. 01856 751414

Brough of Birsay, NW of
Kirkwall, Orkney
T. 01856 841815 (Skara Brae)

Caerlaverock Castle,
Nr Dumfries,
Dumfries and Galloway
T. 01387 770244

Cairnpapple Hill, Torphichen,
Edinburgh and Lothians
T. 01506 634622

Cardoness Castle, Nr Gatehouse
of Fleet, Dumfries and Galloway
T. 01557 814427

Castle Campbell and Gardens,
Dollar Glen
T. 01259 742408

Corgarff Castle, Nr Strathdon,
Grampian
T. 01975 651460

Craigmillar Castle, Edinburgh
and Lothians
T. 0131 661 4445

Craignethan Castle, Lanark,
Greater Glasgow
T. 01555 860364

Crichton Castle, Nr Pathhead,
Edinburgh and Lothians
T. 01875 320017

Crossraguel Abbey, Nr Maybole,
Greater Glasgow
T. 01655 883113

Dallas Dhu Historic Distillery,
Nr Forres, Grampian
T. 01309 676548

Dirleton Castle and Gardens,
Dirleton, East Lothian
T. 01620 850330

Doune Castle, Doune
T. 01786 841742

Dryburgh Abbey, Nr Melrose,
Borders
T. 01835 822381

Duff House, Banff, Grampian
T. 01261 818181

Dumbarton Castle, Dumbarton,
Greater Glasgow
T. 01389 732167

Dunblane Cathedral, Dunblane
T. 01786 823388

Dundonald Castle, Dundonald,
Greater Glasgow
T. 01563 851489

Dundrennan Abbey,
Nr Kirkcudbright,
Dumfries and Galloway
T. 01557 500262

Dunfermline Abbey and Palace,
Dunfermline, Fife
T. 01383 739026

Dunstaffnage Castle,
Nr Oban, Argyll
T. 01631 562465

Edinburgh Castle, Edinburgh
and Lothians
T. 0131 225 9846

Edzell Castle and Garden,
Edzell, Angus
T. 01356 648631

Elcho Castle, Nr Bridge of Earn,
Perthshire
T. 01738 639998

Elgin Cathedral, Elgin, Highlands
T. 01343 547171

Fort George, Nr Ardersier
village, Highlands
T. 01667 460232

Glasgow Cathedral, Glasgow
T. 0141 552 6891 or 552 0988

Glenluce Abbey, Nr Glenluce,
Dumfries and Galloway
T. 01557 331856

Hackness Martello Tower and
Battery, Hoy, Orkney
T. 01856 701727

Hermitage Castle,
Nr Newcastleton, Borders
T. 01387 376222

Huntingtower Castle, Nr Perth,
Perthshire
T. 01738 627231

Huntly Castle, Huntly, Grampian
T. 01466 793191

Inchcolm Abbey,
Firth of Forth, Fife
T. 01383 823332/07836 265146

Inchmahome Priory,
Lake of Menteith, Central
T. 01877 385294/07836 313769

Iona Abbey and Nunnery,
Island of Iona, Argyll
T. 01681 700512

Jarlshof Prehistoric and Norse
Settlement, Sumburgh Head,
Shetland T. 01950 460112

Jedburgh Abbey and Visitor
Centre, Jedburgh, Borders
T. 01835 863925

Kildrummy Castle, Nr Alford,
Grampian
T. 01975 571331

Kisimul Castle, Isle of Barra,
Western Isles
T. 01871 810313

Linlithgow Palace, Linlithgow,
West Lothian
T. 01506 842896

Lochleven Castle, Lochleven,
Perthshire
T. 01577 862670

MacLellan's Castle, Kirkcudbright,
Dumfries and Galloway
T. 01557 331856

Maeshowe Chambered Cairn,
Nr Kirkwall, Orkney
T. 01856 851266

Meigle Sculptured Stone
Museum, Meigle, Angus
T. 01828 640612

Melrose Abbey, Melrose, Borders
T. 01896 822562

New Abbey Corn Mill, New
Abbey, Dumfries and Galloway
T. 01387 850260

Newark Castle, Port Glasgow,
Greater Glasgow
T. 01475 741858

Rothesay Castle, Rothesay,
Isle of Bute
T. 01700 502691

St Andrews Castle,
St Andrews, Fife
T. 01334 477196

St Andrews Cathedral,
St Andrews, Fife
T. 01334 472563

St Serf's Church and Dupplin
Cross, Dunning, Perthshire
T. 01764 684497

St Vigeans Sculptured Stones,
Nr Arbroath, Angus
T. 01241 878756

Seton Collegiate Church,
Nr Cockenzie, East Lothian
T. 01875 813334

Skara Brae and Skaill House,
Nr Kirkwall, Orkney
T. 01856 841815

Edinburgh Castle Entrance

Doune Castle

Smailholm Tower, Near
Smailholm, Borders
T. 01573 460365

Spynie Palace, Nr Elgin,
Grampian T. 01343 546358

Stanley Mills, North of Perth
T. 01738 828268

Stirling Castle, Stirling, Central
T. 01786 450000

Sweetheart Abbey, New Abbey,
Dumfries and Galloway
T. 01387 850397

Tantallon Castle, Nr North
Berwick, East Lothian
T. 01620 892727

Threave Castle, Nr Castle
Douglas, Dumfries and Galloway
T. 07711 223101

Tolquhon Castle, Nr Aberdeen,
Grampian
T. 01651 851286

Urquhart Castle, Drumnadrochit,
Highlands
T. 01456 450551

HISTORIC SCOTLAND

Historic Environment Scotland, Longmore House
Salisbury Place, Edinburgh EH9 1SH T. 0131 668 8999
E. members@hes.scot W. www.historicenvironment.scot

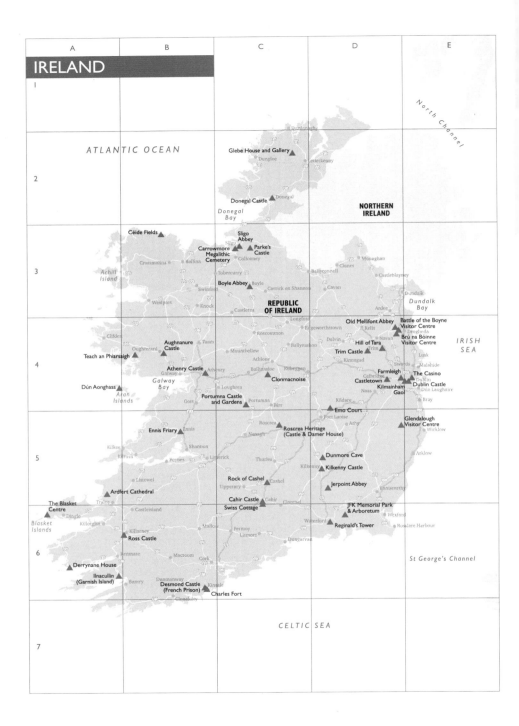

IRELAND

A | B | C | D | E

ATLANTIC OCEAN

NORTH CHANNEL

Dunfanaghy

Glebe House and Gallery
Dungloe
Letterkenny

Donegal Castle ▲ Donegal

Donegal Bay

NORTHERN IRELAND

Céide Fields ▲

Crossmolina
Ballina

Sligo Abbey
Carrowmore Megalithic Cemetery ▲ ▲ Parke's Castle
Collooney

Achill Island

Tobercurry

Monaghan
Clones
Ballyconnell
Castleblayney

Westport
Swinford
Knock
Castlerea

Boyle Abbey ▲ Boyle
Carrick on Shannon
Cavan

Dundalk
Dundalk Bay
Ardee

Clifden
Oughterard
Aughnanure Castle
Tuam
Mountbellew
Ballymahon
Delvin
Kells

Old Mellifont Abbey ▲ Battle of the Boyne Visitor Centre
Drogheda
Brú na Bóinne Visitor Centre

Teach an Phiarsaigh ▲

REPUBLIC OF IRELAND

Roscommon
Edgeworthstown
Longford
Hill of Tara ▲

IRISH SEA

Athenry Castle ▲ Athenry
Galway Bay
Ballinasloe
Athlone
Clonmacnoise ▲

Navan
Trim Castle ▲ Trim
Kinnegad

Farmleigh ▲ The Casino
Swords
Malahide
Celbridge
Castletown ▲ Dublin Castle
Kilmainham Gaol
Dún Laoghaire

Dún Aonghasa ▲
Aran Islands
Loughrea
Gort
Portumna Castle and Gardens ▲ Portumna
Birr

Naas
Kildare
Bray

Emo Court ▲
Port Laoise

Glendalough Visitor Centre ▲ Wicklow

Ennis Friary ▲ Ennis
Roscrea Heritage (Castle & Damer House) ▲
Nenagh

Athy

Arklow

Kilkee
Shannon
Kilrush
Foynes
Limerick
Thurles

Dunmore Cave ▲
Kilkenny Castle ▲

Listowel
Ardfert Cathedral ▲
Tralee
Tipperary
Rock of Cashel ▲ Cashel

Jerpoint Abbey ▲
Enniscorthy

The Blasket Centre
Dingle
Castleisland

Cahir Castle ▲ Cahir
Swiss Cottage
Clonmel

JFK Memorial Park & Arboretum ▲ Wexford

Blasket Islands
Killorglin
Killarney
Mallow
Fermoy
Lismore

Waterford
Reginald's Tower ▲
Dungarvan
Rosslare Harbour

Ross Castle ▲

St George's Channel

Kenmare
Macroom
Cork

Derrynane House ▲
Ilnacullin (Garnish Island) ▲
Bantry
Dunmanway
Desmond Castle (French Prison) ▲ Kinsale
Charles Fort
Clonakilty

CELTIC SEA

Rock of Cashel

Aughnanure Castle

OPW HERITAGE IRELAND

Free entry for English Heritage members

Ardfert Cathedral, Ardfert,
Tralee, Co Kerry
T. +353 (066) 713 4711

Athenry Castle, Athenry,
Co Galway
T. +353 (091) 844797

Aughnanure Castle,
Oughterard, Co Galway
T. +353 (091) 552214

Battle of the Boyne Visitor Centre,
Oldbridge, Co Meath
T. +353 (041) 980 9950

The Blasket Centre, Dún Chaoin,
Dingle Peninsula, Co Kerry
T. +353 (066) 915 6444/
(066) 915 6371

Boyle Abbey, Boyle,
Co Roscommon
T. +353 (071) 966 2604

Brú na Bóinne Visitor Centre,
(Newgrange and Knowth),
Donore, Co Meath
T. +353 (041) 988 0300

Cahir Castle, Castle Street,
Cahir, Co Tipperary
T. +353 (52) 7441011

Carrowmore Megalithic
Cemetery, Carrowmore, Co Sligo
T. +353 (071) 916 1534

Castletown, Celbridge,
Co Kildare
T. +353 (01) 628 8252

Céide Fields, Ballycastle,
Co Mayo
T. +353 (096) 43325

Charles Fort, Summer Cove,
Kinsale, Co Cork
T. +353 (021) 477 2263

Clonmacnoise, Shannonbridge,
Co Offaly
T. +353 (090) 967 4195

Derrynane House, National
Historic Park, Caherdaniel,
Co Kerry
T. +353 (066) 947 5113

Desmond Castle (French Prison),
Cork Street, Kinsale, Co Cork
T. +353 (021) 477 4855

Donegal Castle, Donegal Town,
Co Donegal
T. +353 (074) 972 2405

Dublin Castle, Dame Street,
Dublin 2
T. +353 (01) 645 8813

Dún Aonghasa, Kilmurvey,
Inishmore, Aran Islands,
Co Galway
T. +353 (099) 61008

Dunmore Cave, Castlecomer
Road, Kilkenny
T. +353 (056) 776 7726

Emo Court, Emo, Co Laois
T. +353 (057) 862 6573

Ennis Friary, Abbey Street,
Ennis, Co Clare
T. +353 (065) 682 9100

Farmleigh, Phoenix Park,
Castleknock, Dublin 15
T. +353 (01) 815 5900/815 5981

Above L to R: Ilnacullin (Garnish Island), Kilmainham Gaol and Swiss Cottage.

Glebe House and Gallery,
Churchill, Letterkenny,
Co Donegal
T. +353 (074) 913 7071

Glendalough Visitor Centre,
Glendalough, Co Wicklow
T. +353 404 45352/25

Hill of Tara, Navan, Co Meath
T./F. +353 (046) 902 5903

Ilnacullin (Garnish Island),
Glengarriff, Bantry, Co Cork
T. +353 (027) 63040

Ionad Culturtha an Phiarsaigh,
Conamara, Inbhear, Ros Muc,
Co Galway
T. +353 (091) 574292

Jerpoint Abbey, Thomastown,
Co Kilkenny
T. +353 (056) 772 4623

JFK Memorial Park & Arboretum,
New Ross, Co Wexford
T. +353 (051) 388171

Kilkenny Castle, Kilkenny City,
Co Kilkenny
T. +353 (056) 770 4100

Kilmainham Gaol, Inchicore Road,
Kilmainham, Dublin 8
T. +353 (01) 453 5984

Old Mellifont Abbey, Tullyallen,
Drogheda, Co Louth
T. +353 (41) 982 6459

Parke's Castle, Fivemile Bourne,
Co Leitrim
T. +353 (071) 916 4149

Portumna Castle and Gardens,
Portumna, Co Galway
T. +353 (090) 974 1658

Reginald's Tower, The Quay,
Waterford
T./F. +353 (051) 304220

Rock of Cashel, Cashel,
Co Tipperary
T. +353 (062) 61437

Roscrea Heritage (Castle &
Damer House), Roscrea,
Co Tipperary
T. +353 (0505) 21850

Ross Castle, Killarney, Co Kerry
T. +353 64 6635851

Sligo Abbey, Abbey Street,
Sligo, Co Sligo
T. +353 (071) 914 6406

Swiss Cottage, Kilcommon, Cahir,
Co Tipperary
T. +353 (052) 7441144

The Casino, Cherrymount
Crescent, off the Malahide Road,
Marino, Dublin 3
T. +353 (01) 833 1618

Trim Castle, Trim, Co Meath
T. +353 (046) 943 8619 or
+353 (046) 943 8964

We welcome visitors from near and far and we are particularly delighted to welcome Members of English Heritage and holders of the Overseas Visitor Pass – we look forward to meeting you.

For more information about our sites (including those where admission is free) please visit our website **www.heritageireland.ie**

 Find us on Facebook

Trim Castle

HERITAGE NEW ZEALAND

Fyffe House

English Heritage Members get free entry to all our properties (charges may apply for special events and exhibitions).

New Zealand's built heritage may be considered young in world terms, but many of the properties cared for by Heritage New Zealand are physical reminders of the birth and development of this South Pacific nation and its enduring connection to Great Britain. From the Kerikeri Mission Station in Northland, New Zealand's oldest standing building dating from 1821-22, to Hayes Engineering Works in the gold mining region of Central Otago, Heritage New Zealand cares for 43 properties and sites where you can learn about the people and places that make New Zealand what it is today.

OUR PROPERTIES RANGE FROM IMPRESSIVE HOMESTEADS, CENTRES OF INDUSTRY AND INNOVATION, BATTLE SITES AND SO MUCH MORE, INCLUDING:

Old St Paul's (Wellington) – where stunning stained glass windows help illuminate the glorious native timber interior of this 19th-century Gothic Revival church, a home away from home for US servicemen during the Second World War.

The Kerikeri Mission Station and Stone Store (Northland) – the Mission Station is New Zealand's oldest standing building, built in 1821-22, while the nearby Stone Store is one of the country's most photographed buildings.

Fyffe House (Kaikoura) – where a whale of a time is guaranteed, the property built as part of the early whaling industry and partly on whale vertebrae foundations.

Alberton and Highwic (Auckland) – impressive dwellings that were home to two prominent colonial businessmen.

Totara Estate (Oamaru) – British dinner tables have featured our finest cuts of meat over many years, and Totara Estate is where New Zealand's billion dollar frozen meat industry began.

HERITAGE NEW ZEALAND

More information on heritage sites to visit can be found on Heritage New Zealand's website **www.heritage.org.nz**. Our staff look forward to welcoming you.

ABOUT ENGLISH HERITAGE

As a charity, English Heritage cares for over 400 historic monuments, buildings and sites — from prehistoric stone circles to great medieval castles and abbeys, from magnificent historic houses to a Cold War bunker.

Our sites include Stonehenge, one of the wonders of the world, and the Roman forts of Hadrian's Wall, the frontier of a once mighty empire. We also manage the iconic Blue Plaques scheme in London, celebrating the links between notable figures of the past and the buildings in which they lived and worked.

English Heritage is licensed to manage this collection by the Historic Buildings & Monuments Commission for England.

STEP INTO ENGLAND'S STORY

History gives us all a vital sense of our place in time. But you can't understand the history of England just by reading it.

At our sites across the country, we invite you to stand in the places where history really happened — where William the Conqueror defeated King Harold, where Queen Victoria combined family life with the government of an empire, and where the evacuation of the Dunkirk beaches was masterminded.

English Heritage does more than just show you: we invite you in. You can explore and try stuff on, soak up the atmosphere, climb the ramparts, get your hands dirty, or simply watch, learn and enjoy.

MAKING THE MOST OF YOUR MEMBERSHIP

As an English Heritage Member you enjoy free and unlimited access to all our sites and a host of exclusive events and behind-the-scenes tours. Throughout the year we'll keep you up to speed on all the latest news and stories from properties via our award-winning Members' Magazine and e-newsletters.

You can also keep up to date by visiting our website, including our dedicated Members' Area where you will find a library of digital versions of our Members' Magazine, exclusive online articles and downloads, videos and our new and ever-growing Kids section. You can also register to create your own personalised landing page with carefully selected events and property suggestions just for you, a gallery of all the places you've visited with your membership and a wishlist function so you can bookmark your favourite pages across our website.

GET INVOLVED

Find out more about how to get involved at
www.english-heritage.org.uk

BUILDING FOR THE FUTURE

As we move into our fifth year as a charity, we're continuing to build on a successful start.

Our key projects for the year ahead include the launch of the much-improved visitor facilities at Whitby Abbey, and opening up new areas of the garden at Walmer Castle.

These are just some of the ways we'll be working to secure the future of the unique collection of sites in our care, under our strategic aims of:

- developing inspirational new visitor experiences based around the story of England, including some high-profile flagship projects

- providing an increasing range of opportunities for the public to become involved in our work

- continuing to expertly care for our sites and collections, including the largest conservation programme in our history

- moving towards a position where we are entirely self-funding by increasing earned and donated income, and managing our cost base effectively.

+330,000
schoolchildren
visited our sites

£1.2 million
invested revitalising
Framlingham Castle

£670,000
invested in repairs to
the Archer Pavilion,
Wrest Park

153,000
hours given
by volunteers

337
garden roles filled
by volunteers

23%
rise in numbers visiting
during events

+350,000
YouTube
subscribers

2
pairs of medieval
spectacles conserved

11
cannons conserved
on Tresco

25
properties hosted
community events

£10.6 million
new pledges and contracts
made this year

450
new lines added
in our shops

All of this has been achieved thanks to our Members and supporters. Thank you.

SUPPORTING ENGLISH HERITAGE

We rely on Members, partners and supporters to conserve our heritage and bring history to life. Your support helps in so many ways; from opening our historic places for all to visit, to conserving the objects and buildings in our care and involving others in our work through volunteering and community opportunities.

As a Member you can take pride in knowing that you're helping to care for historic buildings, draw communities closer together and connect people to their past. Thank you for enabling so many visitors to discover, enjoy and share the story of England. Your support makes a difference every day, and will continue to do so for years to come. If you would like to strengthen your ties, there are other ways in which you can play a part in enabling both current and future generations to be inspired by the sites in English Heritage's care.

DONATE TODAY

With conservation challenges to face across the country, your donation will go directly towards enhancing and conserving the buildings, gardens, landscapes and artefacts in our care.

VOLUNTEER

From welcoming visitors and inspiring school children, to learning new skills in gardening and conservation, volunteering is a rewarding opportunity to get involved in protecting and presenting the places where history happened.

LEAVE A LEGACY

Supporting English Heritage with a gift in your Will, however large or small, will help ensure that generations to come can enjoy our collection of historic places just as much as you do today.

BECOME A GUARDIAN

Our new Guardians scheme recognises donors who support English Heritage with gifts of £2,500 or more. As a Guardian, you'll gain a deeper insight into our work of caring for historic properties across the nation.

HOW YOUR SUPPORT HELPS

It's thanks to the generosity of our supporters that many inspiring projects are made possible. We're grateful to the many Members who supported our #LoveCastles campaign last year – your support is enabling us to undertake critical conservation work to protect these incredible structures from the elements and ensure they'll survive to educate and inspire visitors long into the future.

FIND OUT MORE

Please visit www.english-heritage.org.uk/support-us or call the Development Team on 020 7973 3797.

Thank you for your support.

English Heritage gratefully acknowledges support from The Heritage Lottery Fund, as well as numerous charitable trusts and foundations, in helping us to conserve, protect and enhance important historic sites in our care. Generous support from the HLF also enables us to further the enjoyment and appreciation of our sites for all our visitors through learning and volunteer programmes.

PLANNING YOUR VISIT

We want you to enjoy every moment of your day out with us. The following section contains important information about planning your visit and helpful contact details.

ACCESS

Our handbook listings indicate accessible areas of our properties with the use of the 🔍 symbol. Remember that if you are disabled your carer is always admitted free, and many of our sites have accessible parking.

For more detail on access for families and disabled people at each of our sites, please call us on 0370 333 1181, email us at customers@english-heritage.org.uk, or go online at www.english-heritage.org.uk

ADMISSIONS

Admission charges apply to non-Members, and prices are given in this handbook as follows: Adult; Concession (senior citizens, jobseekers and students with relevant ID); Child (age 5-17, under 5s go free). Where available, Family tickets normally admit two adults and three children (may vary at properties not managed by us).

For groups of 11 or more visitors paying together, discounts of 15% (10% at Stonehenge) are available. Please call 0370 333 1181 to book in advance and for a copy of our Group Visits Guide.

If you are visiting from overseas and planning to visit a number of properties, an Overseas Visitors Pass (OVP) may make financial sense, giving unlimited access to all English Heritage properties marked with the OVP symbol over a 9 or 16-day period. Call 0370 333 1182 or visit www.english-heritage.org.uk/ovp

GIFT AID ON ADMISSION

The admission prices shown for each property include Gift Aid where applicable. This voluntary donation of 10% allows us to reclaim 25p tax on every £1 admission, which goes towards helping us to undertake vital conservation and education projects to ensure that our important historic places can continue to be enjoyed by future generations. Non-Gift Aid admission is also available at all of our properties. Please also remember to Gift Aid your membership; it really does make a big difference to our work.

CATERING & PICNICS

Many of our properties offer delicious homemade food and drink. You're welcome to picnic in the grounds of most of our properties.

DOGS

We welcome dogs on leads wherever possible, but please see individual property listings. No restrictions on assistance dogs.

EDUCATIONAL VISITS

Visiting an English Heritage property is an inspiring way to discover more about the past. We believe that experiencing the local historic environment should be central to the curriculum of every school in England. We actively encourage groups for this purpose, offering free self-led educational visits to over 400 historic sites in England, supporting the curriculum across a range of subjects and all key stages. We also

provide a wide range of free online teaching resources, and downloadable hazard information sheets for each of our sites. Find out more at www.english-heritage.org.uk/education

FAMILIES & CHILDREN

With towering castles and underground passages, tales of royal revels and wartime heroes, our sites provide endless entertainment for children. From gardens to headlands, we offer spectacular outdoor locations in which to run freely or enjoy a picnic together. Alongside our events, exhibitions and interactive displays you'll also find kids' activity sheets and reading materials at many of our properties. As you are responsible for the safety of your children, please ensure a sensible ratio of adults to children.

GUIDES & TOURS

You'll find guidebooks and audio tours at many of our sites. We also provide audio guides for children and people with learning difficulties, as well as in different languages. Specialist tours are available at certain sites for pre-booked groups of 11 or more. Many of our properties have specialised guidebooks – including 50 or so in the 'Red Guide' series with their distinctive red spines. Written by experts, these feature a tour of the site together with a more in-depth history of the people who lived and worked there. Packed with plans, reconstruction drawings, eyewitness accounts and beautiful photography, they make essential reading as well as brilliant souvenirs of your visit. Short histories and

descriptions of our free to enter sites are also available on our website.

PHOTOGRAPHY

In some properties we don't allow photography, due to the sensitive nature of some materials. Non-commercial photography is welcome in the gardens and grounds of all our sites.

SAFETY & SMOKING ⚠

Due to their historic nature, some of our sites have potentially hazardous features – please pay attention to all safety notices on site. If you have any doubts, our staff can always advise on safety issues. Please wear suitable footwear to avoid accidents, and do not climb on walls or monuments. In areas of woodland deer pasture there may be a slight risk of ticks, so keep vulnerable parts of your body covered and/or use insect repellent. Note that smoking is not permitted inside any of our properties.

TRAVEL & TRANSPORT

Where possible in the property listings, we have provided public transport information, which has kindly been supplied by the Confederation of Passenger Transport (www.cpt-uk.org). These details were correct at time of going to press. For cycle routes, call 0845 113 0065 or visit www.sustrans.org.uk. OS LandRanger/Explorer map references have also been supplied for each property.

CAR PARKING P

As a charity, we need to make sure that we run our properties and estates as efficiently as possible. This includes ensuring car parks are available to those who visit our historic sites, and finding sustainable ways of managing any maintenance costs. No money earned from any of our sites goes to profit and every penny generated by English Heritage works hard to protect and care for the nation's heritage.

FREE PARKING

Members can now enjoy free parking at the majority of our sites by displaying a current car sticker. Free parking does not apply at sites that are not managed by English Heritage. Full details of parking can be found in the individual listings in this handbook.

EVENTS

Get close to the action at a thrilling joust, take a tour through blooming gardens, go behind the scenes at an exclusive Members' event or get hands-on with history during the school holidays. Our packed programme of events will inspire the whole family, giving you even more ways to explore the story of England.

BLOCKBUSTER EVENTS
Join us at our spectacular blockbuster events for an experience you'll never forget. Watch knights on horseback clash in an adrenaline-fuelled summer joust, or cheer for St George as he takes on the legendary dragon. Watch Normans do battle with Harold's army at Hastings in October, and experience the explosive sights and sounds of the Second World War at Dover Castle in May. Check online to see the full range of breathtaking events.

EVENTS FOR ALL THE FAMILY
Learn what it takes to be a pirate, try your hand at archery, enjoy Victorian pastimes and join historical characters in a medieval court. Take part in games, crafts and activities to fire every imagination.

EASTER ADVENTURES
This Easter, become a time traveller with our range of children's activities, events and Adventure Quests. Meet gladiators, princesses and dragons on a journey through England's history, guaranteed to create an Easter to remember.

FIGHTING KNIGHTS THIS SUMMER
Our brave medieval knights will take on the ultimate challenge at our fiery series of Knights' Tournaments and Grand Jousts this summer.

HALLOWEEN EVENTS

Get into the spirit of Halloween and hunt for ghosts as darkness descends on a ruined castle. Discover spine-tingling tales of ghostly apparitions, dastardly deeds and ghoulish goings-on. Or kick up crackling leaves with the kids and get creative with creepy crafts, fancy dress and spooky trails.

ENCHANTED EVENTS

Make the most of the dark December nights and head out on an adventure through a wonderland of light, colour and sound. Follow the garden trails and explore an illuminated world. Grab the winter woollies and bring your family and friends to experience the most enchanting event of the year. Be sure to book early to avoid missing out.

EXCLUSIVE EVENTS FOR MEMBERS

Meet the experts, find out what it takes to care for our sites and discover the histories of some of England's most fascinating places. Every year we put on over 150 events exclusively for members. Visit the Members' Area of the website or check your Members' Magazine for full details.

SIGN UP FOR EVENT UPDATES

Get regular event updates sent straight to your inbox. Just visit english-heritage.org.uk/newsletter to register. You can also keep up to date with our events programme at english-heritage.org.uk/events or check the latest copy of your Members' Magazine.

HIRING A PROPERTY

For a historic celebration

From iconic London landmarks to medieval castles, an 18th-century villa to Queen Victoria's seaside retreat, host your event in the places where history happened.

Our rich historical settings are perfect for everything from corporate away-days and business meetings to lavish dinners and spectacular showcases. Whether you are looking to host a small private event or a large-scale extravaganza, we have a range of venues guaranteed to make your event unique and memorable.

For a memorable wedding day

Your wedding day is everlasting. It's the start of the next chapter of your story. It's a moment captured in time – through pictures that stand for a lifetime and memories re-lived for years to come.

English Heritage's historic wedding venues share this unique sense of the everlasting. With castles rising above the sea, royal retreats and sweeping views of age-old gardens, our venues give you a connection to the past and an inspiring setting for your future.

PROPERTIES FOR HIRE

Properties available for hire are marked with a ⊤ throughout the handbook. Those also licensed for civil ceremonies are marked with a ♠.

EAST

♠ **Wrest Park**
Bedfordshire 01525 863704

LONDON

♠ **Eltham Palace** 020 8294 2577

♠ **Kenwood** 020 7973 3416

♠ **Ranger's House** 020 8294 2577

Wellington Arch 07867 667714

SOUTH EAST

♠ **Osborne**
Isle of Wight 01983 203055

SOUTH WEST

♠ **Old Wardour Castle**
Wiltshire 01326 310106

♠ **Pendennis Castle**
Cornwall 01326 310106

FIND OUT MORE

www.english-heritage.org.uk/venuehire
hospitality@english-heritage.org.uk

HOLIDAY COTTAGES

Unlock the doors of an English Heritage holiday cottage and enjoy a unique perspective of some of England's most iconic sites. Steeped in history, but equipped with modern comforts, our cottages will be sure to make your holiday a memorable one.

Putting you in touching distance of some of the most famous names in English history – from William the Conqueror to Queen Victoria – staying with us is sure to keep your group inspired and entertained.

FIND OUT MORE

Book or browse the brochure: www.english-heritage.org.uk/holidaycottages or call 0370 333 1187

WHY STAY WITH US?

Exclusive out-of-hours access
One of the great benefits of a stay in our cottages is that you have exclusive access to the grounds once the public have gone home. Explore freely, investigate nooks and crannies and enjoy the atmosphere all by yourselves.

Welcome hamper
On arrival you will be greeted with a welcome hamper with all the essentials for your stay: tea, coffee, milk, bread, eggs, orange juice, marmalade or jam, cheese and a bottle of wine.

Priority access to events
As a guest you can enjoy reduced or complimentary entry to our year-round events. Take the chance to see how our events are set up and watch our re-enactors prepare for the day. Please check what's going on during your stay at www.english-heritage.org.uk/events

Discounts in our shops and in-house catering
For the duration of your stay enjoy a 10% discount on items purchased from English Heritage shops, restaurants and cafés.

STAY WITH US

SOUTH EAST
BATTLE ABBEY South Lodge

CARISBROOKE CASTLE
The Bowling Green Apartment

DOVER CASTLE
The Sergeant Major's House
Peverell's Tower

OSBORNE
Pavilion Cottage
No. 1 & No. 2 Sovereign's Gate

WALMER CASTLE
The Garden Cottage
The Greenhouse Apartment

SOUTH WEST
PENDENNIS CASTLE
The Custodian's House
Callie's Cottage

ST MAWES CASTLE
Fort House

EAST OF ENGLAND
AUDLEY END HOUSE
Cambridge Lodge

EAST MIDLANDS
HARDWICK OLD HALL
East Lodge

KIRBY HALL Peacock Cottage

WEST MIDLANDS
WITLEY COURT Pool House

YORKSHIRE
MOUNT GRACE PRIORY
Prior's Lodge

RIEVAULX ABBEY
Refectory Cottage

NORTH EAST
LINDISFARNE PRIORY
Coastguard's Cottage

SHOPPING

At English Heritage we have a large range of exclusively designed gifts that are inspired by history. Whether you're looking for a souvenir to remind you of your visit, a unique gift for someone special or a tasty treat from our food and drink collection, you'll discover something a little bit different in our gift shops and online store.

- Exclusive and unique gifts; majority made in the UK
- Traditionally made food and drink
- Collectable swords and helmets
- Beautiful tapestries and wall hangings
- Traditional toys and games
- Clothing and accessories
- Decorative and practical gifts for your home and garden
- Stationery, calendars and greeting cards
- Historically inspired books for all ages
- Jewellery for all occasions
- Souvenirs and collectables to remind you of your visit

TO BROWSE AND BUY

Enjoy a great day out and visit one of our historic properties, or shop online at www.english-heritageshop.org.uk

By shopping with English Heritage, you're helping us to carry out vital conservation work at over 400 historic sites and keep the story of England alive for visitors today and in the future.

Thank you for your support.

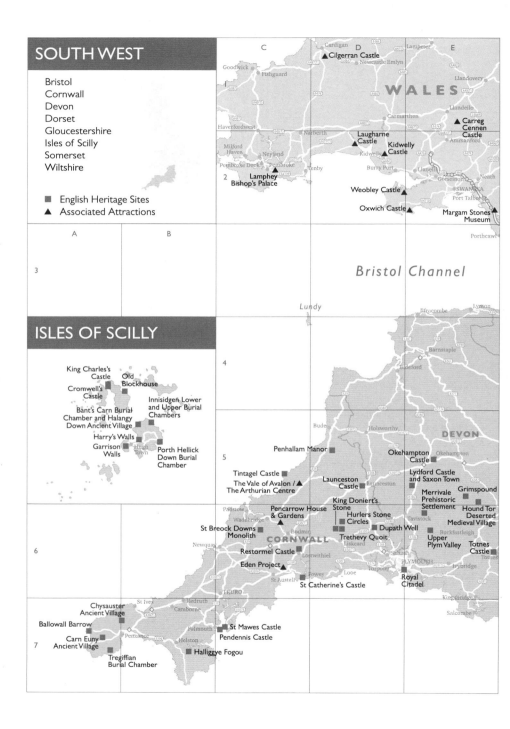

SOUTH WEST

Bristol
Cornwall
Devon
Dorset
Gloucestershire
Isles of Scilly
Somerset
Wiltshire

■ English Heritage Sites
▲ Associated Attractions

A   B

ISLES OF SCILLY

King Charles's
Castle   Old
Blockhouse
Cromwell's
Castle
Bant's Carn Burial   Innisidgen Lower
Chamber and Halangy   and Upper Burial
Down Ancient Village   Chambers
Harry's Walls
Garrison   High   Porth Hellick
Walls   Town   Down Burial
Chamber

Chysauster
Ancient Village
Ballowall Barrow
Carn Euny
Ancient Village
Tregiffian
Burial Chamber

▲ Cilgerran Castle
Cardigan   D   Lampeter   E
Goodwick   Newcastle Emlyn
Fishguard   Llandovery
1
WALES
Haverfordwest   Carmarthen   Llandeilo
▲ Carreg
Cennen
Castle
Milford   Narberth   Laugharne   Ammanford
Haven   Castle
Neyland   Kidwelly ▲ Castle
Pembroke Dock Pembroke Tenby Burry Port Llanelli Neath
2   Lamphey   Gorseinon
Bishop's Palace   SWANSEA
Weobley Castle ▲   Port Talbot
Oxwich Castle ▲   Margam Stones ▲
Museum
Porthcawl

3   Bristol Channel

Lundy   Ilfracombe Lynton
4   Barnstaple
Bideford
DEVON
Bude   Holsworthy
Penhallam Manor ■   Okehampton ■
Castle   Okehampton
5   Tintagel Castle ■   Lydford Castle ■
The Vale of Avalon / ▲   Launceston ■   and Saxon Town
The Arthurian Centre   Castle   Launceston   Merrivale   Grimspound ■
King Doniert's   Prehistoric
Padstow   Pencarrow House ▲   Stone ■   Settlement ■ Hound Tor
Wadebridge   & Gardens   Hurlers Stone ■   Tavistock   Deserted
St Breock Downs ■   Circles ■   Dupath Well ■   Medieval Village
Monolith   Bodmin   Trethevy Quoit ■   Buckfastleigh
Newquay   CORNWALL   Liskeard   Upper Totnes
6   Restormel Castle ■   Lostwithiel   Saltash   Plym Valley   Castle ■
Eden Project ▲   PLYMOUTH   Ivybridge
Fowey   Looe   Torpoint
St Austell   St Catherine's Castle ■   Royal
Citadel ■
Kingsbridge
TRURO
St Ives   Redruth   Salcombe
Camborne
Penzance   St Mawes Castle ■
Falmouth   Pendennis Castle ■
7   Helston   ■ Halliggye Fogou

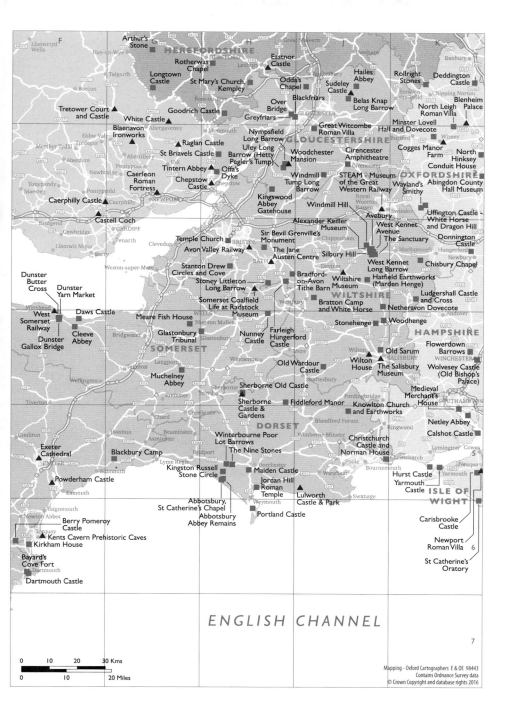

Llanwrtyd Wells
Arthur's Stone
Hay-on-Wye
HEREFORDSHIRE
Eastnor Castle
Great Malvern
Evesham
Banbury
Rotherwas Chapel
Ledbury
Tewkesbury
Hailes Abbey
Rollright Stones
Deddington Castle
Longtown Castle
St Mary's Church, Kempley
Odda's Chapel
Sudeley Castle
Stow-on-the-Wold
Chipping Norton
Talgarth
Brecon
Blackfriars
Belas Knap Long Barrow
North Leigh Roman Villa
Blenheim Palace
Tretower Court and Castle
Goodrich Castle
Over Bridge
GLOUCESTER
Minster Lovell
White Castle
Greyfriars
Great Witcombe Roman Villa
Hall and Dovecote
Ebbw Vale
Abergavenny
Monmouth
Nympsfield Long Barrow
GLOUCESTERSHIRE
Burford
Witney
Blaenavon Ironworks
Merthyr Tydfil
Tredegar
Raglan Castle
Uley Long Barrow (Hetty Pegler's Tump)
Woodchester Mansion
Cirencester Amphitheatre
Cogges Manor Farm
North Hinksey Conduit House
Abertillery
St Briavels Castle
Barrow
Aberdare
Pontypool
Usk
Tintern Abbey
Offa's Dyke
Cirencester
OXFORDSHIRE
Newbridge
Caerleon Roman Fortress
Chepstow Castle
Chepstow
Windmill Tump Long Barrow
STEAM - Museum of the Great Western Railway
Wayland's Smithy
Abingdon County Hall Museum
Tonypandy
Maesteg
Pontypridd
NEWPORT
Kingswood Abbey Gatehouse
Windmill Hill
Royal Wootton Bassett
Caerphilly Castle
Caerphilly
Windmill Hill
Swindon
Uffington Castle - White Horse and Dragon Hill
Bridgend
Castell Coch
CARDIFF
Alexander Keiller Museum
Avebury
West Kennet Avenue
Donnington Castle
Cowbridge
Sir Bevil Grenville's Monument
Chippenham
The Sanctuary
Marlborough
Hungerford
Llantwit Major
Penarth
Clevedon
Temple Church
BRISTOL
The Jane Austen Centre
Silbury Hill
West Kennet Long Barrow
Newbury
Chisbury Chapel
Barry
Avon Valley Railway
BATH
Weston-super-Mare
Stanton Drew Circles and Cove
Bradford-on-Avon
Devizes
Wiltshire Museum
Hatfield Earthworks (Marden Henge)
Dunster Butter Cross
Dunster Yarn Market
Stoney Littleton Long Barrow
Bradford-on-Avon Tithe Barn
WILTSHIRE
Ludgershall Castle and Cross
West Somerset Railway
Daws Castle
Meare Fish House
Somerset Coalfield Life at Radstock Museum
Westbury
Bratton Camp and White Horse
Netheravon Dovecote
Andover
Minehead
WELLS
Shepton Mallet
Stonehenge
Woodhenge
HAMPSHIRE
Dunster Gallox Bridge
Cleeve Abbey
Bridgwater
Glastonbury Tribunal
Glastonbury
Nunney Castle
Farleigh Hungerford Castle
Mere
Wilton
Old Sarum
Flowerdown Barrows
SOMERSET
Langport
Wincanton
Old Wardour Castle
Wilton House
SALISBURY
The Salisbury Museum
WINCHESTER
Wolvesey Castle (Old Bishop's Palace)
Taunton
Muchelney Abbey
Shaftesbury
Sherborne
Fordingbridge
Wellington
Ilminster
Sherborne Old Castle
Medieval Merchant's House
SOUTHAMPTON
Tiverton
Chard
Crewkerne
Yeovil
Sherborne Castle & Gardens
Fiddleford Manor
Knowlton Church and Earthworks
Ringwood
Netley Abbey
Crediton
Honiton
Beaminster
Axminster
Blandford Forum
Wimborne Minster
Christchurch Castle and Norman House
Calshot Castle
Exeter Cathedral
EXETER
Winterbourne Poor Lot Barrows
Bridport
Wimborne Minster
Christchurch
Lymington
Cowes
Blackbury Camp
The Nine Stones
DORSET
Poole
Bournemouth
Yarmouth
Newport
Sidmouth
Lyme Regis
Kingston Russell Stone Circle
Dorchester
Maiden Castle
Wareham
Hurst Castle
Yarmouth Castle
ISLE OF
Powderham Castle
Jordan Hill Roman Temple
WIGHT
Exmouth
Abbotsbury, St Catherine's Chapel
Lulworth Castle & Park
Swanage
Teignmouth
Newton Abbot
Weymouth
Portland Castle
Carisbrooke Castle
Berry Pomeroy Castle
Abbotsbury Abbey Remains
Torquay
Kents Cavern Prehistoric Caves
Newport Roman Villa
Kirkham House
Bayard's Cove Fort
Dartmouth
St Catherine's Oratory
Dartmouth Castle

ENGLISH CHANNEL

0	10	20	30 Kms
0	10	20 Miles	

Mapping - Oxford Cartographers E & OE 98443
Contains Ordnance Survey data
© Crown Copyright and database rights 2016

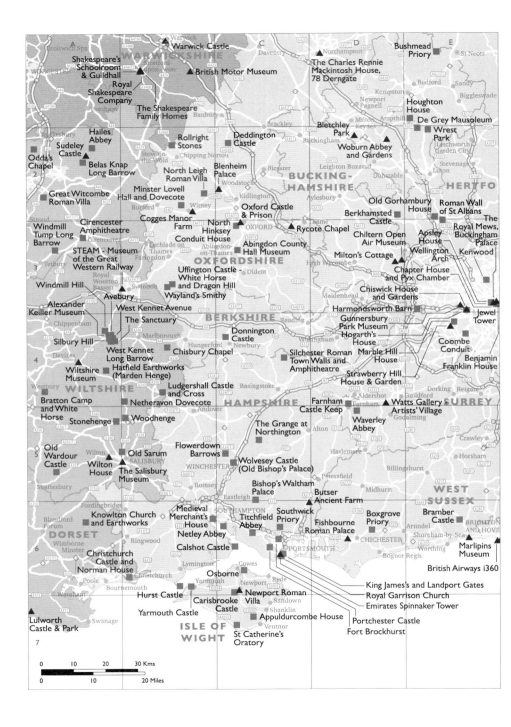

Warwick

Warwick Castle

Shakespeare's
Schoolroom
& Guildhall

Royal
Shakespeare
Company

The Shakespeare
Family Homes

British Motor Museum

Northampton

The Charles Rennie
Mackintosh House,
78 Derngate

Bushmead
Priory

St Neots

Houghton
House

De Grey Mausoleum

Bletchley
Park

Woburn Abbey
and Gardens

Wrest
Park

Hailes
Abbey

Sudeley
Castle

Odda's
Chapel

Belas Knap
Long Barrow

Rollright
Stones

Deddington
Castle

Great Witcombe
Roman Villa

Minster Lovell
Hall and Dovecote

North Leigh
Roman Villa

Blenheim
Palace

BUCKING-
HAMSHIRE

HERTFO

Windmill
Tump Long
Barrow

Cirencester
Amphitheatre

Cogges Manor
Farm

Oxford Castle
& Prison

Old Gorhambury
House

Roman Wall
of St Albans

The
Royal Mews,
Buckingham
Palace

Berkhamsted
Castle

North
Hinksey
Conduit House

OXFORD

Rycote Chapel

Chiltern Open
Air Museum

Apsley
House

STEAM - Museum
of the Great
Western Railway

Abingdon County
Hall Museum

Milton's Cottage

Wellington
Arch

Kenwood

Windmill Hill

Uffington Castle -
White Horse
and Dragon Hill

Chapter House
and Pyx Chamber

OXFORDSHIRE

Avebury

Wayland's Smithy

Chiswick House
and Gardens

Alexander
Keiller Museum

West Kennet Avenue

Harmondsworth Barn

Jewel
Tower

The Sanctuary

BERKSHIRE

Gunnersbury
Park Museum

Silbury Hill

Donnington
Castle

Hogarth's
House

Marble Hill
House

Coombe
Conduit

West Kennet
Long Barrow

Chisbury Chapel

Silchester Roman
Town Walls and
Amphitheatre

Benjamin
Franklin House

Wiltshire
Museum

Hatfield Earthworks
(Marden Henge)

Strawberry Hill
House & Garden

WILTSHIRE

Ludgershall Castle
and Cross

HAMPSHIRE

Guildford

Bratton Camp
and White
Horse

Netheravon Dovecote

Farnham
Castle Keep

Watts Gallery
Artists' Village

SURREY

Stonehenge

Woodhenge

Waverley
Abbey

The Grange at
Northington

Old
Wardour
Castle

Flowerdown
Barrows

Old Sarum

Wilton
House

The Salisbury
Museum

WINCHESTER

Wolvesey Castle
(Old Bishop's Palace)

Bishop's Waltham
Palace

Butser
Ancient Farm

WEST
SUSSEX

Knowlton Church
and Earthworks

Medieval
Merchant's
House

Titchfield
Abbey

Southwick
Priory

Boxgrove
Priory

Bramber
Castle

BRIGHTON
AND HOVE

DORSET

Netley Abbey

Fishbourne
Roman Palace

CHICHESTER

Calshot Castle

Christchurch
Castle and
Norman House

PORTSMOUTH

Marlipins
Museum

British Airways i360

Hurst Castle

Osborne

Newport Roman
Villa

King James's and Landport Gates

Royal Garrison Church

Carisbrooke
Castle

Emirates Spinnaker Tower

Yarmouth Castle

Appuldurcombe House

Portchester Castle

Fort Brockhurst

Lulworth
Castle & Park

ISLE OF
WIGHT

St Catherine's
Oratory

0   10   20   30 Kms

0   10   20 Miles

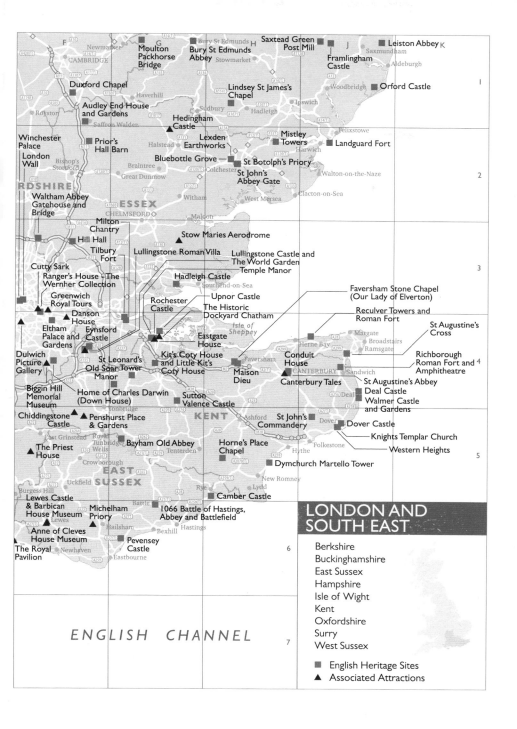

F · G · H · J · K

Newmarket
CAMBRIDGE
Moulton Packhorse Bridge
Bury St Edmunds
Bury St Edmunds Abbey
Stowmarket
Saxtead Green Post Mill
Leiston Abbey
Saxmundham
Aldeburgh
Framlingham Castle

Duxford Chapel
Haverhill
Royston
Audley End House and Gardens
Saffron Walden
Sudbury
Hadleigh
Ipswich
Lindsey St James's Chapel
Woodbridge
Orford Castle

1

Hedingham Castle
Lexden Earthworks
Mistley Towers
Felixstowe
Landguard Fort

Winchester Palace
London Wall
Prior's Hall Barn
Halstead
Bishop's Stortford
Braintree
Great Dunmow
Colchester
Bluebottle Grove
St Botolph's Priory
St John's Abbey Gate
Walton-on-the-Naze
Harwich
West Mersea
Clacton-on-Sea

2

RDSHIRE
Waltham Abbey Gatehouse and Bridge
ESSEX
CHELMSFORD
Witham
Maldon
Milton Chantry
Hill Hall
Tilbury Fort
Stow Maries Aerodrome
Lullingstone Roman Villa
Lullingstone Castle and The World Garden

3

Cutty Sark
Ranger's House – The Wernher Collection
Greenwich Royal Tours
Danson House
Eltham Palace and Gardens
Eynsford Castle
Rochester Castle
Hadleigh Castle
Southend-on-Sea
Temple Manor
Upnor Castle
The Historic Dockyard Chatham
Isle of Sheppey
Eastgate House
Herne Bay
Margate
Broadstairs
Ramsgate
Faversham Stone Chapel (Our Lady of Elverton)
Reculver Towers and Roman Fort
St Augustine's Cross
Richborough Roman Fort and Amphitheatre

4

Dulwich Picture Gallery
St Leonard's Old Soar Manor
Kit's Coty House and Little Kit's Coty House
Maison Dieu
Faversham
Conduit House
CANTERBURY
Sandwich
St Augustine's Abbey
Deal Castle
Deal

Biggin Hill Memorial Museum
Home of Charles Darwin (Down House)
Sutton Valence Castle
KENT
Ashford
Canterbury Tales
St John's Commandery
Dover
Walmer Castle and Gardens

Chiddingstone Castle
Penshurst Place & Gardens
Tonbridge
Royal Tunbridge Wells
Bayham Old Abbey
Tenterden
Horne's Place Chapel
Hythe
Dover Castle
Knights Templar Church
Western Heights

5

The Priest House
East Grinstead
Crowborough
Uckfield
EAST SUSSEX
Rye
Lydd
New Romney
Folkestone
Dymchurch Martello Tower

Lewes Castle & Barbican House Museum
Michelham Priory
Battle
Camber Castle
1066 Battle of Hastings, Abbey and Battlefield

Anne of Cleves House Museum
Hailsham
Bexhill
Hastings

6

The Royal Pavilion
Newhaven
Pevensey Castle
Eastbourne

Burgess Hill
Lewes

LONDON AND SOUTH EAST

Berkshire
Buckinghamshire
East Sussex
Hampshire
Isle of Wight
Kent
Oxfordshire
Surry
West Sussex

■ English Heritage Sites
▲ Associated Attractions

7

ENGLISH CHANNEL

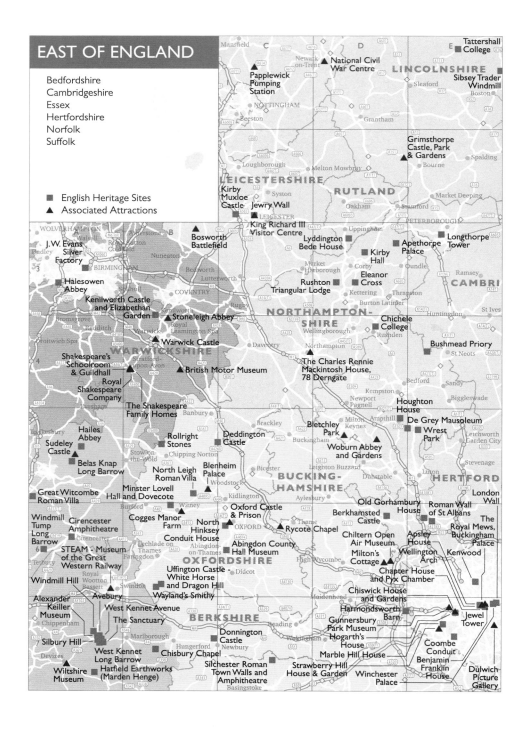

EAST OF ENGLAND

Bedfordshire
Cambridgeshire
Essex
Hertfordshire
Norfolk
Suffolk

■ English Heritage Sites
▲ Associated Attractions

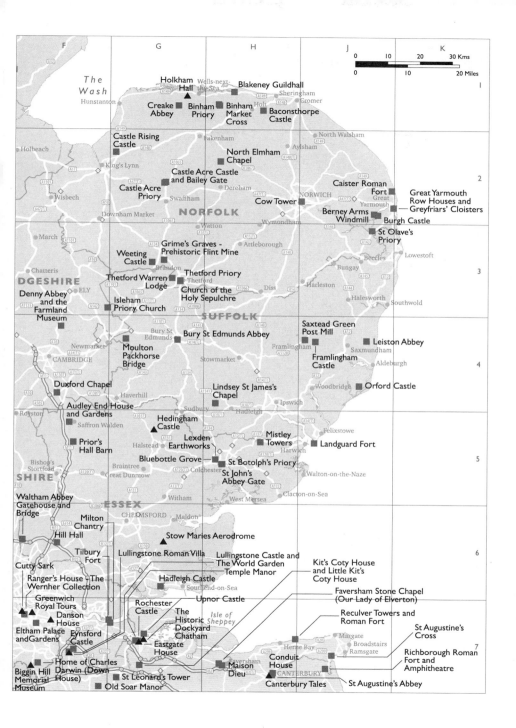

The Wash

F

Holkham Hall
Wells-next-the-Sea
Blakeney Guildhall
Sheringham
Hunstanton
Holt
Cromer
Creake Abbey
Binham Priory
Binham Market Cross
Baconsthorpe Castle
Holbeach
Castle Rising Castle
Fakenham
North Walsham
King's Lynn
North Elmham Chapel
Aylsham
Wisbech
Castle Acre Castle and Bailey Gate
Dereham
Caister Roman Fort
Great Yarmouth Row Houses and Greyfriars' Cloisters
DGESHIRE
Castle Acre Priory
Swaffham
NORWICH
Great Yarmouth
Downham Market
Cow Tower
Berney Arms Windmill
Burgh Castle
March
NORFOLK
Watton
Wymondham
St Olave's Priory
Chatteris
Grime's Graves - Prehistoric Flint Mine
Attleborough
Beccles
Lowestoft
Denny Abbey and the Farmland Museum
Weeting Castle
Brandon
ELY
Thetford Warren Lodge
Thetford
Diss
Harleston
Bungay
Halesworth
Southwold
Isleham Priory Church
Thetford Priory
Church of the Holy Sepulchre
SUFFOLK
Bury St Edmunds
Bury St Edmunds Abbey
Saxtead Green Post Mill
Leiston Abbey
Newmarket
Moulton Packhorse Bridge
Stowmarket
Framlingham
Saxmundham
CAMBRIDGE
Framlingham Castle
Aldeburgh
Duxford Chapel
Haverhill
Lindsey St James's Chapel
Woodbridge
Orford Castle
Royston
Audley End House and Gardens
Sudbury
Hadleigh
Ipswich
Saffron Walden
Hedingham Castle
Felixstowe
Prior's Hall Barn
Halstead
Lexden Earthworks
Mistley Towers
Landguard Fort
Bishop's Stortford
Braintree
Bluebottle Grove
Coggeshall
St Botolph's Priory
Harwich
Walton-on-the-Naze
SHIRE
Great Dunmow
Colchester
St John's Abbey Gate
Waltham Abbey Gatehouse and Bridge
Witham
West Mersea
Clacton-on-Sea
ESSEX
CHELMSFORD
Maldon
Milton Chantry
Hill Hall
Stow Maries Aerodrome
Tilbury Fort
Lullingstone Roman Villa
Lullingstone Castle and The World Garden
Kit's Coty House and Little Kit's Coty House
Cutty Sark
Temple Manor
Ranger's House - The Wernher Collection
Hadleigh Castle
Southend-on-Sea
Faversham Stone Chapel (Our Lady of Elverton)
Greenwich Royal Tours
Upnor Castle
Reculver Towers and Roman Fort
Danson House
Rochester Castle
The Historic Dockyard Chatham
Isle of Sheppey
St Augustine's Cross
Eltham Palace and Gardens
Eynsford Castle
Eastgate House
Margate
Broadstairs
Richborough Roman Fort and Amphitheatre
Home of Charles Darwin (Down House)
Herne Bay
Ramsgate
Biggin Hill Memorial Museum
St Leonard's Tower
Old Soar Manor
Maison Dieu
Conduit House
CANTERBURY
St Augustine's Abbey
Canterbury Tales

G   H   J   K

0   10   20   30 Kms
0   10   20 Miles

1

2

3

4

5

6

7

MAPS 341

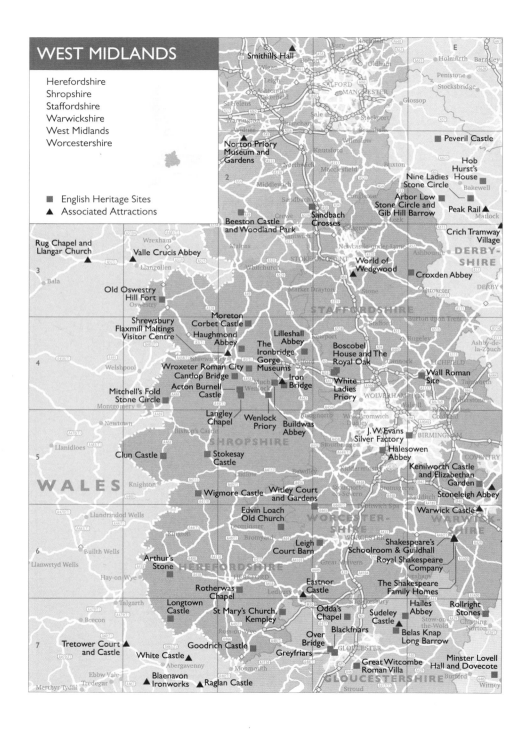

WEST MIDLANDS

Herefordshire
Shropshire
Staffordshire
Warwickshire
West Midlands
Worcestershire

■ English Heritage Sites
▲ Associated Attractions

Smithills Hall

Norton Priory
Museum and
Gardens

Peveril Castle

Hob
Hurst's
Nine Ladies House
Stone Circle

Arbor Low
Stone Circle and
Gib Hill Barrow

Peak Rail

Beeston Castle
and Woodland Park

Sandbach
Crosses

Crich Tramway
Village

Rug Chapel and
Llangar Church

Valle Crucis Abbey

World of
Wedgwood

DERBY-
SHIRE

Croxden Abbey

Old Oswestry
Hill Fort

Moreton
Corbet Castle

Shrewsbury
Flaxmill Maltings
Visitor Centre

Haughmond
Abbey

Lilleshall
Abbey

The
Ironbridge
Gorge
Museums

Boscobel
House and The
Royal Oak

Wall Roman
Site

Wroxeter Roman City

Cantlop Bridge

Iron
Bridge

White
Ladies
Priory

Acton Burnell
Castle

Mitchell's Fold
Stone Circle

Langley
Chapel

Wenlock
Priory

Buildwas
Abbey

J. W. Evans
Silver Factory

BIRMINGHAM

Clun Castle

Stokesay
Castle

Halesowen
Abbey

Kenilworth Castle
and Elizabethan
Garden

WALES

Wigmore Castle

Witley Court
and Gardens

Stoneleigh Abbey

Edvin Loach
Old Church

Warwick Castle

Leigh
Court Barn

Shakespeare's
Schoolroom & Guildhall

Arthur's
Stone

Royal Shakespeare
Company

The Shakespeare
Family Homes

Rotherwas
Chapel

Eastnor
Castle

Hailes
Abbey

Rollright
Stones

Longtown
Castle

St Mary's Church,
Kempley

Odda's
Chapel

Sudeley
Castle

Blackfriars

Belas Knap
Long Barrow

Tretower Court
and Castle

White Castle

Goodrich Castle

Over
Bridge

Greyfriars

Great Witcombe
Roman Villa

Minster Lovell
Hall and Dovecote

Blaenavon
Ironworks

Raglan Castle

GLOUCESTERSHIRE

Monk Bretton Priory
Adwick le Street
Scunthorpe
Grimsby
Cleethorpes

Brodsworth Hall and Gardens
Doncaster
Brigg

NORTH EAST LINCOLNSHIRE

Swinton
Conisbrough Castle
Gainsthorpe Medieval Village

Rotherham
Roche Abbey
Gainsborough
Market Rasen
Louth
Mablethorpe

SHEFFIELD
Mattersey Priory
Gainsborough Old Hall

Sutton Scarsdale Hall
Bolsover Cundy House
Retford
Worksop

Creswell Crags Museum and Prehistoric Gorge
LINCOLN
Lincoln Medieval Bishops' Palace
Alford

Bolsover
Lincoln Castle
Horncastle

Bolsover Castle
Rufford Abbey
North Hykeham
Spilsby
Skegness

Mansfield
Woodhall Spa
Bolingbroke Castle

NOTTINGHAM- SHIRE
Hardwick Old Hall
Tattershall College
Tattershall Castle

Wingfield Manor
Newark-on-Trent
National Civil War Centre

LINCOLNSHIRE
Sibsey Trader Windmill

Papplewick Pumping Station
Sleaford
Boston

Ilkeston
NOTTINGHAM
Hunstanton

The Wash

Beeston
Grantham

Ashby de la Zouch Museum

Ashby de la Zouch Castle
Loughborough
Melton Mowbray
Spalding
Holbeach
King's Lynn
Castle Rising Castle

LEICESTERSHIRE
Coalville
Bourne

1620s House & Gardens
Syston
RUTLAND
Oakham
Market Deeping
Wisbech
Downham Market

Kirby Muxloe Castle
Jewry Wall
LEICESTER
Stamford
PETERBOROUGH

King Richard III Visitor Centre
Uppingham
Longthorpe Tower
March

Bosworth Battlefield
Lyddington Bede House
Apethorpe Palace

Bedworth
Market Harborough
Corby
Kirby Hall
Oundle
Ramsey
Chatteris
ELY
Weeting Castle
Brandon

Lutterworth
Eleanor Cross
Kettering
Thrapston

Rushton Triangular Lodge
Burton Latimer
Huntingdon
St Ives
CAMBRIDGESHIRE

Rugby
NORTHAMPTON- SHIRE
Chichele College
Denny Abbey and the Farmland Museum
Isleham Priory Church

Daventry
Wellingborough
Rushden

Northampton
Bushmead Priory

BEDFORD
St Neots

British Motor Museum
The Charles Rennie Mackintosh House, 78 Derngate
Bedford
Sandy

Banbury
Houghton House
Biggleswade

Brackley
Newport Pagnell
Ampthill

Deddington Castle
Bletchley Park
Milton Keynes
Buckingham
De Grey Mausoleum
Wrest Park

North Leigh Roman Villa
Blenheim Palace
Bicester
Woburn Abbey and Gardens
Leighton Buzzard
Dunstable
Roman Wall of St Albans

Woodstock
BUCKING- HAMSHIRE
Old Gorhambury House

Cogges Manor Farm
Kidlington
Aylesbury
Luton
ST ALBANS

Oxford Castle & Prison
Berkhamsted Castle
Thame
OXFORD
Berkhamsted

EAST MIDLANDS

Derbyshire
Leicestershire
Lincolnshire
Northamptonshire
Nottinghamshire
Rutland

■ English Heritage Sites
▲ Associated Attractions

NORTH SEA

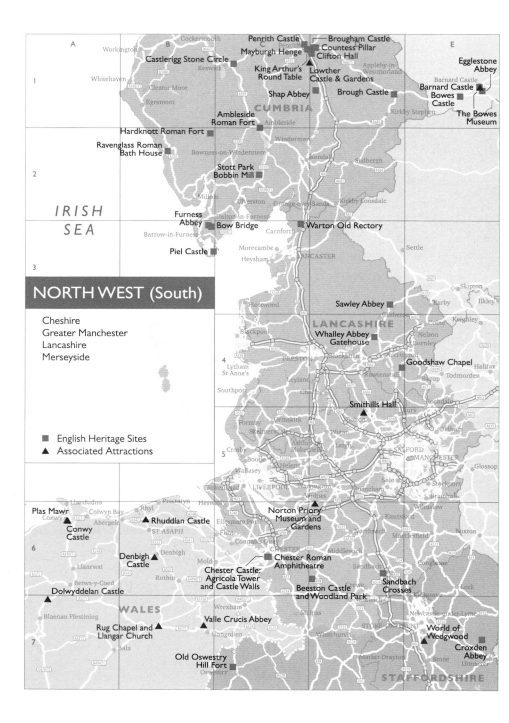

NORTH WEST (South)

Cheshire
Greater Manchester
Lancashire
Merseyside

- ■ English Heritage Sites
- ▲ Associated Attractions

Workington
Cockermouth
Whitehaven
Cleator Moor
Keswick
Castlerigg Stone Circle
Egremont
Penrith Castle
Mayburgh Henge
King Arthur's Round Table
Shap Abbey
Ambleside Roman Fort
Ambleside
CUMBRIA
Brougham Castle
Countess Pillar
Clifton Hall
Lowther Castle & Gardens
Appleby-in-Westmorland
Brough Castle
Kirkby Stephen
Penrith
Egglestone Abbey
Barnard Castle
Bowes Castle
The Bowes Museum

Hardknott Roman Fort
Ravenglass Roman Bath House
Windermere
Bowness-on-Windermere
Kendal
Sedbergh

Millom
Stott Park Bobbin Mill
Ulverston
Grange-over-Sands
Kirkby Lonsdale

IRISH SEA

Furness Abbey
Dalton-in-Furness
Bow Bridge
Carnforth
Warton Old Rectory

Barrow-in-Furness
Morecambe
Heysham
LANCASTER
Settle

Piel Castle
Skipton
Ilkley
Settle

Fleetwood
Sawley Abbey
Barby
Keighley

Blackpool
LANCASHIRE
Colne
Nelson
Burnley

Lytham St Anne's
Whalley Abbey Gatehouse
PRESTON
Blackburn
Accrington
Rawtenstall
Bacup
Todmorden
Halifax
Goodshaw Chapel

Southport
Leyland
Chorley
Rochdale

Formby
Ormskirk
Skelmersdale
Bolton
Smithills Hall
Bury
Oldham

Crosby
Bootle
Wallasey
Ashton-in-Makerfield
Wigan
Leigh
SALFORD
MANCHESTER
Glossop

Birkenhead
LIVERPOOL
St Helens
Warrington
Widnes
Sale
Altrincham
Stockport
Bramhall

Llandudno
Conwy
Colwyn Bay
Abergele
Rhyl
Prestatyn
Heswall
Wilmslow
Knutsford
Norton Priory Museum and Gardens
Ellesmere Port
Flint
Connah's Quay
Northwich
Macclesfield
Buxton

Plas Mawr
Conwy Castle
Rhuddlan Castle
ST ASAPH
Denbigh Castle
Denbigh
Mold
CHESTER
Chester Roman Amphitheatre
Chester Castle: Agricola Tower and Castle Walls
Middlewich
Sandbach
Sandbach Crosses
Congleton
Leek

Llanrwst
Ruthin
Beeston Castle and Woodland Park
Nantwich
Crewe

Berws-y-Coed
Dolwyddelan Castle
WALES
Wrexham
Malpas
Newcastle-under-Lyme

Blaenau Ffestiniog
Valle Crucis Abbey
Llangollen
Whitchurch
STOKE-ON-TRENT
World of Wedgwood

Rug Chapel and Llangar Church
Bala
Old Oswestry Hill Fort
Oswestry
Market Drayton
Stone
Croxden Abbey
Uttoxeter
STAFFORDSHIRE

Auckland Castle Deer House
The Auckland Project
Piercebridge Roman Bridge
Stanwick Iron Age Fortifications
Richmond Castle
Gisborough Priory
Whitby Abbey
North Yorkshire Moors Railway

Easby Abbey
Green Howards Museum
Georgian Theatre Royal Richmond
Mount Grace Priory, House & Gardens
Wheeldale Roman Road
Scarborough Castle

Middleham Castle
St Mary's Church, Studley Royal
Marmion Tower
Rievaulx Abbey
Helmsley Castle
Byland Abbey
Pickering Castle
North Yorkshire Moors Railway

Fountains Abbey & Studley Royal Water Garden
Aldborough Roman Site
Castle Howard
Kirkham Priory
Wharram Percy Deserted Medieval Village
Burton Agnes Manor House

Richard III & Henry VII Experience
Merchant Adventurers' Hall
Skipsea Castle

Spofforth Castle
York Cold War Bunker
Barley Hall
Clifford's Tower
DIG: archaeological adventure

EAST RIDING OF YORKSHIRE

Jorvik Viking Centre
York's Chocolate Story
Steeton Hall Gateway
Howden Minster

KINGSTON UPON HULL

St Peter's Church
Thornton Abbey and Gatehouse

NORTH LINCOLNSHIRE

Monk Bretton Priory
Brodsworth Hall and Gardens

Conisbrough Castle
Roche Abbey
Gainsthorpe Medieval Village

NORTH EAST LINCOLNSHIRE

Peveril Castle
Hob Hurst's House
Bolsover Cundy House
Mattersey Priory
Gainsborough Old Hall

Nine Ladies Stone Circle
Sutton Scarsdale Hall
Creswell Crags Museum and Prehistoric Gorge
Lincoln Medieval Bishops' Palace

Bolsover Castle
Rufford Abbey
Lincoln Castle

Hardwick Old Hall
Peak Rail

NOTTINGHAM-SHIRE

DERBYSHIRE

Crich Tramway Village
Wingfield Manor
Papplewick Pumping Station
National Civil War Centre

Arbor Low Stone Circle and Gib Hill Barrow

YORKSHIRE

East Riding of Yorkshire
North East Lincolnshire
North Lincolnshire
North Yorkshire
South Yorkshire
West Yorkshire

■ English Heritage Sites
▲ Associated Attractions

NORTH SEA

NORTH YORKSHIRE

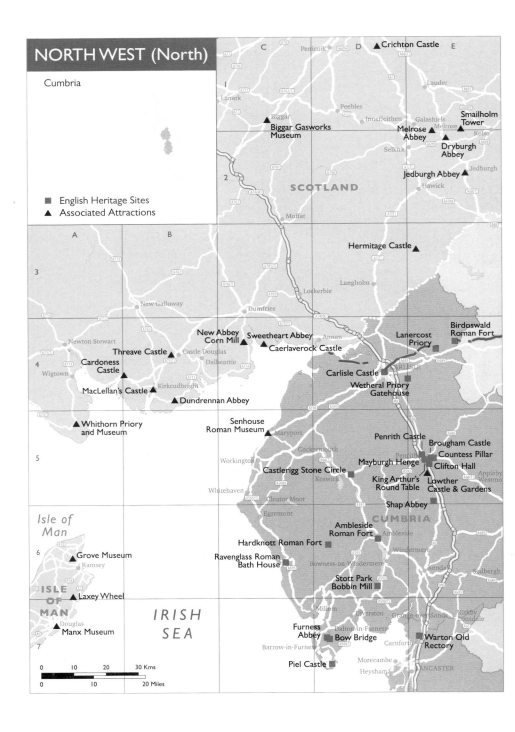

NORTH WEST (North)

Cumbria

■ English Heritage Sites
▲ Associated Attractions

Penicuik   ▲ Crichton Castle

Lauder

Lanark

Peebles

Biggar   Innerleithen   Galashiels   Smailholm Tower

▲ Biggar Gasworks Museum   Melrose   Melrose Abbey   Kelso

Selkirk   ▲ Dryburgh Abbey

SCOTLAND   Jedburgh Abbey ▲   Jedburgh

Hawick

Moffat

Hermitage Castle ▲

Langholm

New Galloway   Lockerbie

Dumfries

New Abbey Corn Mill ▲   Sweetheart Abbey ▲   Annan   Lanercost Priory ■   Birdoswald Roman Fort ■

Newton Stewart   Threave Castle ▲   Castle Douglas   Caerlaverock Castle

Cardoness Castle ▲   Dalbeattie   CARLISLE   Carlisle Castle ■

Wigtown   Kirkcudbright   Wetheral Priory Gatehouse ■

MacLellan's Castle ▲

▲ Dundrennan Abbey

▲ Whithorn Priory and Museum   Senhouse Roman Museum ▲   Maryport

Cockermouth   Penrith Castle ■   Brougham Castle ■

Penrith   Countess Pillar ■

Workington   Mayburgh Henge ■   Clifton Hall ■

Castlerigg Stone Circle ■   Appleby

Keswick   King Arthur's Round Table ■   Lowther Castle & Gardens ■   Westmo

Whitehaven   Cleator Moor   Shap Abbey ■

Egremont   CUMBRIA

Isle of Man   Ambleside Roman Fort ■   Ambleside

Hardknott Roman Fort ■   Windermere

▲ Grove Museum   Ravenglass Roman Bath House ■   Bowness-on-Windermere   Kendal   Sedbergh

Ramsey

Stott Park Bobbin Mill ■

ISLE OF MAN   ▲ Laxey Wheel

Milom   Ulverston   Grange-over-Sands   Kirkby Lonsdale

IRISH SEA

▲ Douglas   Furness Abbey ■   Dalton-in-Furness   Carnforth   Warton Old Rectory ■

Manx Museum   Bow Bridge ■

Barrow-in-Furness   Morecambe

Piel Castle ■   Heysham   LANCASTER

0   10   20   30 Kms
0   10   20 Miles

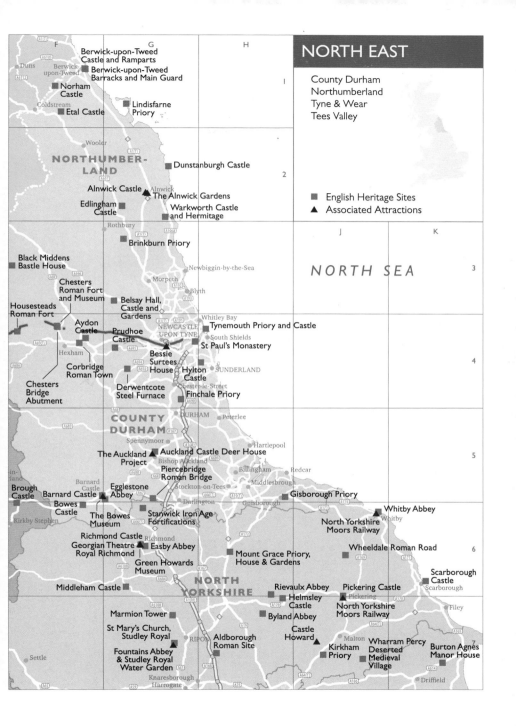

NORTH EAST

County Durham
Northumberland
Tyne & Wear
Tees Valley

■ English Heritage Sites
▲ Associated Attractions

NORTH SEA

NORTHUMBER-LAND

Berwick-upon-Tweed Castle and Ramparts
Berwick-upon-Tweed Barracks and Main Guard
Norham Castle
Etal Castle
Lindisfarne Priory
Duns
Berwick-upon-Tweed
Coldstream
Wooler

Dunstanburgh Castle

Alnwick Castle ▲ Alnwick
The Alnwick Gardens
Edlingham Castle
Warkworth Castle and Hermitage
Rothbury

Brinkburn Priory

Black Middens Bastle House
Newbiggin-by-the-Sea
Morpeth
Chesters Roman Fort and Museum
Belsay Hall, Castle and Gardens
Blyth
Housesteads Roman Fort
Whitley Bay
Aydon Castle
Prudhoe Castle
NEWCASTLE UPON TYNE
Tynemouth Priory and Castle
South Shields
St Paul's Monastery
Hexham
Bessie Surtees House
Corbridge Roman Town
Derwentcote Steel Furnace
Hylton Castle
SUNDERLAND
Chester-le-Street
Finchale Priory
Chesters Bridge Abutment

COUNTY DURHAM

DURHAM
Peterlee
Spennymoor
Hartlepool
The Auckland Project
▲ Auckland Castle Deer House
Bishop Auckland
Piercebridge Roman Bridge
Billingham
Redcar
Brough Castle
Barnard Castle
Egglestone Abbey
Stockton-on-Tees
Middlesbrough
Gisborough Priory
Barnard Castle
Darlington
Guisborough
Bowes Castle
Kirkby Stephen
The Bowes Museum
Stanwick Iron Age Fortifications
Whitby Abbey
Whitby
North Yorkshire Moors Railway
Richmond Castle
Richmond
Wheeldale Roman Road
Georgian Theatre Royal Richmond
▲ Easby Abbey
Green Howards Museum
Mount Grace Priory, House & Gardens
Scarborough Castle
Scarborough
Middleham Castle

NORTH YORKSHIRE

Rievaulx Abbey
Pickering Castle
Helmsley Castle
Pickering
North Yorkshire Moors Railway
Filey
Marmion Tower
Byland Abbey
St Mary's Church, Studley Royal
RIPON
Aldborough Roman Site
Castle Howard
Malton
Kirkham Priory
Wharram Percy Deserted Medieval Village
Burton Agnes Manor House
Fountains Abbey & Studley Royal Water Garden
Knaresborough
Harrogate
Settle
Driffield

ENGLISH HERITAGE

ARE YOU IN?

As an English Heritage Member, we would like you to give us permission to contact you. Say 'yes' and we'll help you to make the most of your membership with exclusive offers and ideas for things to see and do, along with information about our latest work, appeals and what your support has helped us to achieve.

To help us keep you in the picture, go to
www.english-heritage.org.uk/keepintouch

✓ WITHOUT
YOUR TICK
WE'LL LOSE TOUCH

Registered charity no. 1140351 (England)
Registered company no. 07447221 (England)

Details of OS LandRanger and Explorer map references are provided for easy location of each property, with specific map numbers (LandRanger; Explorer) followed by the grid reference.

NB. Contains Ordnance Survey data © Crown Copyright and database rights 2016. Additional map information © English Heritage 2018. Map created by Oxford Cartographers Ltd.

English Heritage Handbook 20.

For English Heritage:
Luke Whitcomb, Johanna Lovesey, Tersia Boorer, Charles Kightly, Tony Dike, Peter D'Ambrosio, Tom Dennis, Lucy Dennison, Tom Moriarty.

Design and Publishing:
Ledgard Jepson Ltd.

For Ledgard Jepson Ltd:
David Exley, Bev Turbitt, Andrea Rollinson, Liam Atkinson.

Print: Pindar Scarborough Ltd.

Images: All images in this handbook are © English Heritage or © Historic England unless otherwise stated.

MIX
Paper from responsible sources
FSC® C011127
www.fsc.org

The following symbols indicate facilities available at the English Heritage properties listed in this handbook.

ACQ.1945	Date property came into the National Collection
🎧	Audio tours
	Baby changing facilities
🅰	Children's play area
♿	Disabled access
🐕	Dogs allowed on leads
	Educational resources
	Events
E	Exhibition
f	Facebook
	Family learning resources
	Film/TV location
	Gardens
	Guidebook available

🍸	Hire of properties for corporate and private events
⌂	Holiday cottage to let
🔔	Licensed for civil ceremonies
⇄	Local railway station
🚹🚺	Male/female toilet
M	Museum
	Assistance dogs allowed only
OVP	OVP – admission free for Overseas Visitor Pass holders
♣	Park
P	Parking
🅿	Picnic area
🍴	Restaurant
🏠	Shop
☕	Tearoom
♿	Toilets with disabled access
🐦	Twitter
⚠	Site may contain hazardous features